GCSE/KEY STAGE 4

GUIDES

HIGHER LEVEL
MATHEMATICS

Brian Speed

Longman

LONGMAN REVISE GUIDES

SERIES EDITORS:
Geoff Black and Stuart Wall

TITLES AVAILABLE:
Art and Design
Biology*
Business Studies
Chemistry*
Computer Studies
Economics
English*
English Literature*
French
Geography
German
Home Economics
Information Systems*
Mathematics*
Mathematics: Higher Level*
Music
Physics*
Religious Studies
Science*
Sociology
Spanish
Technology*
World History

* new editions for Key Stage 4

Longman Group Ltd,
Longman House, Burnt Mill, Harlow,
Essex CM20 2JE, England
and Associated Companies throughout the world.

First Published 1989
Second Edition 1994

ISBN 0 582 23775 0

British Library Cataloguing-in-Publication Data

A catalogue record for this book is
available from the British Library

Set by 16QQ in 10/12pt Century Old Style
Printed in Great Britain by William Clowes Ltd.,
Beccles & London

CONTENTS

EDITORS' PREFACE

Longman Revise Guides are written by experienced examiners and teachers, and aim to give you the best possible foundation for success in examinations and other modes of assessment. Examiners are well aware that the performance of many candidates falls well short of their true potential, and this series of books aims to remedy this, by encouraging thorough study and a full understanding of the concepts involved. The Revise Guides should be seen as course companions and study aids to be used throughout the year, not just for last minute revision.

Examiners are in no doubt that a structured approach in preparing for examinations and in presenting coursework can, together with hard work and diligent application, substantially improve performance.

The largely self-contained nature of each chapter gives the book a useful degree of flexibility. After starting with the opening general chapters on the background to the GCSE, and the syllabus coverage, all other chapters can be read selectively, in any order appropriate to the stage you have reached in your course.

We believe that this book, and the series as a whole, will help you establish a solid platform of basic knowledge and examination technique on which to build.

Geoff Black and Stuart Wall

ACKNOWLEDGEMENTS

I would like to thank the following people for their contributions to the production of this book: Geoff Black and Stuart Wall for their efficient editing and encouragement; Terry Mullen for sharing his thoughts and insights during the preparation of the book; my pupils at Pope Pius X School for their constant inspiration and questioning that has helped to make this book relevant to GCSE students at large; my mother, Mrs Elsie Speed for her dedication to the typewriter and to finding spelling corrections; Gillian my wife who has now learned to cope with my working into the early hours; and finally to my lads, James, John and Joseph who found an alternative sport to 'Dad baiting' for a while.

I am also indebted to the following Examination Boards for giving me permission to use some of their GCSE questions in this book.

University of London Examinations and Assessment Council (ULEAC)
Midland Examining Group (MEG)
Northern Examinations and Assessment Board (NEAB)
Northern Ireland Schools Examinations and Assessment Council (NISEAC)
Oxford and Cambridge Schools Examination Board (OCSEB)
Welsh Joint Education Committee (WJEC)

The above groups do not accept any responsibility for the answers I have given to their questions. All suggestions and any mistakes in the answers are entirely my responsibility. I would be most grateful to any reader who informs me of any errors should they occur.
Brian Speed

The publishers are grateful to the following schools and colleges for their co-operation:

Bishop Fox's School, Taunton; Chase High School, Malvern; Derby Tertiary College, Mackworth; Impington Village College, Cambridge; Poole Grammar School; Popelius Comprehensive Roman School, Rotherham; Queensbury School, Bradford; Rugby School; St Helena School, Chesterfield; St Christopher School, Letchworth; St Mary's High School, Cheshunt; Shildon Sunnydale Comprehensive School; Sir William Perkins's School, Chertsey; South Park Sixth Form College, Middlesborough; Thrybergh Comprehensive School, Rotherham; Waddesdon Church of England Secondary School, Aylesbury; Wollaston School, Wellingborough.

HIGHER LEVEL MATHEMATICS

HIGHER LEVEL OF ENTRY

COURSEWORK

SCHEMES OF ASSESSMENT

ASSUMED KNOWLEDGE

HIGHER LEVEL

ADDRESSES OF THE EXAMINATION BOARDS

GETTING STARTED

GCSE mathematics is at present unique in that it allows three levels of entry; basic, intermediate and higher. The higher level is intended *only* for those candidates who stand a reasonable chance of gaining a grade A*, A or B.

If the highest grade you expect to gain is a C, then you should enter for the intermediate level, as there you will have the best chance to show what you can do. This book is written specifically for those entering the *higher level* and aiming to obtain grade A*, A or B. This first chapter considers the different requirements and details from the various examination boards. (If you are entering for intermediate or basic level then you should refer to the Longman/GCSE Key Stage 4 Revise Guide "Mathematics".)

As you work through this book you will be taken through the *essential principles* of each major topic area. You will find many *worked examples* and *exercises* (with solutions at the end of the chapter). You will also find many past *examination questions* (with answers) on that topic area, together with *student's answers* and examiners' comments on these answers.

INTRODUCING HIGHER MATHEMATICS

1 ▷ HIGHER LEVEL OF ENTRY

The target grades at this level are A*, A and B. A grade C can however be awarded, but if you do not achieve this standard then you will be unclassified.

As has already been noted, you should only be entered for this level if there is a *realistic chance* of your gaining a grade A*, A or B. If this is so and you have a bad day, then you should still end up with a grade C. If you are unclassified, then it will indicate that you were incorrectly entered. Unless a major change occurs in your learning or circumstances, then when you *next* take the exam you would be well advised to take the intermediate level examination.

2 ▷ COURSEWORK

Coursework has been an important element within the GCSE in Mathematics. From 1994 its maximum contribution has been set at 20% of the total marks. Coursework is covered in detail in the Longman GCSE/Key Stage 4 Revise Guide 'Mathematics'. Some syllabuses provide an end-of-course examination to replace the coursework component. You need to check with your syllabus (see below) and teacher to find out how your particular course is to be assessed.

3 ▷ SCHEMES OF ASSESSMENT

UNIVERSITY OF LONDON EXAMINATIONS AND ASSESSMENT COUNCIL (ULEAC)

Option A

Foundation tier	will sit Paper 1 and Paper 2
Intermediate tier	will sit Paper 3 and Paper 4
Higher tier	will sit Paper 5 and Paper 6.

There is no choice of question on any paper and each paper is worth 40% of the final total, with the coursework worth 20%, assessed over a two year period by your own centre.

Option B

The papers are set as for option A, but here the 20% coursework component consists of 'final tasks' to be set by ULEAC but assessed by the centre.

Option C

The papers are set as for options A and B, but here the 20% 'final tasks' are set *and* assessed by ULEAC.

SMP (see MEG SMP, below)

NORTHERN EXAMINATIONS AND ASSESSMENT BOARD (NEAB)

Syllabus A

Basic tier (P)	will sit Paper P1 and P2
Intermediate tier (Q)	will sit Paper Q1 and Q2
Higher tier (R)	will sit Paper R1 and R2

There is no choice of questions on any of the papers. Each paper is worth 40% of the total marks with coursework worth a further 20%. Coursework is given and assessed by your own centre.

Syllabus B

The papers are set as for Syllabus A and each is worth 40%. However, the final 20% is obtained from a terminal examination paper, set and assessed by NEAB, rather than from coursework.

Syllabus C

This is a *modular* examination with the following features:

one terminal examination paper, worth 50%;
two modular examination papers, worth 15% each;
coursework tasks, worth 20%.

MIDLAND EXAMINING GROUP (MEG)

Syllabus Mathematics (with coursework)

Each tier, Basic, Central and Further, will take the following form:

a short and longer answer paper (40%);
a structured extended answer paper (40%);
coursework (20%).

Syllabus Mathematics (without coursework)

The papers are as above, but with each paper worth 50%.

Syllabus Mathematics (SMP 11–16)

Candidates may enter any one of 5 tiers:

Green	(level 3, 4, 5)
Blue	(level 4, 5, 6)
Red	(level 5, 6, 7)
Yellow	(level 6, 7, 8, 9)
Yellow extension	(level 7, 8, 9, 10)

For each tier there are two final examination papers (40% each) with coursework at 20%.

SOUTHERN EXAMINING GROUP (SEG)

SEG offer five versions, all of which include:

two written examination papers (35% each);
coursework at 20%
aural test (10%)

The tiers available are   Foundation (F)
Intermediate (I)
Higher (H)

WELSH JOINT EDUCATION COMMITTEE (WJEC)

Syllabus A

This will consist of two parts, written papers and coursework, each part in the ratio of 200:50 (ie 80%:20%)

a)   Two written papers, each worth 100 marks. They are taken as:

Basic tier ⎫
Intermediate tier ⎬   each tier having two papers
Higher tier ⎭

b)   The coursework. This will consist of 'tasks' provided by the Examination Board, which combined together are worth 50 marks.

Syllabus B

As for syllabus A. However, here there is a third paper which will assess the mathematics which would otherwise have been tested by coursework.

NORTHERN IRELAND SCHOOLS EXAMINATIONS AND ASSESSMENT COUNCIL (NISEAC)

There are *three* parts to the assessment at each level.

a) Written papers
    At each level you sit *two written papers,* each of which will consist of *short answer questions* and *long questions* (most of which will be *structured*). There is no choice of question offered. Each paper is worth 35% of the final assessment.

b) Aural and computation
    There will also be an aural and computation test, which is set for each level. This will test your mental arithmetic and how well you can understand a spoken instruction regarding information available on a separate document. This test is worth 10% of the assessment.

c) Coursework
    You will normally have to hand in *three* assignments for assessing. Your teacher will tell you what these assignments are. They could include work on topics such as practical geometry, measurement, statistics, everyday application of mathematics and investigations. This coursework element is worth 20% of the assessment.

INTERNATIONAL GENERAL CERTIFICATE OF SECONDARY EDUCATION (IGCSE)

This syllabus has been designed to meet international mathematical needs while being based on the United Kingdom's national criteria as published by the SEAC.

There are only *two* levels available: the basic level being included in the *lower level* of the two which is called the *core curriculum* where the only grades available are C to G; the *higher level* being called the *extended curriculum,* where the only available grades are from A to E. There is also an *optional* coursework element in place of part of the written papers. The assessment will be in *three* parts:

a) a *written* paper of *short answer* questions.
b) a *written* paper of *structured* questions.
c) a *written* paper of *problems* **or** the *school based assessment*.

There is *no* choice of question on any paper. The combination of the different parts of the assessment are:

CORE:	a) first paper	35%
	b) second paper	40%
	c) third paper	25%

EXTENDED:	a) first paper	37.5%
	b) second paper	37.5%
	c) third part	25%

The school based assessment which is *optional* consists of four coursework assignments (20%) and two aural tests (10%). The four coursework assignments will be on the four areas of:

■ statistics and/or probability;
■ geometry;
■ investigations;
■ practical applications of mathematics

The aural tests will be about fifteen minutes of single response questions aimed at each different level.

You may use a suitable calculator in each part of the assessment and, if you wish, four figure tables also. For centres that are in areas where electronic calculators are not readily and cheaply obtainable, there is an alternative version of the examination available.

HIGHER MATHEMATICS

Since this book is aiming only at the higher level, it will be assumed that you have a basic knowledge of mathematics already. In this chapter we list this *assumed* knowledge, and indicate the *mathematical content* of the *higher level*. You need to check this part of the chapter for yourself to see exactly which topics do relate to you.

Number	Different types of number, eg. integers, odd, even, prime, multiples, factors, irrationals, rationals, prime factors, sequences, standard form, squares and square roots.
Fractions	Vulgar and decimal with the four rules. Conversion from vulgar to decimal and vice versa. Percentage and its uses.
Directed number	The four rules of.
Approximation	Rounding off to significant figures and decimal places.
Household finance	Simple and compound interest, taxation, loans, wages and salaries.
Tables and Charts	Being able to read them as well as construct them.
Ratio	Scale factors, best buys, scale drawing. Proportion, both direct and inverse. Speed, and foreign currency exchange rates.
Formulae	Flowcharts, use of simple equations, transposition of.
Algebra	Factors, simplification, simple linear equations and inequalities.
Indices	Integral, both positive and negative.
Co-ordinates	Plotting points and drawing graphs from given data.
Graphs	Interpreting different types of graphs, such as travel graphs and conversion graphs. Gradients as found from a graph. Solution of simultaneous, linear equations by a graph.
Angles	In triangles, parallels, polygons, and in semicircles.
Plane figures	Properties of triangles, quadrilaterals, circles and polygons.
Symmetry	Line and rotational.
Solid figures	Their names and their nets.
Perimeter	Of plane figures and circles.
Area	Of rectangles, triangles, parallelograms and circles.
Volume	Of cuboids, cylinders and prisms.
Trigonometry	Simple right angled triangles.
Pythagoras	As used to solve right angled triangles.
Loci and Constructions	Triangles, rectangles and quadrilaterals from given data. Bisector of lines and angles.
Scale drawings	And when to use them.
Bearings	Compass points and bearings from one point to another.
Transformation geometry	Tessellations, reflections, simple enlargements, rotations of 90° and 180°, and translations.
Statistics	Bar charts, pictograms and pie charts.
Frequency distributions	And their use in constructing charts, with also the use of grouped data. Scatter diagrams.
Averages	Mean, mode and median.
Probability	Simple, equally likely situations and combined events.

5 ⟩ HIGHER LEVEL

The Higher Level of mathematics does not differ from exam board to exam board, or from syllabus to syllabus. The table below will guide you on which parts of the book are relevant to the Higher Level syllabus.

The *Higher Level* is referred to by the different boards as:

ULEAC	Level Z
NEAB	Level R
MEG	Higher
SEG	Level 3
WJEC	Level 3
NISEAC	High
IGCSE	Extended

Chapter and topic

3   Percentage, Compound interest
4   Number Patterns
5   Ratio and Variation
    Direct, inverse and joint proportion
    Similarity, Congruence
6   Quadratic factorization, equations
    Simultaneous equations
    Algebraic fractions
    Fractional indices
    Functions and their combinations
    Limits of accuracy
    Standard Form
    Rational/Irrational numbers
    Inequalities
7   Drawing graphs of inequalities
    Drawing graphs of simultaneous equations
    Area under a graph
    Gradients and their uses
8   Cyclic qudrilaterals
    Angles in a circle
    Axes and planes of symmetry
    Intersecting chord theorem
    Loci
9   Length of arc, area of sector
    Area of trapezium
    Area using sine rule ($\frac{1}{2}$ a.b. sin C)
    Volume of prisms, spheres and cones
    Surface areas
    3D solutions using trigonometry and Pythagoras
    Sine and Cosine rule
10   Vectors
    Matrices
    Transformations and combinations of
    Enlargements with negative or fraction scale factors
11   Cumulative frequency
    Unequal width histograms
    Probabilities (and/or)
    Sampling, standard deviation

6 ⟩ ADDRESSES OF THE EXAMINATION BOARDS

ULEAC   **University of London Examinations and Assessment Council**
Stewart House, 32 Russell Square, London, WC1B 5DN
Tel: 071 331 4000
Fax: 071 631 3369

MEG   **Midland Examining Group**
1 Hills Road, Cambridge, CB1 2EU
Tel: 0223 61111
Fax: 0223 460278

NEAB   **Northern Examinations and Assessment Board**
Devas Street, Manchester, M15 6EX
Tel: 061 953 1180
Fax: 061 273 7572

NISEAC **Northern Ireland Schools Examinations and Assessment Council**
Beechill House, 42 Beechill Road, Belfast, BT8 4RS
Tel: 0232 704666
Fax: 0232 799913

SEG   **Southern Examining Group**
Stag Hill House, Guildford, GU2 5XJ
Tel: 0483 506506
Fax: 0483 300152

WJEC   **Welsh Joint Education Committee**
245 Western Road, Cardiff, CF5 2YX
Tel: 0222 561231
Fax: 0222 571234

IGCSE   **International General Certificate of Secondary Education**
University of Cambridge Local Examinations Syndicate
1 Hills Road, Cambridge, CB1 2EU
Tel: 0223 61111
Fax: 0223 460278

EXAMINATION AND ASSESSMENT TECHNIQUES

CALCULATORS

FORMULAE LIST

REVISION

EXAMINATION ROOM STRATEGY

EXAMINATION EQUIPMENT

EXAMINATION QUESTIONS

USING AND APPLYING MATHEMATICS

PRACTICAL WORK

INVESTIGATIONAL WORK

EXTENDED WORK

GETTING STARTED

It is encouraging to know that if you *have been correctly entered* for the higher level of mathematics then you can do *at least half* of the examination questions well. This should give you a lot of confidence before you go into the examination. Being confident is helpful, since being anxious often means that students make careless mistakes.

Work through the many *worked examples* you will find in each topic based chapter. Try all the *exercises* before checking your work with the answers at the end of the chapter. Also try the many *examination questions* set on each topic yourself before looking at the answers at the end of each chapter. Look carefully at the *examiner comments* to be found alongside each *student answer* at the end of each chapter. There is no better way to prepare for mathematics examinations than to *do* as much practice as you can.

ESSENTIAL PRINCIPLES

1 ▷ CALCULATORS

All GCSE examinations allow you to have your calculator available. The questions will be set on the assumption that you have a calculator suitable to your level. For example, you will be asked some *trigonometry questions* at this high level, so make sure that you have a *scientific* calculator. It is up to **YOU** to be responsible for your calculator and not the exam board, school or college. Do have the right one, and make certain that the batteries are not going to run out on you (perhaps take some spares). Do use a calculator that you are familiar with, and not a strange one borrowed at the last minute.

When using the calculator in the examination, do not forget to *write out* your method of solution, otherwise you will often lose marks. In marking a recent exam paper the answer to one question should have been £1.99. Some candidates gave the answer as £1.98 with *no* working out, so they got no marks at all, even though it is quite likely that they *knew* what they were doing, but had just made a small error, perhaps in rounding off. You will throw marks away if you fail to put down your *method of solution*. Make sure you are familiar with the standard form notation on your calculator and how to use this with large or very small numbers. This is covered in Chapter 5 of this book.

2 ▷ FORMULAE LIST

Each Examination Board will supply a formulae list for each syllabus, and for each level in that syllabus. You are advised to become familiar with this list, so that you know where to find the formulae when needed. It is also important that you practise using those formulae. If you have practised using the formulae *before* the exam, then this will give you confidence in using them in the examination itself.

3 ▷ REVISION

There is of course no substitute for hard work *throughout* the course, and for regularly doing homework and classwork assignments. Revision is, however, important and should be started well before the examination, best of all *before* the Easter holiday leading to the examination. The best way to revise mathematics is to *do* it. You should try as many questions as you can beforehand, this is why there are a lot of questions at the end of each chapter. Do not be afraid of going through the same question more than once during your revision. This will be helpful practice in using the correct technique for answering that type of question, and it should help boost your confidence. Do not revise for too long at a single sitting! You are advised to revise in short periods of between 45 to 60 minutes then to have a break before doing any more. Of course, this will vary with individuals but, if you've started your revision early enough, this is usually the best way rather than a last final fling!

Use this book to remind you of the things you have been taught. Go through the *worked examples*; then try the *exercises* for yourself, *checking* the answer before going any further. Finally, try the *exam questions* at the end of each chapter, making sure that you put down all your working out, just as you will have to do in the examination itself.

4 ▷ EXAMINATION ROOM STRATEGY

Remember, you can do *at least half* the questions, and there will always be some that cause problems. You must use your time properly, so do not waste it. The majority of GCSE examinations use 'Question and Answer Books', which means that there is space for you to work out your answer and to give an answer on the exam paper itself. So it doesn't matter in what *order* you do the questions. Go through the paper and answer the questions *you can do* first, then go back and attempt the ones you've left out. If a question causes you particular problems and you cannot see what to do, then leave it, go on to another and come back to it later. In other words, 'do what you can do well' first. This will help you to 'put marks into the bank' and will help you to gain confidence before you tackle the more 'difficult' questions.

Most examination papers will tell you *how many marks* are available to a question; the more difficult a question is, the more marks are generally given to it. So if you come across a question worth 5 marks and one worth 2 marks, you should expect the 2 mark question to be answered more easily than the 5 mark question. If you have managed to do the 5 mark question very easily, perhaps more easily than the 2 mark question, just check that you have in fact done the question that has been set and have not misread it!

If you're answering on an answer booklet, do also use the *number of lines* left for your answer as a guide to the amount you should write. If there is only one line left for working, then you should not need to do a lot of working out. If, however, five lines have been left for working, then you should expect to need to complete a number of stages to get to the answer.

The number of marks per question will also give you some idea of how much *time* to spend on each question. Suppose an examination paper lasts $2\frac{1}{2}$ hours (150 minutes) and there are 100 marks, then each mark has an average time of $1\frac{1}{2}$ minutes, and hence a five mark question should not take more than 8 minutes. Of course you should perhaps allow 10 minutes at the start of the exam for reading through the paper (or booklet) carefully and for choosing your early questions, and perhaps 10 minutes for checking at the end. In this case you would be able to use the 'rule of thumb' that you have just over one minute per mark. Working out the *minutes per mark* should not be taken *too* far, but it does give you some idea on how to use your time well in the examination.

Finally, do not forget to *check* those answers, especially the sense and the accuracy of your answer. If you have calculated the cost of a car to be £6, you ought to suspect that your answer is wrong and check it. Year after year examiners always mark papers where 'stupid' answers are given, such as a man being paid a salary of £45 a year! Do check your answers, it will gain you marks. Also, check that you have *rounded off* suitably. Many questions will say 'round your answer to 1 decimal place', etc., in which case you could obtain marks for rounding off. But other questions might simply say 'calculate the distance . . .', and if your answer is something like 8.273419 km, you are quite likely to lose a mark for your answer since it is not given to a suitable degree of accuracy. You must round off sensibly or be prepared to lose marks.

You ought to be doing many of these checks whilst answering the question the first time, but do go through the routine as a check at the end. It may be boring, but if it gains you a number of marks you would otherwise lose, and this makes the difference between grades, it will have been well worth doing.

 **5 > EXAMINATION EQUIPMENT**

You will be required to calculate, draw and construct. You must therefore have the right equipment for the job. Do not rely on the school providing it, since if you provide the equipment you are familiar with, you can be more confident that you can use it and rely on it. Make certain you have the following:

calculator	pencil sharpener
batteries for calculator	rubber
ruler	protractor
sharp pencils	pair of compasses
pen (and a spare pen)	set square

6 > EXAMINATION QUESTIONS

There are different *types* of question that you could meet: eg. multiple choice, short answer, structured and combination.

SHORT-ANSWER QUESTIONS

This type of question is usually given one or two marks, and you may only have a line or two on which to answer the question. You must first assess what you have to do, then be sure to write down the *method* you are using as well as the answer, suitably rounded off.

Example 1

Find the value of x such that $90 < x < 180$ and $\sin x° = 0.4567$ (NEAB)

Here you need to notice that the answer you want is between 90 and 180, hence the calculator answer to 0.4567 $\boxed{\text{INV}}$ $\boxed{\text{SIN}}$ which gives 27.17 (rounded off), needs to be taken away from 180, hence $180 - 27.17 = 152.83$ should be written down. If you showed no method of solution here, and wrote an incorrectly rounded answer of 152.9° only, then you are likely to gain no marks at all.

STRUCTURED QUESTIONS

These are the longer questions that will use one answer *as part of the next question*. This may occur perhaps two or three times in the one question. It is also vital that you show *all* your method of solution here, as one wrong answer early on could make all subsequent answers wrong. To gain marks you must show exactly what you have done.

Example 3

Karl won £2000 in a competition and put it into a Building Society account that paid him 5% interest every 6 months. How much will he have in the account after:

a) 6 months?
b) 1 year?   (NEAB)
c) 2 years?

You can see how you use the answer to part a) to find the answer to part b) and then this answer to find the final answer to part c), and that any mistakes made earlier will make a wrong answer appear later . . . so it is vital that you show all your method of solution in each section of the question. If you did this question correctly, then you would find that your final answer to part c) was £2431.0125, which should be rounded off to give £2431 or £2431.01.

COMBINATION QUESTIONS

A longer question is often a *combination* of short answer and structured questions.

Example 4

A fruit cake is a cylinder of height 7 cm and radius 9 cm. It is to have its top and sides covered in marzipan.

a)   i) The top covering is 0.7 cm thick. Calculate this volume of marzipan.
     ii) A strip of marzipan 7.7 cm wide is to be wrapped around the side of the cake. Show that it must be about 57 cm long.
    iii) This strip is 0.5 cm thick. Calculate the volume of marzipan needed for the whole cake.
b) A family baker makes 12 such cakes. He buys marzipan in 500 g packs. Each pack has a volume of 180 cm³. How many packs will he need to cover the 12 cakes?   (MEG)

You should set out the parts a) i) and ii) as short answer questions, with your method clearly stated. The final part a) iii) is done by combining the answer to part a) i) with information in part ii) to find the total volume of marzipan. Then the final answer to part b) is calculated by multiplying the volume of the marzipan for one cake (396 cm³) found in part a), by 12, then dividing by 180 to give 26.4. Hence the baker needs to buy 27 packs of marzipan.

   These answers must be clearly written down, since it is possible for you to have made a mistake in one of the earlier parts and the examiner marking your paper needs to be able to see what *you* have done, rather than have to do your calculation *himself* as a means of checking what you really have done!

SUMMARY

To summarise this section we can simply say that at all stages you should show the method of solution, unless you are certain that there is only one mark for the question and that no method is being looked for.

COURSEWORK

7 ▷ USING AND APPLYING MATHEMATICS

As we have already seen, Attainment Target 1 (AT1) involves 'using and applying mathematics'. This Attainment Target can be assessed either by coursework activities or by an examination at the end of the course. Table 2.1 provides a more detailed breakdown of the skills and understanding you need to display to reach Levels 6 to 10 in this attainment target.

	i) Applications	ii) Communication	iii) Reasoning, logic and proof
Level 6	Pose their own questions or design a task in a given context.	Examine critically the mathematical presentation of information.	Make a generalisation giving some degree of justification.
Level 7	Follow new lines of enquiry when investigating within mathematics itself or when using mathematics to solve a real-life problem.	Use appropriate mathematical language and notation when solving real-life problems or commenting on generalisations or solutions.	Examine and comment constructively on generalisations or solutions.
Level 8	Make reasoned choices when exploring a mathematical task.	Use mathematical language and symbolism effectively when presenting logical accounts of work stating reasons for choices made.	Understand the role of counter-examples in disproving generalisations or hypotheses.
Level 9	Co-ordinate a number of features or variables in solving problems.	Use mathematical language and symbolism effectively when presenting logical accounts of work and produce concise justifications of their solutions to complex problems.	Justify their solutions to problems involving a number of features or variables.
Level 10	Explore independently and constructively a new area of mathematics.	Apply mathematical language and symbolism confidently when handling abstract concepts. Present logical and concise accounts of work resulting from an independent exploration of a new area of mathematics, commenting on alternative solutions.	Handle abstract concepts of proof and definition when exploring independently a familiar or new area of mathematics.

Table 2.1 Levels of Attainment in 'Using and Applying' Mathematics.

8 ▷ PRACTICAL WORK

You will be assessed on:

a) How you planned the task, how you carried it out and how accurate you were. Evidence of these three stages is necessary.

b) Whether you have demonstrated that you understand the use of equipment. For example in weighing, that you have used an appropriate set of scales.
c) Your actual skill in using the equipment.
d) Your ability to communicate what you are doing. You could well be asked to explain whey you did a certain thing, or why you used a piece of equipment in a particular way.

The tasks set will be at the level for which you are being considered. If you have moved up a level during the course, then you should have been given an opportunity of doing the practical work appropriate to this higher level.

INVESTIGATIONAL WORK

You will be assessed on:

a) How you planned and prepared the set task.
b) How much relevant information you were able to obtain and use.
c) Your ability to communicate what you have done. You could be asked to talk about the investigation as well as to write a clear solution.
d) The extent to which you were able to draw a valid conclusion.
e) How far you went with the investigation. Was it exhaustive?

Very often the same investigation will be set for *all* levels. It is up to you to demonstrate how well you have been able to pursue the investigation and to decide at what point you stop.

EXAMPLE INVESTIGATION

Four straight lines all intersect each other. How many intersections will there be for other numbers of lines?

a) This work can be planned in such a way that it can become an investigation. First you can draw two lines, then three, then four, and so on.
b) You now need to look for a *pattern*. If you *can* identify a pattern you can start *predicting* how many intersections there will be for the next sets of lines without having to draw them. At the Higher Level it is vital that you are able to generalise the patterns found. In this case you should be able to find that for n lines there are $\dfrac{n(n-1)}{2}$ intersections.
c) The work must be written up clearly. Start with an *introduction*, telling the assessor what you were trying to do. Follow this by outlining the *method* you chose to pursue your investigation. Present a *table of results,* giving an indication of what patterns you noticed.
d) Can you draw a *conclusion*? For example, can you state how you can find the number of intersections for any given number of straight lines, say 50?
e) How far have you been able to see a pattern? Can you write a *formula* for n lines, and how many intersections will this give?

In an investigation it is up to *you* to go as far as you can. But be *clear* and *logical* in how you set about conducting the investigation. Make sure that you write up your results neatly and on the lines suggested; introduction → method → results → conclusion.

EXTENDED WORK

Usually the task set will be defined by the school or college from some particular starting point. Then it is up to you to determine where you take it and how far you develop it. The main points being looked for in an extended piece of work will be:

a) *The comprehension of the task.*
    Did you understand the problem and were you able to define what you were going to do?

b) *Planning*.
Were you able to plan out the task into different set stages to enable you to complete the task?

c) *Performance of the task*.
How well did you undertake the set task? Did you choose appropriate methods? Did you use appropriate equipment? How have you interpreted the results from that equipment?

d) *Communication*.
This will be both written and oral. Again a well set out introduction → method → results → conclusion will be important. Have you used helpful diagrams/tables etc? In oral work, were you able to respond to unexpected queries?

EXAMPLE OF EXTENDED WORK

Square numbers 1, 4, 9 . . . can be built up in a pattern such as in Fig. 2.1,

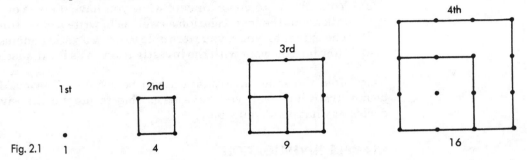

Fig. 2.1

and the nth square number is found by n^2.
Investigate patterns in triangle numbers, pentagonal numbers, etc.
Here, you could find the pattern for triangle, pentagonal and hexagonal numbers as:

■ **Triangle numbers**

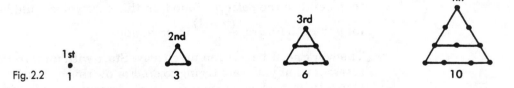

Fig. 2.2

the nth triangular number is given by $\dfrac{n(n+1)}{2}$

■ **Pentagonal numbers**

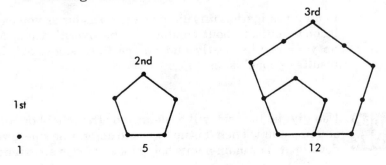

Fig. 2.3

the nth pentagonal number given by $\dfrac{n}{2}(3n-1)$

■ **Hexagonal numbers**

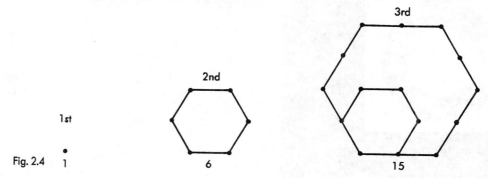

Fig. 2.4

the nth hexagonal number given by $n(2n - 1)$

As you see, this task will involve some imagination and quite a bit of mathematical exploring (investigation). You will have to decide *which* numbers to include *as well as* the triangle and pentagonal numbers given. You would need to *build up* the patterns for each number type, then to look for some principle or *rule* behind the way in which each pattern is building up, and then to *generalise* that rule. Here I have only written down the results. You would, in an extended piece of work, give the method of solution, including the way in which you found the rule behind each pattern, together with any illustrations of how the rule works. You would probably also be finding the patterns for octagonal numbers and maybe more!

FINALLY

Your coursework tasks should be assessed at frequent, but appropriate, times during the course. Assessed coursework will help you to be aware of how well you are doing. If you do have shortcomings, you can then work on improving them *before* the next time such material is assessed. Yet in every case, the coursework component comes down to you, since it really does assess the way in which *you*:

■ plan the work
■ do the work
■ communicate the work.

It is all up to you!

You can find more specific help on your approach to Coursework topics in Longman GCSE/Key Stage 4 Revise Guide 'Mathematics'.

PERCENTAGE AND INTEREST

SIMPLE PERCENTAGE

INCREASE AND DECREASE

BACKWARD PERCENTAGE

COMPOUND INTEREST

QUANTITY AS PERCENTAGE

G E T T I N G   S T A R T E D

The application of mathematics is often examined with the use of *percentages*. In this chapter we focus on those aspects likely to be met in the examination.

Sensible *rounding off* at the appropriate time is always needed here and we show you when and how to do this so that you will not lose marks for incorrect rounding. You can find more on rounding off under 'Limits of accuracy' in Chapter 4.

USEFUL DEFINITIONS

Discount	A deduction from the usual price.
Principal (amount)	Usually means the amount of money you start with in a bank account etc.
Simple Interest	Interest is paid on an *unchanged* principal amount. There is then a single formula to work out the amount of interest your money will earn.
Compound Interest	Interest is paid at regular intervals (usually each year or half year), so the principal amount *changes* from year to year.

ESSENTIAL PRINCIPLES

 **SIMPLE PERCENTAGE**

All of this chapter is devoted to percentage, and as we will be assuming the general use of a calculator, then we will always use percentage in the *decimal* form.

Eg.   1% = 0.01,   15% = 0.15,   130% = 1.30, etc.

WORKED EXAMPLE 1

Find 15% of £2.50.
15% of £2.50 is found by £2.50 × 0.15 = £0.375; we round up to give £0.38.

EXERCISE 1

Which is the larger, 81% of £5.99 or 5% of £95.99?

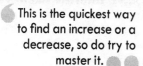 **INCREASE AND DECREASE**

INCREASE

To *increase* any amount by x%, use the simple routine:

change % to decimal
↓
add on 1
↓
multiply by amount.

WORKED EXAMPLE 2

Increase Gillian's wage of £126 by $6\frac{1}{2}$%.
$6\frac{1}{2}$% = 0.065, so to find the increased wage; £126 × 1.065 = £134.19.

This is the quickest way to find an increase or a decrease, so do try to master it.

EXERCISE 2

When Sheffield Wednesday gained promotion to the first division their average attendance of 25 756 was expected to increase by about 22%. What was their new, expected, average attendance?

DECREASE

To *decrease* any amount by x%, use a similar routine of:

change % to decimal
↓
subtract from 1
↓
multiply by amount.

WORKED EXAMPLE 3

After the Red Plague, the 526 000 population of Gallilee fell by 32%. What was the population after the Red Plague?
32% = 0.32, hence population is now 526 000 × (1 − 0.32)
    = 526 000 × 0.68 = 357 680.

EXERCISE 3

I bought a car for £900, then sold it one year later at a loss of 30%. What did I sell it for?

 **BACKWARD PERCENTAGE**

We are often told a given percentage of some amount and then need to work out the amount.
For example, the 5% of the voters who voted for M. Slater totalled 917. How many voters were there?
In this situation, we again have a simple routine which basically finds 1%, then multiples by 100 to find the whole amount. So follow this routine:

divide given amount by %

↓

then multiply by 100.

WORKED EXAMPLE 4	The $3\frac{1}{2}$ acre woodland of the Duke De Richleaux only represents 8% of his total estate. What acreage is the estate of the Duke? Calculate $3.5 \div 8 \times 100$ to give 43.75 acres.

EXERCISE 4

When Alison Metcalf was transferred from Sheffield FC to Santos Ladies team she received £162 000 which represented 18% of the transfer fee. What was this transfer fee?

WORKED EXAMPLE 5	Mr. Cofield had a pay increase of 5% to give him a new salary of £1092 per month. What was his previous monthly salary? The statement in effect tells us that £1092 is 105% of the previous salary, hence this is $1092 \div 105 \times 100$, which is £1040.

4 ▷ COMPOUND INTEREST

❝ This is like repeated simple interest year after year adding the interest onto the balance each time. ❞

Compound interest is the type of interest used by the commercial sector for calculating interest payments; it is a way of paying interest on your investment. Again, it is calculated by a simple routine as illustrated in the formula:

Final amount $= P \times (1 + R)^n$

where P is the principal amount started with

R is the interest rate quoted

n is the number of times this interest is being applied.

WORKED EXAMPLE 6	£60 is invested in an account that pays 8% compound interest each year. How much will this investment be worth in five years' time? Since the principal amount invested is £60, the rate is 8%, and the number of times the rate is applied will be 5,

the final amount $= £60 \times (1.08)^5 = £88.159685$

$= £88.16$

Note here that it is essential that you do no rounding off *until* the final answer. You should of course have used the $\boxed{x^y}$ button on your calculator to work out the power quite quickly.

WORKED EXAMPLE 7	A new-born octopus is know to increase in body weight quite steadily at the rate of $5\frac{1}{2}$% a day over the first few months of its life. What will be the weight of a baby octopus after 4 weeks if when it was born it weighed 4 kg?

❝ This is compound interest, you need to recognise it when it is needed. ❞

The principal amount is 4 kg, the rate of increase is $5\frac{1}{2}$% each day for 28 days. Hence final weight $= 4 \times (1.055)^{28}$

$= 17.9$ kg

EXERCISE 5

When John started work he was given a starting wage of £50 a week and told it would increase by 4% every six months. How much will his weekly wage be after 5 years?

5 ▷ QUANTITY AS PERCENTAGE

This is usually asked for as a percentage profit or loss. It is a simple extension of changing a fraction to a percentage by multiplying the fraction by 100.

WORKED EXAMPLE 8	Divinder had paid £575 for an old bike, done it up and then sold it for £750. What was his profit as a percentage of his original cost? This profit was £750–£575 which is £175. This as a percentage of the original cost of £575 is found by calculating $175 \div 575 \times 100$ which is 30.4% (rounded off).

EXERCISE 6

When a metal bar is heated to 300°C it expands from 41 cm to 41.3 cm. What is the expansion as a percentage of the original length?

S O L U T I O N S   T O   E X E R C I S E S

S1

81% of £5.99 = 0.81 × 5.99 = 4.8519
5% of £95.99 = 0.05 × 95.99 = 4.7995
hence 81% of £5.99 is larger than 5% of £95.99.

S2

25 756 × (1 + 0.22) = 25 756 × 1.22 = 31 422 (rounded off).

S3

£900 × (1 − 0.3) = £900 × 0.7 = £630.

S4

£162 000 ÷ 18 × 100 = £900 000.

S5

Principal amount is £50, rate is 4% applied 10 times.
   Hence final wage = $50 \times (1.04)^{10} = £74.01$ (or £74).

S6

Expansion is 0.3 cm. As a % of the original this will be 0.3 ÷ 41 × 100 = 0.73%.

E X A M   T Y P E   Q U E S T I O N S

Q1

DISCOUNTPRINT
30% BIGGER COLOUR PRINTS
Check your bigger print size here

FILM SIZES	135	110/DISC	126
DISCOUNTPRINTS	6 × 4	5¼ × 4	4 × 4
STANDARD	5 × 3½	4½ × 3½	3½ × 3½

Fig. 3.1

a)   Use the dimensions given in the table in Fig. 3.1 to see if the '30% bigger' claim is true for film size 135. Show all your working.

b)   Figure 3.2 shows the actual sizes for a standard and a discount print for size 135.

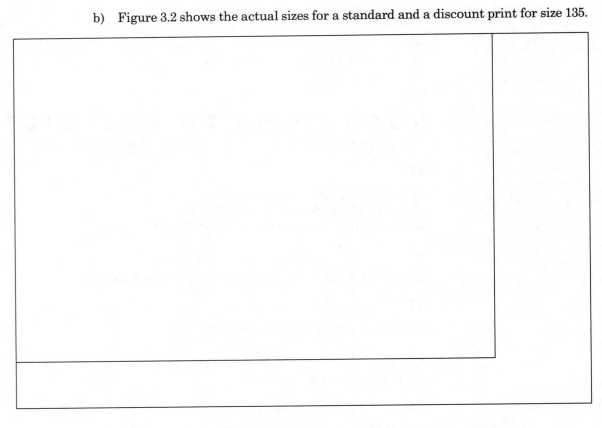

Fig. 3.2

Measure these prints and check the claim from your measurements.

c)   Comment on the results in a) and b).   (MEG)

Q2

32ND ISSUE CERTIFICATES
52%
NO TAX, NO RISK, NO HASSLE, NO FEAR OF FALLING INTEREST RATES.

The interest that you can earn from National Savings Certificates is TOTALLY free from Income Tax and Capital Gains Tax. You don't even have to declare it on your Income Tax return.

The 32nd Issue offers a guaranteed return of 52% after five years. This is equivalent to 8.75% a year over the five years.

You can invest from £25 to £5,000, in addition to any other Issues you already hold.

Each member of your family can invest up to the full amount in their own names.

For full details ask at your bank or post office.

We guarantee freedom from tax, with high performance and absolute safety. There is nothing to touch National Savings Certificates.

NATIONAL SAVINGS

Fig. 3.3

The advertisement in Fig. 3.3 contains the following statement.
The 32nd Issue offers a guaranteed return of 52% after 5 years.
This is equivalent to 8.75% a year over the five years.

a) Investigate the truth of this statement by completing the table in Fig. 3.4 to show the year by year growth of an initial investment of £1000 at 8.75% a year.

	Amount at end of year
Year 1	
Year 2	
Year 3	
Year 4	
Year 5	

Fig. 3.4

From this table, write down, correct to one decimal place, the total percentage increase over the five years.

b) Given that National Savings Certificates are bought in multiples of £25, find the minimum amount of money which would have to be invested initially in order to produce a total of at least £1000 at the end of the five years.　(NEAB)

Q3

Sally put £250 into a savings account which paid interest at the rate of 8% per annum.

a) Find the amount in the account at the end of one year.
She leaves this amount of money in the account for another year. During this year the rate of interest is 9.75% per annum for the whole year.

b) Find, to the nearest penny, the amount in the account at the end of the second year.　(ULEAC)

Q4

A trade union negotiates the following rise in wages on behalf of its members:

5% of weekly wage or £6 per week, whichever is the greater

One employee finds that, for him, there is no difference between a rise of 5% and a rise of £6 per week. Calculate this employee's weekly wage before the rise.　(NEAB)

Q5

Supergrowth Unit Trust claims that the value of its units is likely to grow by 21% compound interest per annum. Assuming that this claim is true, calculate the value, after 5 years, of an investment of £1000 in Supergrowth Unit Trust.　(MEG)

Q6

Figure 3.5 shows a floppy disc for a microcomputer. The useful area is shaded. Find the percentage of the area of the disc that is useful.　(MEG)

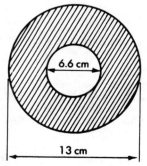

6.6 cm

13 cm

Fig. 3.5

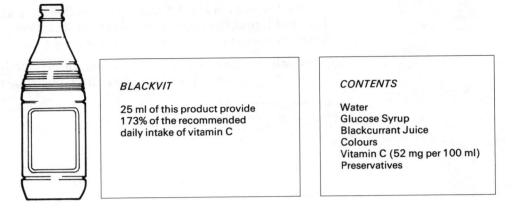

BLACKVIT

25 ml of this product provide
173% of the recommended
daily intake of vitamin C

CONTENTS

Water
Glucose Syrup
Blackcurrant Juice
Colours
Vitamin C (52 mg per 100 ml)
Preservatives

Fig. 3.6

Q7

The information in Fig. 3.6 was given on two labels taken from a bottle of 'Blackvit', a blackcurrant drink. Calculate, from the information provided, the recommended daily intake of vitamin C. (NEAB)

Q8

Mr. & Mrs. Williams invest £1000 in an investment account which pays 10.5% per annum interest.

a) How much interest do they get in a year?
b) They have to pay tax on this interest at the rate of 27p in the £1. How much tax do they pay? How much of the interest is left after paying tax?
c) What percentage is this 'after tax' interest of their £1000 investment?
(WJEC)

Q9

A flower is placed in a vase. During the course of each day, it loses 5% of its water content. It will begin to droop after losing 25% of its original water content.

a) What percentage of its original water content will it lose in two days?
b) If the flower had drooped after x days, what is the minimum possible value of x? (NEAB)

Q10

A man invests £200 in a savings account at an annual rate of interest of 7%. He makes no further deposits or withdrawals. Interest is added each year and then itself earns extra interest (ie. compound interest).

a) How much will he have in his account at the end of the second year?
b) After how many complete years will he first have more than £300 in his account? (MEG)

Q11

a) A function p is defined by $p(x) = (1 + x)(1 - 0.6x)$ for the domain $0 \leqslant x \leqslant 0.5$.
   i) Complete the table in Fig. 3.7.

x	0	0.05	0.10	0.15	0.20	0.25	0.30	0.35	0.40	0.45	0.50
$1 + x$	1	1.05	1.10	1.15		1.25		1.35	1.40		1.50
$1 - 0.6x$	1	0.97	0.94	0.91		0.85		0.79	0.76		0.70
$p(x)$	1	1.019	1.034	1.047		1.063		1.067	1.064		1.050

Fig. 3.7

ii) Draw the graph of p(x) for the domain $0 \leqslant x \leqslant 0.5$.

b) A theatre finds that when it raises its prices, the percentage increase in the price is directly proportional to the percentage decrease in the number of people attending the theatre. When the prices were increased by 10%, 6% fewer people came.

   i) What percentage reduction in the audience will there be for a 1% rise in prices?

   ii) What percentage change in the takings will there be for a 1% rise in prices?

   iii) Using your graph drawn in part a), find what percentage rise in prices will give the greatest rise in takings.

c) The theatre takes £380 per night before the rise. What is the most it can take after the rise?

                                                    (WJEC)

OUTLINE ANSWERS TO EXAM QUESTIONS

A1

a) Standard size area = $5 \times 3.5 = 17.5$
Discount size area = 24, an increase of 6.5.
The percentage increase is $\dfrac{6.5}{17.5} \times 100 = 37\%$.
Yes, the claim is true for the size 135.

b) Standard size area = $12.9 \times 8.8 = 113.52$
Discount size area = $15 \times 10.2 = 153$, an increase of 39.48.
The percentage increase is $\dfrac{39.48}{113.52} \times 100 = 34.8\%$.
Yes, the claim is true for these measurements.

c) The given sizes which are probably rounded off imperial measurements, and the metric sizes both give more than 30% increase, which is what the advertisement is saying—at least 30% bigger.

A2

a) The table can be built up by multiplying each previous figure by 1.0875 to give the figures:
     year 1 → 1087.5
     year 2 → 1182.6563 (1182.66)
     year 3 → 1286.1387 (1286.14)
     year 4 → 1398.6758 (1398.68)
     year 5 → 1521.0599 (1521.06)
(The rounding off should only be done after all the calculations.)
The percentage increase will be $\dfrac{1521.06 - 1000}{1000} \times 100 = 52.1\%$.
Hence the statement is true.

b) If £x is invested then after 5 years it will be worth

     $x \times (1.0875)^5 = 1.52106x$
     For this investment to be at least £1000, then $1.52106x \geqslant 1000$
     hence $x \geqslant £1000 \div 1.52106$
     $x \geqslant £657.44$.
     Yet this value must be a multiple of 25, hence the value of x will be £675.

> ❝❝ You ought to put down enough information to indicate what you are doing. ❞❞

A3

a) £250 × 1.08 = £270.

b) £270 × 1.0975 = £296.325 = £296.33 (to nearest penny).

A4

If his wage before the rise is £x, then 5% is 0.05x, which equals £6.
Hence x = £6 ÷ 0.05 = £120.

A5

Principal amount is £1000, rate is 21%, applied 5 times, to give the final
amount = 1000 × (1.21)^5
          = £2593.74

A6

Inner circle = $\pi \times (3.3)^2$
Outer circle = $\pi \times (6.5)^2$
Useful area = $\pi(6.5^2 - 3.3^2)$
So the percentage of disc that is useful is given by:

$$\frac{\pi(6.5^2 - 3.3^2)}{\pi(6.5^2)} \times 100 = 74.2\%$$

A7

Bottle contains vitamin C at 52 mg per 100 ml, that is $\frac{52}{4}$ mg per 25 ml, which
is 13 mg.

Hence 173% of recommended dose = 13 mg, so recommended dose = $\frac{13}{173} \times 100 =$

7.51 mg.

A8

a) £1000 × 0.105 = £105

b) 105 × 27p × 2835p = £28.35 tax paid.
    Interest left = £(105 − 28.35) = £76.65

c) $\frac{76.65}{1000} \times 100 = 7.665\%$.

A9

a) After the first day it has 0.95% of its original water content, then after 2 days
    it will have (0.95)^2% of its original water content, which is 0.9025, hence the
    plant has lost (100 − 90.25)% which is 9.75%.

b) If the flower has drooped after x days, then (0.95)^x < 0.75,
    By trial of x = 1, x = 2, etc. we find that (0.95)^5 = 0.77378
                                      and (0.95)^6 = 0.73509.
    So the smallest integer value of x to satisfy the situation is 6.

A10

> ❝❝ Do say so when your
> method is trial and
> improvement, it is quite
> acceptable as long as you
> indicate that is what you
> have done and you've tried a
> few trials. ❞❞

a) £(200) × (1.07)^2 = £228.98.

b) 200 × (1.07)^x ⩾ 300
    →   (1.07)^x ⩾ 1.5
    By trial of x = 1, 2, 3 . . . we find that 1.07^5 = 1.40
                                      and 1.07^6 = 1.5007.
    So after 6 complete years there will be more than £300 in the account.

A11

a) i) The final figures to put in the table will be
       $p(0.2) = 1.056$ $p(0.3) = 1.066$ $p(0.45) = 1.0585$.
   ii) You should have a smooth quadratic curve like the top of a small hill.

b) % increase in price (P) $\propto$ % decrease in audience (A).
    Hence P = KA (K being the constant of proportionality).
    When P = 10, A = 6,

    hence $10 = 6K \rightarrow K = \dfrac{5}{3}$

    i) When P = 1, $A = 1 \div \dfrac{5}{3} = \dfrac{3}{5} = 0.6\%$.

   ii) (Original takings) $\times 0.994 \times 1.01 =$ (Original takings) $\times 1.003\,94$.
       So the change in takings will be 0.394% increase.

   iii) We can now see that the horizontal x axis represents the % change
        in prices, while the vertical $p(x)$ represents the % change in takings.
        The top of the hill on the graph will give us the maximum rise in
        takings. This is where the graph is at $x = 0.33$. So the percentage rise
        in prices is 33%.

c) From the graph, when $x = 0.33$, $p(x) = 1.067$, which represents the increase.
    So the most the threatre could take would be £380 $\times$ 1.067, which is £405.46,
    which should be rounded off to give a final answer of £405.

GRADE CHECKLIST

For a Grade B you should:

Be able to: solve numerical problems.

For a Grade A you should also:

Be able to: use a calculator to investigate compound interest problems.

A STUDENT'S ANSWER WITH EXAMINER'S COMMENTS

Question

In January 1988, an engineering firm made 20% profit on their cost prices by selling machines for £3200. The cost of manufacturing the machines was made up of wages, raw materials, electricity and maintenance in the ratios 16:6:2:1. During the year wages rose by 6%, the cost of raw materials rose by 15%, electricity charges rose by 12% and maintenance went up by 30%.

a) Find the manufacturer's cost price in January 1988.
b) Find the increase in the total cost of manufacturing during the year.
c) After these rises the firm decided to reduce its profit to 18% of the cost price. Find the new selling price.
d) Calculate the percentage profit at the end of the year if the selling price did not change from the beginning of the year.

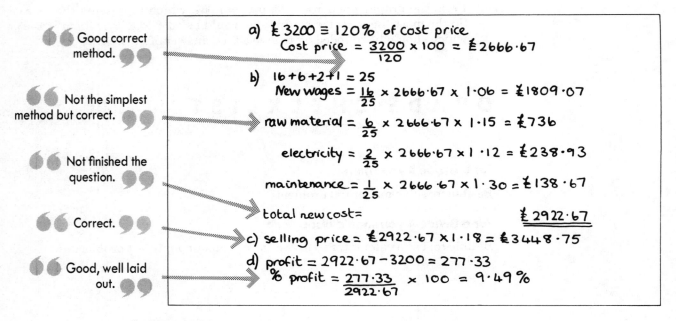

❝ Good correct method. **❞**

❝ Not the simplest method but correct. **❞**

❝ Not finished the question. **❞**

❝ Correct. **❞**

❝ Good, well laid out. **❞**

a) £3200 ≡ 120% of cost price
   Cost price = $\frac{3200}{120}$ × 100 = £2666·67

b) 16 + 6 + 2 + 1 = 25
   New wages = $\frac{16}{25}$ × 2666·67 × 1·06 = £1809·07
   raw material = $\frac{6}{25}$ × 2666·67 × 1·15 = £736
   electricity = $\frac{2}{25}$ × 2666·67 × 1·12 = £238·93
   maintenance = $\frac{1}{25}$ × 2666·67 × 1·30 = £138·67
   total new cost =   £2922·67

c) selling price = £2922·67 × 1·18 = £3448·75

d) profit = 2922·67 − 3200 = 277·33
   % profit = $\frac{277·33}{2922·67}$ × 100 = 9·49%

❝ This good answer was somewhat spoilt by the simple error of not finishing the question in part b). Otherwise, the answer has been very clearly presented showing what has been done. **❞**

GETTING STARTED

At the higher level of GCSE you are expected to be able to *generalise* a number pattern and then to use this to make *predictions*. These patterns and iterations will occur in combination with quite a few other topics also, as you will see in the exam questions.

USEFUL DEFINITIONS

Generalisation An algebraic rule to represent a pattern you have identified.

Iterative A mathematical procedure in which repetition of the same process produces results getting closer and closer to some unknown value.

Limits of Accuracy The possible lowest and highest true values of a stated measurement *before* any rounding-off has taken place.

Percentage error $\dfrac{\text{error}}{\text{possible value}} \times 100$

Standard Form $A \times 10^n$ where $1 \leqslant A \leqslant 10$ and n is an integer.

ESSENTIAL PRINCIPLES

1 ▷ PATTERNS IN NUMBER

Both in coursework, and in your final end of course examination, you will be expected to investigate, work out and recognise a variety of number patterns.

Some of these will be based on the following:

Prime numbers
 2, 3, 5, 7, 11, 13, 17, 19, 23 . . .

Square numbers
 1, 4, 9, 16, 25, 36, 49, 64, 81 . . .

These two sequences must be learned and therefore readily recognised in unfamiliar places.

WORKED EXAMPLE 1

Find the next three numbers in the sequence,

 4, 9, 25, 49, –, –, –

First recognise that all the numbers are square numbers, and hence can re-write the series as:

 $2^2, 3^2, 5^2, 7^2$

Now recognise that it is the prime numbers being squared, so the next three will be:

 $11^2, 13^2, 17^2$, which is 121, 169, 289.

EXERCISE 1

Find the next three numbers in the sequence 1, 16, 36, 64, 81, –, –, –

2 ▷ SEARCHING FOR PATTERN

The most common way is to look at the *differences*. This will in fact help you to find most of the patterns and then to continue them.

WORKED EXAMPLE 2

Find the next three numbers in the sequence 3, 7, 11, 15, 19, –, –, –
Looking at the *differences* we see:

 3→ 7→ 11→ 15→ 19→
 +4   +4   +4   +4

so the pattern can be continued by simply adding on 4 each time, to give 23, 27 and 31.

WORKED EXAMPLE 3

Find the next three numbers in the sequence 5, 6, 8, 11, 15, 20, –, –, –
Looking at the differences we see:

 5→ 6→ 8→ 11→ 15→ 20→
 +1   +2   +3   +4   +5

so the pattern can be continued by adding on 6 then 7 then 8 to give 26, 33, 41.

EXERCISE 2

Find the next three numbers in each of the following sequences:

  i) 4, 6, 9, 14, 21, 32, –, –, –
  ii) 100, 95, 90, 85, –, –, –
  iii) 10, 11, 15, 24, 40, –, –, –

It is vital that you look at the differences in a number sequence to help you find the pattern. However, sometimes you will need to consider the 'second differences' to continue the pattern.

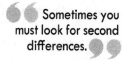

WORKED EXAMPLE 4

Find the next three numbers in the sequence 2, 3, 7, 17, 36, –, –, –
Looking at the differences we see:

$$
\begin{array}{ccccccccc}
2 & \rightarrow & 3 & \rightarrow & 7 & \rightarrow & 17 & \rightarrow & 36 \\
& +1 & \rightarrow & +4 & \rightarrow & +10 & \rightarrow & +19 & \\
& & +3 & & +6 & & +9 & &
\end{array}
$$

It is now in the 'second differences' that we notice a pattern and can continue it to give:

$$
\begin{array}{ccccccccc}
& & 36 & \rightarrow & 67 & \rightarrow & 113 & \rightarrow & 177 \\
& +19 & \rightarrow & +31 & \rightarrow & +46 & \rightarrow & +64 & \\
+9 & & +12 & & +15 & & +18 & &
\end{array}
$$

> Sometimes you must look for second differences.

hence the next three numbers are 67, 113 and 177.

EXERCISE 3

Find the next three numbers in the sequence 1, 3, 6, 11, 20, 37, –, –, –

This technique of looking for differences can, if required, be continued on to the 'third differences', or even further. When answering this type of question you should always illustrate *how* you found your pattern.

These patterns will very often be part of a longer investigation type question where you would probably also be asked for the general term or the *n*th term, which we consider later in this chapter.

3 ▷ GENERATING A SEQUENCE

At times you will be given a rule to follow so as to generate a number pattern.

WORKED EXAMPLE 5

U_n is the *n*th term in a sequence. If $U_n = \dfrac{n(n+1)}{2}$ then generate the first five terms of this sequence and describe the type of numbers, generated.

The first five terms are found by substituting into the formula $U_n = \dfrac{n(n+1)}{2}$ the numbers $n = 1, 2, 3, 4, 5$ to give

$$
\frac{1 \times 2}{2}, \quad \frac{2 \times 3}{2}, \quad \frac{3 \times 4}{2}, \quad \frac{4 \times 5}{2}, \quad \frac{5 \times 6}{2},
$$
$$
= 1, \quad 3, \quad 6, \quad 10, \quad 15,
$$

This pattern is the 'triangle numbers' usually found by considering *triangular patterns* as in Fig. 4.1

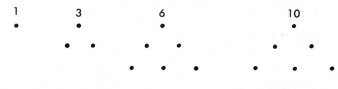

Fig. 4.1

EXERCISE 4

Generate the first few terms of the sequence given by: $U_n = n(2n - 1)$.

Alternative Notation

This can also be done by defining how the terms use the *one before* to build upon. For example, the *n*th term of a sequence could be given by the formula

$$U_n = 3 + 2.U_{(n-1)}$$

So where

$U_1 = 5$ then we would calculate the following terms as:
$U_2 = 3 + 2 \times 5 = 13$
$U_3 = 3 + 2 \times 13 = 29$
$U_4 = 3 + 2 \times 29 = 61$ etc.

This process is more commonly used in *iterations* which come later in the chapter.

4 ⟩ GENERALISING

❝❝ Being able to do this will show that you are a grade B or better. ❞❞

This is where, from a given pattern of numbers, you try to state the pattern *algebraically*, as in the section above. This can be a long investigation by trial and error, but if you can learn some simple patterns to recognise, and some simple rules to follow, then you will find the generalisations more quickly.

Rules to follow

a) Look first to see if it is an obvious pattern or one you've remembered.
b) Look at the *differences* to see what type of relationship you are looking for. If the *first* differences do not reveal anything, try the *second* or *third* differences, and so on.
c) Break the sequences up into *factors* to see what other links you can find.

We now look in more detail at these procedures.

a) COMMON PATTERNS

i) $2, 4, 6, 8, 10$ .... $2n$

ii) $2, 4, 8, 16$ .... 2^n

iii) $1, 4, 9, 16, 25$ .... n^2

iv) $1, 3, 6, 10, 15$ .... $\dfrac{n(n+1)}{2}$

iv) are the triangle numbers, well worth recognising when you see them.

b) LOOKING AT DIFFERENCES

Same difference

If between each term you find the same difference, d, then where 'a' is the first number in the sequence, the nth term will be given by

$$U_n = a + d(n-1)$$

WORKED EXAMPLE 6

Find the nth term in the sequence $4, 7, 10, 13, 16 \ldots$
We notice that the difference is always 3, and the first term is 4, hence the nth term will be $4 + 3(n-1)$, which could be simplified to $3n + 1$.

EXERCISE 5

Find the nth term in the following sequence $7, 12, 17, 22 \ldots$

Multiple differences

If the differences give recognisable multiples of, say, m, then where the first term is 'a' the nth term will be given by

$$U_n = a + m\frac{n(n-1)}{2}$$

WORKED EXAMPLE 7

Find the nth term in the sequence $1, 4, 10, 19, 31 \ldots$
We notice that the differences are $3, 6, 9, 12$, the multiples of 3, and that the first term is 1, hence the nth term will be give by

$$U_n = 1 + 3\frac{n(n-1)}{2}$$

EXERCISE 6

Find the nth term of the sequence $8, 15, 29, 50, 78 \ldots$

Square differences

If the differences give the square numbers, ie. $1, 4, 9, 16, 25 \ldots$ then where the first term is 'a', the nth term will be given by

$$a + \frac{n}{6}(n+1)(2n+1)$$

WORKED EXAMPLE 8

Find the nth term of the sequences $6, 7, 11, 20, 36 \ldots$
We notice that the differences are $1, 4, 9, 16, \ldots$, and that the first term is 6, hence the nth term is given by

$$U_n = 6 + \frac{n}{6}(n + 1)(2n + 1)$$

Triangle differences

If the differences give the well known triangle numbers, ie. $1, 3, 6, 10, 15, \ldots$, and a first term of a, then the nth term will be given by

$$U_n = a + \frac{n}{6}(n + 1)(n + 2)$$

There are lots of different differences that can now link to one of the above types, and hence you can generalise the sequence. However, do look carefully at the differences as they may be a multiple or a factor of one of the above types.

WORKED EXAMPLE 9

Find the nth term of the sequence $8, 10, 16, 28, 48, \ldots$
We notice the differences are $2, 6, 12, 20 \ldots$ which are not recognisable until you halve them to get $1, 3, 6, 10 \ldots$ (the triangle numbers). Hence the nth term will be given by

$$U_n = 8 + 2 \times \frac{n}{6}(n + 1)(n + 2)$$

$$U_n = 8 + \frac{n}{3}(n + 1)(n + 2)$$

EXERCISE 7

Find the nth term of the sequence $1, 9, 25, 49 \ldots$

c) FIND FACTORS

Sometimes we look at the differences and see nothing, we go to second differences and see nothing. If this is the case then we can look at *factors* of the sequence and see how they are being built up. For example, look at the triangle numbers:

$1, 3, 6, 10, 15, 21 \ldots$

Looking at the differences gives us $2, 3, 4, 5, \ldots$, but how does this help us to find U_n? Well actually it can do, but that would be taking us into much higher mathematics. Suppose instead that we write down the *factors* of each term; we then have:

1	3	6	10	15	21
↓	↓	↓	↓	↓	↓
1×1	1×3	2×3	2×5	3×5	3×7

There seems nothing to see first of all; but then on closer inspection we see that if we *double* the *smaller of each factor* we get the interesting pattern:

1	3	6	10	15	21
↓	↓	↓	↓	↓	↓
1×1	1×3	2×3	2×5	3×5	3×7

double 1 term:

(1×2)	(2×3)	(4×3)	(4×5)	(6×5)	(6×7)
↓	↓	↓	↓	↓	↓
$\frac{1}{2}(1 \times 2)$	$\frac{1}{2}(2 \times 3)$	$\frac{1}{2}(3 \times 4)$	$\frac{1}{2}(4 \times 5)$	$\frac{1}{2}(5 \times 6)$	$\frac{1}{2}(6 \times 7)$
↓	↓	↓	↓	↓	↓
U_1	U_2	U_3	U_4	U_5	U_6

which gives us very neatly

$U_n \rightarrow \frac{1}{2}n(n + 1)$.

So, when looking for patterns:

a) look for *familiar* patterns you've seen before
b) look at the *differences*
c) look at the *factors*.

EXERCISE 8

Find the nth term of the sequence 3, 8, 15, 24 . . .

---

5 > ITERATION

An *iteration* is when a *generating term*, U_n, is used to *keep generating terms* until a certain situation is satisfied.

Example — A solution to the equation $x^2 - 2x - 3 = 0$ can be found by re-writing the equation in the form: $x^2 = 3 + 2x$

Dividing by x gives $\qquad x = \dfrac{3}{x} + 2$

Suppose we assume a *starting solution* x_1 to this equation as being $x_1 = 2$. We now find the value this 'starting solution' makes the right hand side of the equation. We find that

$$x_2 = \frac{3}{x_1} + 2 = \frac{3}{2} + 2 = 3.5$$

We then use this value of $x_2 = 3.5$ as a *better solution* in the equation. We now get

$$x_3 = \frac{3}{3.5} + 2 = 2.857 \text{ (the rest is in the calculator)}.$$

> **This is ideal to work through on a computer, have a go and just see how accurate it can be.**

By *continuing* this process we find:

$x_4 = 3.05$
$x_5 = 2.98$
$x_6 = 3.01$
$x_7 = 3.00$
$x_8 = 3.00$

The process was continued until the value to 2 decimal places was the same two times. The actual calculator value was used each time in the iteration. Hence the solution here is $x = 3$, which can be shown to be correct.

WORKED EXAMPLE 10

Show that an iteration formula to solve the equation

$$x^3 - 5x + 1 = 0 \text{ is } x_{n+1} = \frac{x_n{}^3 + 1}{5}.$$

Starting with $x_1 = 0$, continue the iteration until you get a solution correct to 3 decimal places.

The equation $x^3 - 5x + 1 = 0$ can be re-written to give

$$5x = x^3 + 1$$
$$\text{hence} \quad x = \frac{x^3 + 1}{5}$$

This can be solved using the iteration method where $x_{n+1} = \dfrac{(x_n)^3 + 1}{5}$

Working the iteration out to four decimal places (but keeping the accurate figure in the calculator)

$x_1 = 0$
$x_2 = (0 + 1)/5 = 0.2$
$x_3 = (0.2^3 + 1)/5 = 0.2016$
$x_4 = \qquad\qquad 0.2016.$

Hence a solution to the equation is $x = 0.2016$.

EXERCISE 9

Solve the equation, *to 3 decimal places,* $x^2 + 3x - 1 = 0$ by the iteration formula

$$U_{n+1} = \frac{1 - (U_n)^2}{3}$$ (starting with $U_1 = 0$), and show it as a solution.

6 > **LIMITS OF ACCURACY**

Whenever we round off or approximate we immediately bring a slight *error* into the figures. For example, if I said that my height is 173 cm, then I could be as small as 172.5 cm or as tall as 173.499 999 cm. This is because:

- the smallest figure that can *round up* to 173 cm is 172.5 cm
- the largest figure that can *round down* to 173 cm is 173.499999 . . . cm

These lowest and highest values are called the *limits of the accuracy.*

Any stated measurement is rounded off to some *degree of accuracy*. This determines the possible true values *before* the rounding took place. In other words, the degree of accuracy used in the rounding process will determine the limits of the accuracy of the stated measurement.

Examples:

> *Finding the limits of the accuracy when rounding-off has taken place.*

i) A length of 32.7 cm is rounded to 1 decimal place:
  - the smallest possible value is 32.65
  - the largest possible value is 32.749 999 9 . . .
    or rather $32.65 \leqslant$ length < 32.75.
ii) A weight of 5.34 kg is rounded to 2 decimal places:
  - it can have values $5.335 \leqslant$ weight < 5.345.
iii) A weight of of 200 grams is rounded to 1 significant figure:
  - it can have values $150 \leqslant$ weight < 250.
iv) A length of 6.203 m is rounded to 3 decimal places:
  - it can have values $6.2025 \leqslant$ length < 6.2035.

EXERCISE 10

Write down the limits of accuracy for the values of the following measures.

1. 8 cm.
2. 6.3 m
3. 9.17 cm
4. 20 cm

7 > **PERCENTAGE ERROR**

The error made by the rounding off can be expressed as a *percentage error.*

$$\text{percentage error} = \frac{\text{error}}{\text{possible value}} \times 100$$

The greatest *absolute* errors occur at the limits of accuracy.

WORKED EXAMPLE 11

Calculate the greatest % error of a given height of 26 cm.

Solution
The possible values are $25.5 \leqslant$ height < 26.5
The greatest errors then are at 25.5 and at 26.5, both of which give an

absolute error of 0.5 cm.

■ At 25.5 cm the % error is $\dfrac{0.5}{25.5} \times 100 = 1.96\%$.

■ At 26.5 cm the % error is $\dfrac{0.5}{26.5} \times 100 = 1.89\%$.

The greatest % error is 1.96%.

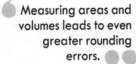

The greatest % error is always at the lower limit of accuracy.

EXERCISE 11

Find the greatest percentage error of each of the following measures.

1. a) 9 m   b) 14 kg
2. a) 1.6 m   b) 0.5 kg
3. Tommy has 30 marbles. He weighs one marble at 75 g.
   a) What is the largest weight of his 30 marbles?
   b) What is the lowest weight of his 30 marbles?
   c) What is his greatest percentage error?
   d) What is his lowest percentage error?

Measuring areas and volumes leads to even greater rounding errors.

Problems involving % errors and limits of accuracy

When we measure *areas* and *volumes* then the errors will be compounded upon each other to make still larger errors from the rounding process.

WORKED EXAMPLE 12

A rectangle has sides given as 5 cm and 8 cm.

Calculate
a) the greatest possible area that this rectangle could have.
b) the greatest percentage error in the calculated area.

Solution
a) The upper limit of each side is just under 5.5 cm and 8.5 cm respectively. Hence the greatest possible area is just under $5.5 \times 8.5 = 46.75$. So the greatest area is slightly less than 46.75 cm².
b) The greatest percentage error is at the *lower limit* of each side, giving an area of 4.5×7.5 which is 33.75 cm².
   The *given* lengths produce an area of $5 \times 8 = 40$ cm².
   Hence we have a possible error of $40 - 33.75 = 6.25$ cm².

   Greatest percentage error $= \dfrac{6.25}{33.75} \times 100 = 18.5\%$.

EXERCISE 12

1. A rectangular plot of land has its sides measured to the nearest metre. The measurements recorded are 5 m and 3 m.
   Find:
   a) the limits of accuracy for each measurement.
   b) What is the maximum possible area of the plot.
   c) What is the minimum possible value of the perimeter of the plot.
   d) What is the maximum percentage error on the area.
2. The volume of a cuboid is 154 000 cm³. The area of the base is 618 cm². Both measurements are rounded to three significant figures.
   Find the limits of accuracy on the height of the cuboid.

8 STANDARD FORM

Standard form is written as a number between 1 and 10 multiplied by ten raised to a power (index). This is a widely used method for displaying the multiplication of very large (and very small) numbers.
Here are some examples of standard form numbers:

$$9.134 \times 10^1 \qquad 5.6 \times 10^3 \qquad 3.45 \times 10^{16} \qquad 7.035 \times 10^{27}$$

Write down ten more standard form numbers of your own. Notice how standard form numbers are made up of *two parts*:

- The *first part* being a number between 1 and 9.9999 . . . (less than 10).
- The *second part* being the number 10 raised to a power (or index).

In Short . . .

Standard form is
$$A \times 10^n \text{ where } 1 \leqslant A < 10$$
$$\text{and } n \text{ is an integer}$$

To Change A Number to Standard Form

Follow the rules:
  i)   Move the decimal point so that it lies between the first two digits. This gives the number A.
  ii) Count how many places you have moved the decimal point in order for it to be in that position. This gives n (the power).

Examples
$$215\,000 \quad = 2.15 \times 100\,000 \quad = 2.15 \times 10^5$$
$$809 \qquad = 8.09 \times 100 \qquad = 8.09 \times 10^2$$
$$60\,000\,000 = 6.0 \times 10\,000\,000 = 6.0 \times 10^7 \text{ (we could have written } 6 \times 10^7\text{)}$$

EXERCISE 13

Find the square of each number below and give your answer in standard form

a) 3715   b) 650   c) 299   d) 5 million   e) $6\frac{1}{2}$ million.

To Change A Standard Form Number Back To 'Normal' Number

Here we reverse the process we previously followed. For example,
$$9.6 \times 10^4 = 96\,000$$

Notice how we move the decimal point one place over the 6, and then a further three more places. So we put three zeros after 96.

Examples
$$7.31 \times 10^5 \ = 731\,000$$
$$1.9 \times 10^6 \quad = 1\,900\,000$$
$$4.345 \times 10^2 = 434.5$$
$$6.07 \times 10^1 = 60.7$$
$$4.156 \times 10^3 = 4156$$

EXERCISE 14

First convert the following standard form numbers back to normal, then find their *square roots*.

a) 2.56×10^4 b) 6.4×10^3 c) 2.25×10^6

Standard Form For Numbers Less Than 1

How can we write 0.000 53 in standard form?

To answer the above question we start by doing exactly what we did before, i.e. following our two rules. However, the four places of decimal we have moved are in the opposite *direction* to that when the numbers are greater than 1. So this time we put in a negative sign to go with the power.

This gives us 5.3×10^{-4}.

> Notice how we use a negative power (index) to indicate the standard form of a number smaller than 1.

Examples
$$0.932 \qquad = 9.32 \times 10^{-1}$$
$$0.045\,1 \qquad = 4.51 \times 10^{-2}$$
$$0.000\,000\,71 = 7.1 \times 10^{-7}$$

If the product of two numbers is 1, then they are reciprocals of each other.

The Meaning Of A Negative Power (Index)

It is worth remembering that if we divide by a number, it is the same as multiplying by the reciprocal of that number.

Examples
$12 \div 6 = 12 \times \frac{1}{6} = 2$
$18 \div 3 = 18 \times \frac{1}{3} = 6$

In the same way, when we divide by 10 raised to some power, it is the same as multiplying by '1 over 10 raised to some power'.

Examples
$800 \div 10^2 = 800 \times \dfrac{1}{10^2} = 8$

$936 \div 10^3 = 936 \times \dfrac{1}{10^3} = 0.936$

Now, we write $\dfrac{1}{10^2}$ as 10^{-2}, and $\dfrac{1}{10^3}$ as 10^{-3}, and so on.

> In general, $10^{-n} = \dfrac{1}{10^n}$

So, when we use a negative power in the standard form notation, it tells us that we are multiplying by 1 over 10 raised to that power.

Examples
$6.4 \times 10^{-2} = 6.4 \times \dfrac{1}{10^2} = 0.064$

$9.7 \times 10^{-3} = 9.7 \times \dfrac{1}{10^3} = 0.0097$

Rounding Off Using Standard Form

Generally, when dealing with standard form numbers, you would want to round off to 1, 2 or 3 significant figures. Remember, it is only the first part of the number that would be rounded off.

Examples
Round off the following:
a) 5.621×10^{17} to one significant figure
b) 7.053×10^{-8} to two significant figures

 It is only the *first part* of the standard form number that is rounded off.

Working
a) $5.621 \times 10^{17} \approx 6 \times 10^{17}$ (*Note*: We do **not** use 6.0, *as this would*
b) $7.053 \times 10^{-8} \approx 7.1 \times 10^{-8}$ *be **two** significant figures.*)

EXERCISE 15

1.   Convert the following fractions to decimal numbers. Then express each decimal in standard form correct to three significant figures.
     a) $\frac{1}{121}$ b) $\frac{4}{125}$ c) $31\frac{5}{36}$
2.   Write the answers to the following in standard form, correct to two significant figures.

     a) 215^2 b) $\sqrt{(3710)}$ c) $(0.00031)^3$ d) $\sqrt{\left(\dfrac{1}{\pi}\right)}$

ESTIMATION, APPROXIMATION AND OTHER USES OF STANDARD FORM

We can estimate the rough size of some awkward arithmetic problems by using our work on standard form, as in the following examples. Notice how we break down each number in the problem separately into standard form before solving.

WORKED EXAMPLE 13

Find an approximate value of $390\,000 \times 62\,100\,000$.

Working

We first approximate $390\,000$ to $400\,000$ and $62\,100\,000$ to $60\,000\,000$, then change each number to standard form, giving:

$4 \times 10^5 \times 6 \times 10^7$

We now rearrange to give:

$4 \times 6 \times 10^5 \times 10^7$

That gives

24×10^{12}

which gives

2.4×10^{13}

 Recall that $10^m \times 10^n = 10^{m+n}$.

WORKED EXAMPLE 14

Find an approximate value for $731\,520\,000 \times 0.000\,815\,34$.

Working

$731\,520\,000 \approx 700\,000\,000$
$0.000\,815\,34 \approx 0.000\,8$

We change each number to standard form, giving:

$7 \times 10^8 \times 8 \times 10^{-4}$

We now rearrange, to give

$7 \times 8 \times 10^8 \times 10^{-4}$

That gives

56×10^4

which gives

5.6×10^5

WORKED EXAMPLE 15

Find a rough estimate to the following problem:

$0.000\,000\,005\,82 \div 0.000\,016\,45$

Working

We first approximate and change each number to standard form, giving:

$6 \times 10^{-9} \div 2 \times 10^{-5}$

We now rearrange to give

$(6 \div 2) \times (10^{-9} \div 10^{-5})$

That gives 3×10^{-4} (*since* $-9 - (-5) = -4$)
which is $0.000\,3$

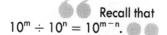 Recall that $10^m \div 10^n = 10^{m-n}$.

WORKED EXAMPLE 16

Find a rough estimate to the following problem:

$$\frac{(615\,800\,000 \times 0.005\,971)}{0.081\,62}$$

Working

We first find an approximation and change each number to standard form, giving:

$$\frac{6 \times 10^8 \times 6 \times 10^{-3}}{8 \times 10^{-2}}$$

We now rearrange to give

$$\frac{(6 \times 6)}{8} \times \frac{(10^8 \times 10^{-3})}{10^{-2}}$$

That gives $\dfrac{36}{8} \times 10^{(8-3--2)}$

which gives 4.5×10^7

EXERCISE 16

Use the idea of 'standard form' to find rough estimates to the following problems, leaving your answer in a suitable form.

a) $91\,500 \times 710\,000$

b) $156\,100 \times 0.008\,156$

c) $0.000\,615 \times 0.007\,59$

d) $\dfrac{(2\,410\,000 \times 0.003\,14)}{3600}$

e) $\dfrac{(580\,000 \times 0.790\,01)}{0.013\,0}$

AWKWARD CALCULATIONS IN STANDARD FORM

You really are being assessed on your use of the calculator when evaluating such questions as

$$\frac{6.85 \times 10^9 \times 7.1 \times 10^{17}}{3.85 \times 10^4 \times 7.2 \times 10^8}$$

You should let the calculator do all the hard work, and one efficient way to cope with such a problem is to recognise that you need to keep the denominator (bottom part of the fraction) in the memory first.

Follow through the calculator sequence for the above problem and compare it with your calculator.

3.85	EXP	4	×	7.2	EXP	8	=	Min

6.85	EXP	9	×	7.1	EXP	17	÷	MR	=

this should give you a result of 1.75×10^{14}

EXERCISE 17

Evaluate the answers to the following in standard form, to three significant figures.

1. $\dfrac{4.08 \times 10^4 \times 1.89 \times 10^5}{9.15 \times 10^{-6} \times 4.95 \times 10^{-3}}$

2. $\dfrac{8.7 \times 10^5 + 2.61 \times 10^7}{9.2 \times 10^4 - 8.5 \times 10^2}$

S O L U T I O N S   T O   E X E R C I S E S

S1

The sequence can be rewritten as 1^2, 4^2, 6^2, 8^2, 9^2, these are the squares of the non-prime integers, hence the next three numbers are 10^2, 12^2 and 14^2 which are 100, 144 and 196.

S2

i) Differences are the prime numbers, hence the next three numbers are 45, 62 and 81.
ii) Differences are -5 in each case, hence the next three numbers are 80, 75 and 70.
iii) Differences are the square numbers, hence the next three numbers are 65, 101 and 150.

S3

Look at second differences, these are 1, 2, 4, 8, (16, 32, 64) used to build down to give the next three numbers as 70, 135 and 264.

S4

$U_1 = 1, U_2 = 6, U_3 = 15, U_4 = 28$.

S5

The difference is always 5, and the first term is 7, hence the nth term is given by $7 + 5(n - 1)$ which could be simplified to $5n + 2$.

S6

The differences are 7, 14, 21, 28 which are the multiples of 7. The first term is 8, hence the nth term is $8 + 7\dfrac{n(n - 1)}{2}$.

S7

These are $1^2, 3^2, 5^2, 7^2$, the odd numbers squared. Hence we need to link up

$$1\text{st term} \rightarrow 1^2$$
$$2\text{nd term} \rightarrow 3^2$$
$$3\text{rd term} \rightarrow 5^2$$
$$4\text{th term} \rightarrow 7^2$$

hence the nth term $\rightarrow (2n - 1)^2$

S8

The differences helped me to predict the next few terms but not the nth term so readily. However, on looking at the factors I noticed:

U_1	U_2	U_3	U_4	U_n
↓	↓	↓	↓	↓
3	8	15	24	
1×3	2×4	3×5	4×6	$n \times (n + 2)$

hence $U_n = n(n + 2)$.

S9

The iteration to three decimal places is:

$$U_2 = 0.333$$
$$U_3 = 0.296$$
$$U_4 = 0.304$$
$$U_5 = 0.302$$
$$U_6 = 0.303$$
$$U_7 = 0.303$$

so the solution is $x = 0.303$.

By substituting $x = 0.303$ into $x^2 + 3x + 1$ we get 0.0009, showing it to be very close to zero.

S10

1. $7.5 \leqslant$ measure < 8.5
2. $6.25 \leqslant$ measure < 6.35
3. $9.165 \leqslant$ measure < 9.175
4. $15 \leqslant$ measure < 25

S11

1. a) $\dfrac{0.5}{8.5} \times 100 = 5.9\%$ b) $\dfrac{0.5}{13.5} \times 100 = 3.7\%$

2. a) $\dfrac{0.05}{1.55} \times 100 = 3.2\%$ b) $\dfrac{0.05}{0.45} \times 100 = 11.1\%$

3. a) $30 \times 75.5 \text{ g} = 2265 \text{ g}$ b) $30 \times 74.5 \text{ g} = 2235 \text{ g}$

   c) $\dfrac{0.5}{74.5} \times 100 = 0.67\%$ d) 0%, he could be accurate!

S12

1. a) $4.5 \leqslant$ length $< 5.5, 2.5 \leqslant$ width < 3.5

   b) $5.5 \times 3.5 = 19.25 \text{ m}^2$ c) $(4.5 + 2.5) \times 2 = 14 \text{ m}$

   so greatest $< 19.25 \text{ m}^2$ d) $\dfrac{5 \times 3 - 11.25}{5 \times 3} \times 100 = 25\%$

2. least height is $\dfrac{\text{least volume}}{\text{greatest area}} = \dfrac{153\,500}{618.5} = 248.18$

   greatest height is $\dfrac{\text{greatest volume}}{\text{least area}} = \dfrac{154\,500}{617.5} = 250.2$

hence the limits of accuracy are $248.18 \leqslant$ height < 250.2

S13

a) 1.38×10^7 b) 4.23×10^5 c) 8.94×10^4
d) 2.5×10^{13} e) 4.23×10^{13}

S14

a) 160   b) 80   c) 1500

S15

1. a) 4.76×10^{-2} b) 3.20×10^{-2} c) 3.11×10^{1}
2. a) 4.6×10^{4} b) 6.1×10^{1} c) 3.0×10^{-11} d) 5.6×10^{-1}

S16

a) 6.4×10^{10} b) 1.2×10^{3} c) 4.8×10^{-6} d) 2 e) 3.5×10^{7}

S17

1. 1.70×10^{17} 2. 2.96×10^{2}

EXAM TYPE QUESTIONS

Q1

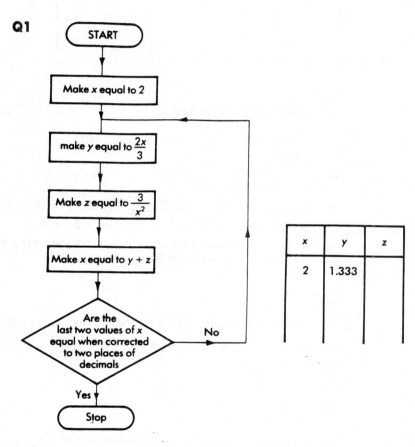

Fig. 4.2

a) Work through the flow diagram writing down the value of x, y and z in a table, as shown in Fig. 4.2, recording only the first three decimal places of your answers.

b) Cube the last value of x and comment on the result.

c) Give the last value of x correct to two decimal places.   (MEG)

> Try to make your comment on some mathematical insight you can notice.

Q2

The nth term of a sequence is given by the formula

$$U_n = \frac{1}{1 + U_{n-1}} \text{ and } U_4 = 3$$

a) Calculate the value of U_5.

b) Calculate the value of U_3.   (NEAB)

Fig. 4.3

Q3

Four rods are used to make a square, as shown in Fig. 4.3.

Rods are then addded to make a row of 2 squares, then 3 squares, and so on, as in Fig. 4.4.

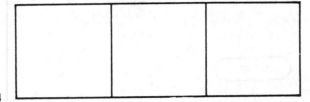

Fig. 4.4

a)   How many rods are needed to make a row of
  i) 5 squares
  ii) 6 squares
  iii) 15 squares?
b)   Find the formula which gives the number of rods, r, needed to make a row of s squares in the form: $r =$
c)   Use your formula to find how many squares could be made with 70 rods.
d)   Re-arrange your formula in b) into the form: $s =$
e)   What is the greatest number of squares you can make in a row with 120 rods? How many rods will you have left over?   (WJEC)

Q4

Write down the missing TWO numbers in each of the sequences:

a)   64, 32, 16, –, –, 2
b)   1, 2, 6, –, –, 720   (ULEAC)

Q5

In a sequence of fractions, the next term after $\dfrac{x}{y}$ is $\dfrac{x+y}{2x+y}$.

The first term is $\dfrac{2}{3}$.

a)   Write down the next six terms of the sequence $\dfrac{2}{5}, \dfrac{5}{7}, –, –, –, –, –$

b)   Find the *squares* of the values of these six terms to as many decimal places as your calculator will give. What do you notice about these squares of values?

c)   Find the term in the sequence which comes immediately before $\dfrac{2378}{3363}$

d)   One term in the sequence is $\dfrac{p}{q}$. Find, in terms of p and q, the term which comes immediately before $\dfrac{p}{q}$.   (MEG)

Q6

A computer has been programmed to generate a sequence of numbers. The first six numbers that it produces are:

9, 16, 23, 30, 37, 44.

a) Write down the next two numbers of the sequence that will appear.
b) Work out the 60th number to appear.
c) Write down an expression for the rth term of the sequence.
d) How many terms of the sequence will the computer have produced when the first number over 2000 appears? (NEAB)

Q7

Figure 4.5 shows part of the graph of $f : x \rightarrow x^3 - 2x - 1$ and the solution $x = w$ of the equation $x^3 - 2x - 1 = 0$.

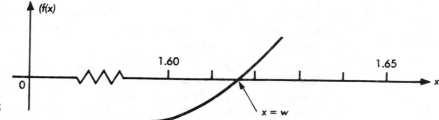

Fig. 4.5

a) From this diagram, estimate the value of w correct to two decimal places.

b) Show that $x^3 - 2x - 1 = 0$ may be written as $x = \sqrt{\left(2 + \dfrac{1}{x}\right)}$

c) Using $x_{n+1} = \sqrt{\left(2 + \dfrac{1}{x_n}\right)}$ and taking x_1 to be the value you obtained as your estimate for w in part a), calculate x_2, x_3 and x_4. In each case, write down all the digits shown on your calculator.

d) Continue this iteration until you can give the value of w correct to five decimal places. Write down this value of w. (ULEAC)

Q8

a) Here is a sequence of numbers 2, 4, 8, 16, 32, 64.
   i) Write down a formula for the nth number in this sequence.
      You can get from any number of this sequence to the next number by adding on as in Fig. 4.6.

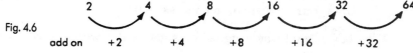

Fig. 4.6

add on   +2   +4   +8   +16   +32

   ii) The 'add on' numbers also form a sequence. What do you notice about this sequence?
   iii) Use algebra to explain why this happens.
b) Now write down this sequence 3, 9, 27, 81, 243, 729.
   i) Write down the 'add on' numbers for this sequence.
   ii) What is the connection between the 'add on' sequence and the original sequence?
   iii) Use algebra to explain why this happens.
c) If instead of starting with 2 or 3, the original sequence starts: a, a², a³, a⁴, what is the connection between the 'add on' sequence and the original sequence?

d) Here is an 'add on' sequence: $+20, +100, +500, +2500$.
    i) If the original sequence is of the type described in c) write down the first five numbers of the original sequence.
    ii) Write down the first five numbers of a different original sequence (not of the type described in c)) which has the same 'add on' sequence.
    iii) Write down a formula for the nth number in the sequence you have given in ii).
                                                                            (OCSEB)

Q9

a) The symbol $n!$ (usually called "factorial n") is used to stand for the result of multiplying together the first n whole numbers; so that, for example

$$10! = 1 \times 2 \times 3 \times 4 \times 5 \times 6 \times 7 \times 8 \times 9 \times 10$$

My calculator gives the value of 10! to be 3628800. Explain how you could tell, without actually doing the multiplication, that the value of 10! ends in just two zeros.

b) The value of 100! is too large to be found on the calculator. Find, without using your calculator, how many zeros there are at the end of 100! Explain your reasoning clearly.

c) A book of tables states that 100! is approximately 9.33×10^{157}. Putting this together with b), we know how many digits there are in 100!, that some are certainly zero and that some are certainly not zero. Making the assumption that each of the digits $0, 1, 2, \ldots 9$ occurs about the same number of times amongst the remaining digits, estimate how many zeros there are altogether in 100! when it is written out in full. Show your working.   (OCSEB)

Q10

Ranjit measures the dimensions of a rectangular field, correct to the nearest metre. He finds that the length is 105 m and the width is 63 m.

a) Between what bounds must the true length lie?
b) Calculate the upper and lower bounds for the area of the field.

Q11

The price of gold is £348.50 per ounce. The density of gold is 19.3 g/cm^3 (i.e. 1 cm^3 of gold weighs 19.3 g). There are 28.35 grams in one ounce. These figures can be treated as **exact** measurements.

A solid gold bar, in the shape of a cuboid, has sides 4.15 cm, 2.04 cm and 5.96 cm. These measurements are made to the nearest 0.01 cm.

a) What is the range of prices for this bar of gold?
    Give your answers to the nearest £10.

The bar of gold was weighed on some scales which gave a value of 974 g to the nearest gram.

b) Estimate the range of prices for the gold bar using this value.
c) Explain why the weighing method appears to be better.

Q12

Given that the numbers 2.4, 4.3 and 0.8 are accurate to 1 decimal place, calculate upper and lower bounds for the calculation

$$\frac{2.4 + 4.3}{0.8}$$

Q13

a) A distance is measured as 100 m, correct to the nearest metre. What is the least value that the actual distance could be?

b) A student runs the distance in 14.3 seconds correct to 1 decimal place. What is the greatest time the athlete could have taken?

c) Calculate the least and greatest average speeds for the athlete in metres per second.

Q14

A light year is approximately 5 878 000 000 000 miles. Write this number in standard form.

Q15

i) Express 43.6×10^{-3} in standard index form.

ii) Calculate the value of $(1.3221 \times 10^{-2})(1.17 \times 10^{-4})$.

Q16

$$D = 1000 - 1.28 \times 16^2$$

Use the formula to find the value of D.

Q17

The mass, M, of the Earth is 5.98×10^{24} kg.
The mass, m, of the Moon is 7.35×10^{22} kg.

a) Explain how it is possible to say which of these masses is greater, without doing any working.

b) Calculate the value of $\dfrac{M}{m}$. Give your answer in standard form.

Q18

Given that $m = 5 \times 10^{-2}$ and $n = 4 \times 10^3$, calculate, giving each answer in standard form

i) mn ii) m^3 iii) $\dfrac{1}{m} + n$

Q19

a) When buying his groceries in a supermarket, George estimates the maximum amount he will have to pay by rounding up the price of each article to the nearest 10p (unless it is already a multiple of 10p). For example, an article costing £2.21 is rounded up to £2.30 and an article costing £1.58 is rounded up to £1.60.

On one particular occasion, he bought 12 articles and his estimate was £8.30.

What is the smallest possible total of the actual prices of the 12 articles? Show your working clearly.

b) Alyson uses a similar method but she rounds the price of each article to the nearest 10p (up or down as necessary with 5p always being rounded up). For example, an article costing £2.21 is rounded down to £2.20 and an article costing £1.58 is rounded up to £1.60.

She bought 20 articles whose total price was £12.56.

Calculate the greatest and least possible values of her estimate. Explain your method.

Q20

A **packet** of custard cream biscuits costs 33p and contains 24 biscuits.
A **bargain box** of the same type of biscuits costs £3.29 and has a weight (excluding the box and packing) of 3.6 kg, correct to the nearest 0.1 kg. All the biscuits, whether from a packet or a box, have the same weight. Once opened, the contents of either a packet or a bargain box should be eaten within five days.

a) Ten of those biscuits were weighed on kitchen scales and found to be heavier than 120 g but lighter than 130 g.

Fig. 4.7

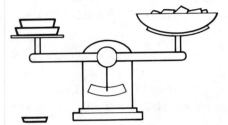

    i) Estimate the weight of the biscuits in one packet.

    ii) Calculate the maximum possible number and the minimum possible number of biscuits in a bargain box.

b) The St. Mithian Pensioners club meets every weekday afternoon (Monday to Friday inclusive) for tea and chat. At these meetings every member present is given four custard cream biscuits with the tea. There are 28 members of the club.

    i) How many packets of biscuits should the secretary buy on a Monday to be sure of providing four biscuits for every members who might be present on a Monday?

The secretary assumes that over the whole week the average daily attendance will be 16 pensioners and on Tuesday she buys sufficient biscuits for the rest of the week.

    ii) Calculate the total cost of biscuits for the week if she buys a bargain box on Tuesday.

    iii) Determine whether it would be cheaper to buy separate packets rather than a bargain box on the Tuesday.

c) The secretary now decides that she wants to buy sufficient biscuits for the whole week on Monday. Calculate the cheapest way of doing this.

OUTLINE ANSWERS TO EXAMINATION QUESTIONS

A1

a)

x	y	z
2	1.333	0.75
2.083	1.388	0.691
2.080		

b) Using the correct calculator value of x I get 9.000 065 8, and cubing 2.08 I get 8.9989, both of which round off to 9. So it would appear that this iteration has found the cube root of 9 to 2 decimal places.

c) 2.08.

A2

a) $U_5 = \dfrac{1}{1 + U_4} = \dfrac{1}{1 + 3} = 0.25$.

b) We need to re-arrange the formula to make $U_{(n-1)}$ the subject,

this is $U_{(n-1)} = \dfrac{1}{U_n} - 1$

hence $U_3 = \dfrac{1}{U_4} - 1 = \dfrac{1}{3} - 1 = -\dfrac{2}{3}$.

A3

a) Build up a table of results to give

number of squares (s)	1	2	3	4	5	6
rods (r)	4	7	10	13	16	19

The difference is 3 each time so the table can easily be continued, and with a difference of 3 each time and a start of 4 then the number of rods $(r) = 4 + 3(s - 1) = 4 + 3s - 3 = 1 + 3s$.

Hence   i) $r = 16$ ii) $r = 19$ iii) $r = 46$.

b) The formula is $r = 1 + 3s$.

c) When $r = 70$, solve the equation $70 = 1 + 3s$ to give $s = 23$.

d) Re-arrange to give $s = \dfrac{r - 1}{3}$.

e) When $r = 120$, $s = \dfrac{119}{3} = 39.6$.

So there will be 39 squares with 2 rods left over.

A4

a) 8, 4

b) The differences will not help here, but looking at the factors will, since

$1 \rightarrow 1$

$2 \rightarrow 1 \times 2$

$6 \rightarrow 1 \times 2 \times 3$

$?$

$?$

$720 \rightarrow 1 \times 2 \times 3 \times 4 \times 5 \times 6$.

So the missing numbers are $(1 \times 2 \times 3 \times 4) = 24$ and $(1 \times 2 \times 3 \times 4 \times 5) = 120$.

A5

a) $\dfrac{2}{5}, \dfrac{5}{7}, \dfrac{12}{17}, \dfrac{29}{41}, \dfrac{70}{99}, \dfrac{169}{239}$

b) 0.444 444 4

0.510 204

0.498 269 9

0.500 297 4

0.499 948 9

0.500 008 7

You should notice that these squares are getting closer to 0.5.

c) You will get a pair of simultaneous equations, $x + y = 2378$

$2x + y = 3363$

which will solve to give $x = 985$, $y = 1393$. So the term is $\dfrac{985}{1393}$.

d) Solve the pair of simultaneous equations: $x + y = p$

$2x + y = q$

to give $x = q - p$ and $y = 2p - q$. So the term is $\dfrac{q - p}{2p - q}$.

A6

a) Looking at the differences, we note they are 7 each time. So the next two numbers are 51 and 58.

b) Since the difference is 7 and the first term is 9, then the nth term is $9 + 7(n - 1)$. So the 60th term is $9 + 7 \times 59 = 422$.

c) rth term $= 9 + 7(r - 1) = 9 + 7r - 7$
$$= 7r + 2.$$

d) When rth term > 2000 then $7r + 2 > 2000$
$$\text{hence } 7r > 1998$$
$$r > 285.4.$$

So after 286 terms the first number over 2000 appears.

A7

a) 1.62.

b) $x^3 - 2x - 1 = 0$, dividing through by x gives
$$x^2 - 2 - \frac{1}{x} = 0,$$

hence $x^2 = 2 + \dfrac{1}{x}$

hence $x = \sqrt{\left(2 + \dfrac{1}{x}\right)}$

c) $x_1 = 1.62$
$x_2 = 1.617\,802\,2$
$x_3 = 1.618\,061\,4$
$x_4 = 1.618\,030\,8$

d) $x_5 = 1.618\,034\,4$; this now gives us the solution to 5 decimal places as $w = 1.618\,03$.

A8

a) i) 2^n.

ii) It is the same sequence as the original.

iii) Consider three consecutive terms in the original sequence, $2^x, 2^{x+1}, 2^{x+2}$.
The 'add ons' will be $2^{x+1} - 2^x$ and $2^{x+2} - 2^{x+1}$
which are $2^x(2 - 1)$ and $2^{x+1}(2 - 1)$
which is 2^x and 2^{x+1}.

So we see the pattern as in Fig. 4.8.

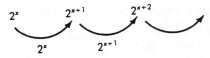

Fig. 4.8

b) i) The 'add ons' are 6, 18, 54, 162, 486.

ii) The 'add on' sequence is exactly double the original.

iii) Consider three consecutive terms of the original sequence $3^x, 3^{x+1}, 3^{x+2}$.
The 'add ons' will be $3^{x+1} - 3^x$ and $3^{x+2} - 3^{x+1}$
which are $3^x(3 - 1)$ and $3^{x+1}(3 - 1)$
which is 2×3^x and $2 \times 3^{x+1}$.

So we see the pattern as in Fig. 4.9.

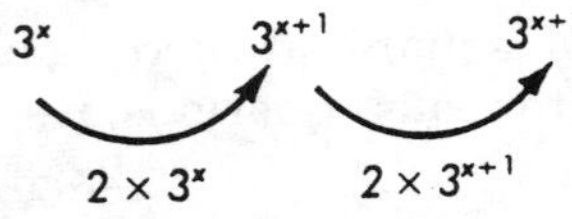

Fig. 4.9

c) The 'add on' sequence will be the original sequence multiplied by $(a - 1)$.

d) i) Then from c) $a(a - 1) = 20$
hence $a^2 - a - 20 = 0$
which is the quadratic having solution $a = 5$ and $a = -4$. The only sensible solution is $a = 5$ which gives the sequence 5, 25, 125, 625, 3125.

ii) 1, 21, 121, 621, 3121 ...

iii) The sequence 1, 21, 121, 621, 3121 ... U_n
Adding 4 on to each term will give 5, 25, 125, 625, 3125 ... $U_n + 4$
The nth term of this sequence is 5^n; hence $U_n + 4 = 5^n$, so the nth term will be $5^n - 4$.

A9

a) Pairs of numbers that multiply to give a multiple of 10 can be found to be (2×5), and then 10 itself, will each give a zero on the end. None of the other numbers can multiply together to give any zeros. So just (2×5) and 10 contribute a zero, hence two zeros.

b) Finding pairs that give multiples of 10, and the multiples of 10 give us $(2 \times 5), (4 \times 15), (6 \times 25), (8 \times 35), (12 \times 45) \ldots (24 \times 95)$ [10 of them]
and $\times 10 \times 20 \times 30 \times 40 \times 50 \times 60 \times 70 \times 80 \times 90 \times 100$ [another 10 of them]
gives 20 zeros altogether. (Note you can only use any number once.)

c) There will be $157 + 1$ digits altogether, 20 of which are known to be zero, this leaves 138 digits. There is a $\frac{1}{10}$ probability of any other digits being a zero, hence I would expect to find one tenth of 138, which is approximately 14, other zeros. So $14 + 20 = 34$ zeros altogether.

A10

a) $104.5 \text{ m} \leqslant \text{length} < 105.5$

b) since $62.5 \leqslant \text{width} < 63.5$ then the smallest value of the area will be given by $104.5 \times 62.5 = 6531.25 \text{ m}^2$ and the greatest by $105.5 \times 63.5 = 6699.25$ hence $6531.25 \text{ m}^2 \leqslant \text{area} < 6699.25 \text{ m}^2$.

A11

a) least weight is $(4.145 \times 2.035 \times 5.955) \times 19.3 \text{ g} = 969.45582 \text{ g}$
(Keep accurate figures in calculator memory)
the cost is $\dfrac{969.45582}{28.35} \times £348.50 = £11\,917.30$
similarly the highest price is £12 024.91
hence the range is $£11\,920 \leqslant \text{price} < £12\,020$.

b) least value is $\dfrac{973.5}{28.35} \times £348.50 = £11\,967.01$
greatest value is $\dfrac{974.5}{28.35} \times £348.50 = £11\,979.30$
the range is $£11\,970 \leqslant \text{price} \leqslant £11\,980$.

c) part c) price range is over £100 between lowest and upper. While b) price range is only over £10, hence it is more reliable.

A12

$$\text{lowest} = \frac{\text{lowest numerator}}{\text{greatest denominator}} = \frac{2.35 + 4.25}{0.85} = 7.7647$$

$$\text{highest} = \frac{2.45 + 4.35}{0.75} = 9.0667.$$

A13

a) 99.5 m

b) 14.35 seconds

c) $\text{least} = \dfrac{99.5}{14.35} = 6.93 \text{ m/s}; \text{greatest} = \dfrac{100.5}{14.25} = 7.05 \text{ m/s}.$

A14

5.878×10^{12}.

A15

i) 4.36×10^{-2} ii) 1.547×10^{-6}.

A16

D = 872.

A17

a)   The Earth, since 10^{24} will make the number greater than 10^{22}.
b) 8.136×10^1.

A18

i) 2×10^2 ii) 1.25×10^{-4} iii)   4020.

A19

a)   He could overestimate by a maximum of 9p each time, making the least total
£8.30 − (12 × 9p) = £7.22.
b)   Greatest value is £12.56 + (12 × 4p) = £13.04.
least value is £12.56 − (12 × 5p) = £11.96.

A20

a)   i) $\dfrac{24 \times 125}{10}$ g = 300 g.

ii) $\dfrac{3.55 \times 1000}{13} = 273$ minimum, $\dfrac{3.65 \times 1000}{12} = 304$

b)   i) $\dfrac{28 \times 4}{24} = 4.67$, so buy 5 packets.

ii)   Total cost = 5 × 33p + £3.29 = £4.94.
iii)   16 × 5 × 4 = 320 biscuits needed in the week.
320 − (24 × 5) = 200 biscuits needed after Monday.
200 ÷ 24 = 8.33, 9 packets needed at a cost of £2.97.
hence cheaper to buy packets.
c)   320 ÷ 24 = 13.33, so 14 packets would last the week . . . £4.62.
320 − 273 = 47 extra to a bargain box $\left.\vphantom{\begin{matrix}1\\2\end{matrix}}\right\}$ £3.95.
47 ÷ 24 = 1.958 . . . 2 packets extra needed
The cheapest option is to buy 1 bargain box
and 2 packets.

G R A D E   C H E C K L I S T

For a Grade B you should:

Be able to: Search and explain number sequences;
Calculate with numbers in standard form;
Solve numerical problems, checking that the results are of the right
size.

For a Grade A you should also:

Be able to: Generalise the number pattern;
Understand upper and lower bounds of numbers expressed to a given
degree of accuracy.

For a Grade A* you should also:

Be able to: Investigate iterations to solve problems;
Determine the possible effects of errors on calculations.

STUDENTS' ANSWERS WITH EXAMINER'S COMMENTS

Question 1
A black ball is placed on a table and is represented by T_1, as shown in the diagram.

It is then surrounded by white balls to form a triangular shape, T_2, as shown in the diagram.

Shape T_3 is formed by surrounding T_2 by black balls, and so on.

> Spelling incorrect, but as long as the word is recognisable then no marks will be lost.

a)   What kind of triangles are formed by the centres of the outside balls?

→ isosolese

> You have ended up in the right place, but have not specifically given the answer.

b)   How many rows of balls will there be in

   i) shape T_7? 1,3,5,6,7,9,11,13

   ii) shape T_n?

   $2n - 1$

> Good generalisation, well done.

c)   How many balls will there be in

   i) shape T_7? 1, 9, 25, 49, 81, 121, 169

   ii) shape T_n?

   $(2n-1)^2$

> What a shame, you have made out a correct table but then not used it properly to find the answer.

d)   What colour balls will be added

   i) to T_{17} to make T_{18}?

   black

> Although the answer is correct, there will be no marks because it does not agree with the part i).

   ii) To T_{2n-1} to make T_{2n}?

   white

Black	White
T_1	T_2
T_3	T_4
T_5	T_6
T_7	T_8
odd	even

e)   How many balls will be added to T_{n-1} to make T_n?

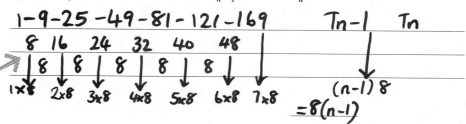

> Very good, clearly showing how the final answer is found.

$1 - 9 - 25 - 49 - 81 - 121 - 169 \qquad T_{n-1} \qquad T_n$

$8 \quad 16 \quad 24 \quad 32 \quad 40 \quad 48$

$8 \quad 8 \quad 8 \quad 8 \quad 8$

$1\times8 \quad 2\times8 \quad 3\times8 \quad 4\times8 \quad 5\times8 \quad 6\times8 \quad 7\times8 \qquad (n-1)8$

$= 8(n-1)$

> A good answer showing high mathematical ability but a tendency to make careless errors which will be costly.

Question 2

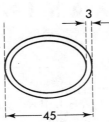

Each link of a chain has an outside length of 45 mm, and the metal is 3 mm thick.
Each measurement is given to the nearest mm.
The diagram below shows a chain which is made up of 4 links.

a) Find the maximum length, in millimetres, of a chain which is made up of
    i) 2 links,
    ii) 3 links,
    iii) 10 links.
b) Find an expression for the maximum length of a chain which is made up of n links.
c) Use your answer to part b) to find the smallest number of links required to make a chain at least 3 metres long.

Good diagrams to help show the situation.

A good generalisation.

Clearly shown the method; good.

poor use of = sign.

A clear correct approach, well done.

a) i) $|45.5| |45.5| = 2 \times 45.5 - 2.5 = 85.5$ but less
    2.5 so max = $\underline{88\,mm}$

    ii) $45.5\,45.5\,45.5$ $= 3 \times 45.5 - 2 \times 2.5 = 131.5 = \underline{131\,mm}$ max

    iii) $10 \times 45.5 - 9 \times 2.5 = 432.5 = \underline{432\,mm}$

b) $n \times 45.5 - (n-1) \times 2.5 - 0.5$

c) $45.5n - 2.5n + 2.5 - 0.5 = 3000$
    $43n = 3000 - 2.5 + 0.5 = 2998$
    $n = 2998/43 \qquad = 69.72$

    answer $n = \underline{70}$

GETTING STARTED

We consider here the ratios of similar shapes and the three different types of variance, all of which appear in the GCSE higher level mathematics syllabuses.

This section will incorporate quite a lot of algebra also.

USEFUL DEFINITIONS

Similar	Two shapes are similar if one is a mathematical enlargement of the other.
Enlargement	When all the respective dimensions of two shapes are in the same ratio.
Scale factor	The ratio which links two similar figures.
Variation	Where one or more variables are connected by an algebraic rule.
Direct Variation	Where there is a simple *multiplying* relationship between the variables involved.
Inverse Variation	Where there is a simple *dividing* relationship between the variables involved.
Partial Variation	Where two or more variables are connected by some 'law of variation' in such a way that the independent variables can be *added* together.
Joint Variation	Where three (or more) variables are connected with each other in combinations of direct and/or inverse proportion.
Proportional	Having a constant ratio.
Surd	An expression left in 'root' notation, e.g. $\sqrt{2}, \sqrt{15}$.

SIMILAR SHAPES

VARIATION

DIRECT VARIATION

INVERSE VARIATION

PARTIAL VARIATION

JOINT VARIATION

ESSENTIAL PRINCIPLES

1 **SIMILAR SHAPES**

Two shapes are said to be *similar* if all their corresponding angles are equal and the ratios of the corresponding lengths are also equal. An example is shown in Fig. 5.1.

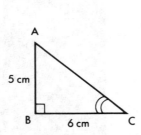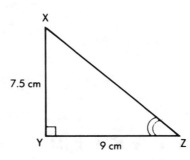

Fig. 5.1

All the corresponding angles are equal and the ratio of each pair of corresponding sides is 2:3

$$\text{ie. } \frac{5}{7.5} = \frac{6}{9} = \frac{2}{3}$$

So if the length AC is 7.8 cm, then the length XZ can be found by equating $\frac{XZ}{7.8} = \frac{3}{2}$

hence $XZ = \frac{3 \times 7.8}{2} = 11.7$ cm. (Note how the ratio has been used.)

RATIOS OF SIMILAR SHAPES

Consider the two shapes shown in Fig. 5.2.

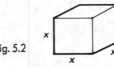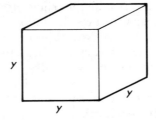

Fig. 5.2

Both these shapes are *cubes*; hence each *corresponding angle* is the same, and each *corresponding side* is in the ratio $x:y$. We can now also see that by considering any *face*, the ratio of the *areas* is $x^2:y^2$. The ratio of the *volumes* is $x^3:y^3$.

We can summarise the situation by saying that for any similar solid that has lengths in the ratio $x:y$ then:

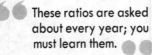

These ratios are asked about every year; you must learn them.

- ratio of lengths $x:y$
- ratio of areas $x^2:y^2$
- ratio of volume $x^3:y^3$

WORKED EXAMPLE 1

Two similar statues, one 8 cm tall, the other 15 cm are on display. The smaller one has a base area of 4 cm^2 and a volume of 30 cm^3.

find a) the base area of the larger statue,

b) the volume of the larger statue.

Working

The length ratio $= \dfrac{15}{8}$

a) ratio of areas $= (\text{ratio of lengths})^2 = \left(\dfrac{15}{8}\right)^2$

so where A is the base area of the larger statue

> The larger value is the numerator because it is the area of the larger statue that we are looking for.

$$\frac{A}{4} = \left(\frac{15}{8}\right)^2$$

$$A = \left(\frac{15}{8}\right)^2 \times 4 = 14.0625$$

Area $= 14 \text{ cm}^2$

b) Volume ratio $= (\text{length ratio})^3 = \left(\dfrac{15}{8}\right)^3$

so where V is the volume of the larger statue

$$\frac{V}{30} = \left(\frac{15}{8}\right)^3$$

$$V = \left(\frac{15}{8}\right)^3 \times 30 = 197.75$$

Volume $= 197.75 \text{ cm}^3$

WORKED EXAMPLE 2

A supermarket sold similar tins of beans.

Small—which has a paper label of area 23 cm²
Medium—which has paper label of area 45 cm²
Large—which has paper label of area 75 cm²

> The sizes of the labels are in direct proportion to the sizes of the tins.

The medium sized tin is 7 cm tall with a weight of 350 g.
Calculate
a) the height of the other two tins.
b) the weight of the other two tins.

Working

(We have to be careful to get the ratios (fractions) the correct way up).
a) Let h be the height of the small tin.
Then, when area ratio $= (\text{length ratio})^2$

$$\begin{array}{l} \text{small tin} \\ \text{medium tin} \end{array} \rightarrow \begin{array}{l} \\ \end{array} \frac{23}{45} = \left(\frac{h}{7}\right)^2 = \frac{h^2}{7^2}$$

> Smaller number on top since it is the height of the smaller tin that we are finding.

i.e. $\qquad h^2 = \dfrac{23}{45} \times 49$

$$h = \sqrt{25.04}$$

$$h \approx 5$$

Let H be the height of the large tin.
Then, where area ratio $= (\text{length ratio})^2$

$$\frac{75}{45} = \left(\frac{H}{7}\right)^2$$

> We put the larger number as the numerator because it is the height of the larger tin that we need to find.

i.e. $H^2 = \dfrac{75}{45} \times 49$

$$H = \sqrt{81.667}$$

$$H \approx 9$$

So the small height is 5 cm and the large height is 9 cm.

Weight is directly
proportional to
volume and so
will behave in the
same way.

b) Let w be the weight of the small tin.
Then the volume ratio = (length ratio)^3
weight ratio = (length ratio)^3

$$\text{Small tin} \quad\rightarrow\quad \frac{w}{350} = \left(\frac{5}{7}\right)^3$$
$$\text{Medium tin} \rightarrow$$

$$w = \left(\frac{5}{7}\right)^3 \times 350$$

$$w \approx 128$$

Let W be the weight of the large tin.
Then weight ratio = (length ratio)^3

$$\text{Large tin} \quad\rightarrow\quad \frac{W}{350} = \left(\frac{9}{7}\right)^3$$
$$\text{Medium tin} \rightarrow$$

$$W = \left(\frac{9}{7}\right)^3 \times 350$$

$$W \approx 744$$

so the weights of the two tins are 128 g and 744 g.

EXERCISE 1

1. Find the volumes of the similar solids in Fig. 5.3. Give the answers correct to 3 significant figures.

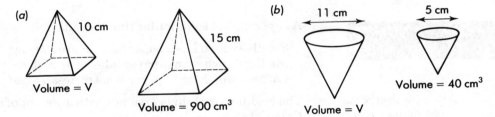

(a) 10 cm Volume = V   15 cm Volume = 900 cm^3

(b) 11 cm   5 cm
Volume = V   Volume = 40 cm^3

Fig. 5.3

2. Find the volumes and lengths as indicated in Fig. 5.4. Give the answers correct to the nearest whole number.

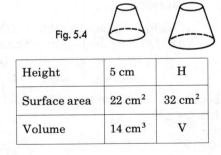

Fig. 5.4

Height	5 cm	H
Surface area	22 cm^2	32 cm^2
Volume	14 cm^3	V

2 ▷ VARIATION

Variation is a term we use when one or more variables can be connected by some algebraic rule.

There are four types of variation—direct, inverse, partial and joint. We now look at each type in turn.

DIRECT VARIATION

Look at these two examples.

- When you cycle at a steady speed, then the distance you travel increases as the time you are cycling increases.
- When you wish to exchange Singapore Dollars for pounds sterling, then the more Singapore Dollars you exchange, the more pounds you will receive.

Both of these are examples of direct variation.

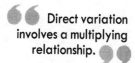 *Direct variation involves a multiplying relationship.*

Direct variation (or proportion) is when there is a simple *multiplying* relationship between the variables involved. So in a two variable situation, as one variable increases so does the other.

The symbol we use for 'varies directly with' or 'is directly proportional to' is $\propto$. Hence the statement 'distance varies directly with time' can be written as:

distance $\propto$ time.

This means that $\dfrac{\text{distance}}{\text{time}}$ is a fixed ratio; we call this 'k'.

We can therefore say that distance = k multiplied by time

$$\text{or } d = kt.$$

This k is called 'the constant of proportionality' and the equation $d = kt$ is known as the 'law of proportionality' or 'the law of variation'.

WORKED EXAMPLE 3

W is directly proportional to N, and W = 8 when N = 5. Find:
a) the law of proportionality;
b) W when N = 12.

Working

$W \propto N$
so $W = kN$ where k is a constant.
Since W = 8 when N = 5 then $8 = 5\,k$

$$k = \frac{8}{5}$$

$$= 1.6$$

a) Hence the law of proportionality is W = 1.6 N
b) When N = 12 then   W = 1.6 × 12
                         W = 19.2

WORKED EXAMPLE 4

The weight of a metal sphere varies directly with the cube of the radius. If the weight of a metal sphere of radius 3 cm is 1.02 kg, find the weight of a metal sphere of radius 5 cm.

Working

Let W be the weight and r the radius.

$W \propto r^3$ so $W = kr^3$ where k is a constant

$W = 1.02$ when $r = 3$

hence $1.02 = k \times 3^3$

$$k = \frac{1.02}{27}$$

(Because it does not evaluate exactly, it is best left in the fraction form.)

hence $$W = \frac{1.02}{27} \times r^3$$

when $r = 5$ then $$W = \frac{1.02}{27} \times 5^3$$

$$= \frac{1.02 \times 125}{27}$$

$$W = 4.72 \text{ kg}$$

EXERCISE 2

If x varies directly with y and $x = 30$ when $y = 24$, find:

a) x when $y = 10$;

b) y when $x = 14$.

INVERSE VARIATION

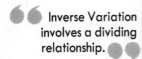 Inverse Variation involves a dividing relationship.

Inverse Variation (or proportion) is when there is a simple *dividing* relationship between the variables involved. So, in a two variable situation, as one variable *increases* the other *decreases*, and decreases in such a way that the product of the two variables is constant.

For example, as I drive home and decide to increase the *speed*, then the *time taken* for the journey decreases. So speed (S) and time taken (T) are inversely proportional and S.T = k where k is some constant.

Suppose you go on a journey of 240 km,

travelling at an average speed of: 40 km/h would take 6 hours
60 km/h would take 4 hours
80 km/h would take 3 hours
120 km/h would take 2 hours

Notice how all these pairs multiply together to give a constant value (k) of 240.

In general,

if A varies inversely with B, then $A \propto \dfrac{1}{B}$

$$A = \frac{k}{B}$$

hence $AB = k$.

WORKED EXAMPLE 5

T is inversely proportional to V and T is 18 when V = 60. Find:

a)   T when V = 30;

b)   V when T = 20.

Working

$T \propto \dfrac{1}{V}$ hence $T = \dfrac{k}{V}$ where k is a constant.

$T = 18$ when $V = 60$, hence $k = 18 \times 60$
$= 1080$

i.e. $TV = 1080$.

a)   When V = 30, $T = \dfrac{1080}{30} = 36$

b)   When T = 20, $V = \dfrac{1080}{20} = 54$

WORKED EXAMPLE 6

The length of paper on a roll varies inversely with the thickness of the paper. A roll holds paper of length 90 m and the thickness of the paper is 0.8 mm. Calculate the length of the paper in a roll if its thickness is 1.2 mm.

Working

Length $\propto \dfrac{1}{\text{thickness}}$ hence $L = \dfrac{k}{t}$ where L is the length, t the thickness and k is a constant.

$$\therefore k = Lt$$

$t = 0.8$ when $L = 90$ hence $k = 0.8 \times 90$
$$= 72$$

i.e. $Lt = 72$

so when $t = 1.2$, $L = \dfrac{72}{1.2}$

$$= 60$$

Length is 60 m.

EXERCISE 3

1. $A \propto \dfrac{1}{\sqrt{B}}$. If $A = 9$ when $B = 16$, find:
    a) A when $B = 25$;
    b) B when $A = 30$.

2. The number of small spheres which can be made from a given volume of metal varies inversely as the cube of the diameter of the spheres. When the diameter is 3 mm, the number of spheres is 240. How many spheres of diameter 2 mm can be made from the same volume of metal?

PARTIAL VARIATION

> The 'independent variables' in a formula are on the right hand side of the equal sign.

Partial variation (or proportion) occurs when two or more variables are connected by some formula or 'law of variation' in such a way that the independent variables can be *added* together.

In these cases there could well be two or more constants to be found (called 'constants of variation' or 'constants or proportionality').

WORKED EXAMPLE 7

R is partly constant and partly varies as V^2. When $V = 40$, $R = 564$, and when $V = 60$, $R = 644$, find:

a) the law of variation;
b) R when $V = 80$.

Working

> Remember, you can use the substitution or elimination method for solving simultaneous equations (see Book 2).

As R is partly constant and partly varies as V^2
then $R = c + kV^2$ where c and k are both constants.

$V = 40$ when $R = 564$,	$564 = c + 1600\,k$	... (i)
$V = 60$ when $R = 644$,	$644 = c + 3600\,k$	... (ii)

Solving the two equations simultaneously, we get

$$k = \frac{80}{2000} = \frac{1}{25}$$

$$c = 564 - \frac{1600}{25} = 500$$

a) the law of variation is $R = 500 + \dfrac{V^2}{25}$

b) When $V = 80$. $R = 500 + \dfrac{6400}{25}$

$$R = 756$$

WORKED EXAMPLE 8

The resistance to a car is partly proportional to its speed and partly proportional to the square of its speed. When the speed is 20 km/h, the resistance is 80 N. When the speed is 30 km/h, the resistance is 150 N. Find the resistance when the speed is 60 km/h.

Working

Let the resistance be R and the speed be V, then $R = cV + kV^2$ where c and k are both constants.

When $V = 20$, $R = 80$, hence $80 = 20c + 400\,k \ldots$ (i)
When $V = 30$, $R = 150$, hence $150 = 30c + 900\,k \ldots$ (ii)

Solving the equations simultaneously, we get $c = 2$, $k = \dfrac{1}{10}$

hence $R = 2V + \dfrac{V^2}{10}$

When $V = 60$, $R = 2 \times 60 + \dfrac{3600}{10}$

$$R = 480 \text{ N}$$

EXERCISE 4

1. W varies partly as Z^2 and partly inversely as T. When $Z = 4$, $T = 6$ and $W = 19$, and when $Z = 5$, $T = 12$ and $W = 35$. Find:
   a) the law of variation;
   b) W when $Z = 6$ and $T = 10$.
2. The distance in which a car can stop after the brakes have been applied varies partly as the speed of the car at the time the brakes are first applied and partly as the square of the speed.
   When the speed is 20 km/h, the stopping distance is 8 m.
   When the speed is 40 km/h, the stopping distance is 24 m.
   Find the stopping distance at 60 km/h.

JOINT VARIATION

Joint variation occurs where three (or more) things vary with each other in combinations of direct and/or inverse proportion. There is just one 'constant of variation' in each case.
For example:

   i) $M \propto PT$, hence $M = k_1\, PT$

   ii) $V \propto \dfrac{A}{B}$, hence $V = k_2\, \dfrac{A}{B}$

   iii) $W \propto \dfrac{PT^2}{\sqrt{L}}$, hence $W = k_3\, \dfrac{PT^2}{\sqrt{L}}$ when k_1, k_2, k_3 are constants.

WORKED EXAMPLE 9

When gold medals of various radii and thickness are weighed, the masses will depend upon both the thickness and the square of the radius of the medal. A gold medal of thickness 2 mm and a radius of 2.5 cm has a mass of 45 g. What is the weight of a gold medal of thickness 3 mm and a radius of 3.5 cm?

Working

If M = mass, R = Radius and T = thickness,
   then $M \propto TR^2$
   hence $M = k\, TR^2$ where k is a constant
$M = 45$ when $T = 2$ and $R = 2.5$,
   so $45 = k \times 2 \times 2.5^2$

   $k = \dfrac{45}{2 \times 2.5^2} = 3.6$

When $T = 3$ and $R = 3.5$, $M = 3.6 \times 3 \times 3.5^2$
$$= 132.3 \text{ g.}$$

> 66 Here, we are talking about proportionality, therefore we need not change all the thickness and radii to the same unit. Just make sure that all the units for thickness are the same (millimetres in this case). 99

WORKED EXAMPLE 10

T varies directly with P and inversely with the square of Q. If T = 6 when P = 180 and Q = 0.03, find:

a) the law of variation;
b) the value of P when T = 3.5 and Q = 0.024.

Working

$$T \propto \frac{P}{Q^2} \quad \text{hence } T = k\frac{P}{Q^2}$$

T = 6 when P = 180 and Q = 0.03

$$\text{so } 6 = k \times \frac{180}{0.03^2}$$

$$k = \frac{6 \times 0.03^2}{180} = 0.000\,03$$

a) $T = \dfrac{0.000\,03\,P}{Q^2}$

b) When T = 3.5 and Q = 0.024

$$\text{then } 3.5 = \frac{0.000\,03 \times P}{(0.024)^2}$$

$$P = \frac{3.5 \times (0.024)^2}{0.000\,03}$$

$$= 67.2$$

EXERCISE 5

1. V varies directly as x and inversely as y^2, V = 4 when $x = 2$ and $y = 3$. Find:

   a) the law of variation;
   b) V when $x = 4$ and $y = 6$.

SOLUTIONS TO EXERCISES

S1

1. a) Ratio of lengths is 10:15 which simplifies to 2:3.
    hence the ratio of volumes = $2^3 : 3^3 = 8:27$

    so $\dfrac{V}{900} = \dfrac{8}{27} \Rightarrow V = \dfrac{900 \times 8}{27} = 266.7$

    rounded gives 267 cm^3

    b) Ratio of lengths is 11:5, ratio of volumes is $11^3 : 5^3$.

    $$\frac{V}{40} = \frac{11^3}{5^3} = \frac{1331}{125} \Rightarrow V = 40 \times \frac{1331}{125} = 425.9$$

    rounded gives 426 cm^3

2. area ratio is 22:32 which simplifies to 11:16
    so length ratio is $\sqrt{11}:\sqrt{16}$, volume ratio is $(\sqrt{11})^3 : (\sqrt{16})^3$

    $\text{missing height} = 5 \times \dfrac{\sqrt{16}}{\sqrt{11}} \qquad \text{missing volume} = 14 \times \dfrac{(\sqrt{16})^3}{(\sqrt{11})^3}$

    $= 6 \text{ cm} \qquad\qquad\qquad\qquad = 25 \text{ cm}^3$

S2

$x = ky; 30 = k \times 24 \Rightarrow k = \dfrac{30}{24}$

a) $x = \dfrac{30}{24} \times 10 = 12.5$

b) $y = 14 \div \dfrac{30}{24} = 14 \times \dfrac{24}{30} = 11.2$

S3

1. $A = \dfrac{k}{\sqrt{B}} \Rightarrow 9 = \dfrac{k}{\sqrt{16}} \Rightarrow k = 9 \times 4 = 36$

   a) $A = \dfrac{36}{\sqrt{25}} = 7.2$ b) $\sqrt{B} = \dfrac{36}{30} = 1.2$

   $B = 1.2^2 = 1.44$

2. $n = \dfrac{k}{r^3} \Rightarrow 240 = \dfrac{k}{3^3} \Rightarrow k = 240 \times 27 = 6480$

   $n = \dfrac{6480}{2^3} = \dfrac{6480}{8} = 810$ spheres

S4

1. a) $W = cZ^2 + \dfrac{k}{T} \Rightarrow 16c + \dfrac{1}{6}k = 19 \ \ldots \text{(i)}$

   $$25c + \dfrac{1}{12}k = 35 \ldots \text{(ii)}$$

   eliminate k by multiplying (ii) through by 2 to give the solution

   $c = 1.5 \qquad k = -30$

   law of variation is $W = \dfrac{3Z^2}{2} - \dfrac{30}{T}$

2. $D = cS + kS^2 \Rightarrow 20c + 400\,k = 8$
   $40c + 1600\,k = 24$

   eliminate c to give the solution $c = \dfrac{1}{5}, k = \dfrac{1}{100}$

   hence $D = \dfrac{S}{5} + \dfrac{S^2}{100}$, when $S = 60, D = 48$ m.

S5

a) $V = k\dfrac{x}{y^2} \Rightarrow 4 = k\dfrac{2}{9} \Rightarrow k = \dfrac{4 \times 9}{2} = 18$

   $V = \dfrac{18x}{y^2}$

b) $V = \dfrac{18 \times 4}{36} = 2.$

EXAM TYPE QUESTIONS

Q1

The electrical resistance, R ohms, of a piece of wire of length one metre is inversely proportional to the square of its diameter, d cm. This can be written as $R = K\left(\dfrac{1}{d^n}\right)$.

a) State the value of n.

b) A metre length of copper wire has resistance of 5 ohms. Find the resistance of a piece of copper wire of the same length which has three times the diameter of the first piece.

(MEG)

Q2

Figure 5.5 shows a measuring scoop used for measuring soap power for a washing machine. It has a diameter of 8 cm and a height of 10 cm.

Ignore the handle, you then have a pair of similar cones.

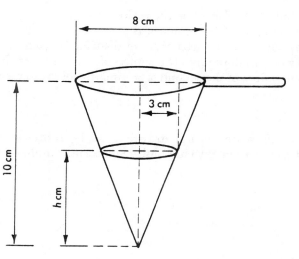

Fig. 5.5

Calculate the height of the powder (h cm) in the scoop when the radius of the soap powder surface is 3 cm.

(NEAB)

Q3

The pressure needed to blow up the balloon in Fig. 5.6 varies as the cube of its radius. When the radius is 5 cm the pressure needed is 80 g/cm^2.

Fig. 5.6

a) What pressure is required when the radius is 15 cm?

b) What is the radius of the balloon when the pressure needed is 640 g/cm^2?

(WJEC)

Q4

Figure 5.7 shows two closed cyclindrical cans, A and B. The radius of A is 4 cm and its height is 12 cm. The radius of B is 8 cm and its height is 6 cm.

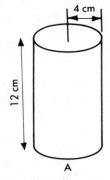

Fig. 5.7

a) Find, in the form $1:n$, the ratio
     i) volume of A: volume of B
     ii) total surface area of A: total surface area of B.
b) Two cylinders have the same volume. The first has radius r and height h. If the radius of the second is $2r$, find its height in terms of h.   (MEG)

Q5

Figure 5.8, which is not drawn to scale, represents a symmetrical white sign fused on to a road with hot molten material. Angle BAC = 2 × angle DAE.

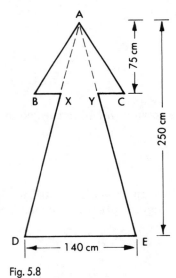

Fig. 5.8

In the following calculations, work to four significant figures and give answers to two significant figures.

a)   i) Use similar triangles to calculate the length XY.
       ii) Calculate the size of angle DAE.
      iii) Calculate the length BC.
       iv) Calculate the surface area of the sign.
b) Each sign is 3 mm in depth and the material for 30 such signs can be poured from a full cylindrical boiler, 40 cm in depth.
      i) Calculate the volume of material used for each sign.
     ii) Calculate the internal radius of the boiler.   (NEAB)

Q6

Information is provided about a sailboard.
A scale model is to be made $\frac{1}{20}$ of the full size.

a)   Calculate the length of the model in centimetres.

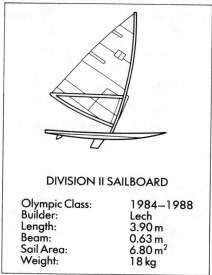

DIVISION II SAILBOARD

Olympic Class:	1984–1988
Builder:	Lech
Length:	3.90 m
Beam:	0.63 m
Sail Area:	6.80 m²
Weight:	18 kg

Fig. 5.9

b)   Calculate the sail area of the model in square centimetres.

Q7

In the triangle shown, XY is parallel to BC.

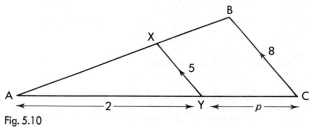

Fig. 5.10

a)   Explain why triangles AXY and ABC are similar.
b)   Write down an equation involving p and solve it.

Q8

A right pyramid stands on a square base of side 20 cm. Its vertical height is 30 cm.
It is cut through by a plane $WXYZ$, parallel to the base, and 15 cm above it.

a)   Work out the length of XY.

b)   Calculate $\dfrac{\text{volume of } OWXYZ}{\text{volume of } OABCD}$

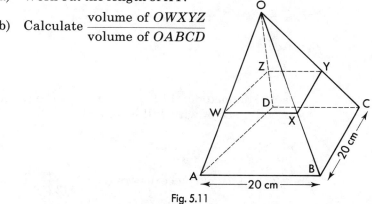

Fig. 5.11

c)   Find the size of the angle which OA makes with the base $ABCD$.

Q9

A small object P is tied to one end of a string and the other end of the string is attached to a fixed point. The object hangs at rest. When P is projected horizontally with a speed u metres per second, it is found to swing through a vertical height h centimetres before swinging back again. The table below shows the values of h (to the nearest whole number) for given values of u.

u (m/s)	1.4	1.7	2.2	2.4
h (cm)	10	14	24	25

a) Find which of the following statements best describes the variation between h and u:
   i) h varies as u^3,
   ii) h varies as u^2,
   iii) h varies as $\sqrt{u}$.
   Explain your reasoning.

b) Deduce an approximate value for h when $u = 3$.

Q10

The frequency of a radio wave is inversely proportional to its wavelength.
Radio One broadcasts at a frequency of 1053 KHz and a wavelength of 285 m.
Radio Two broadcasts at a frequency of 909 KHz.
Calculate the Radio Two wavelength. Write your answer to the nearest metre.

Q11

A variable t is inversely proportional to the square of p and varies directly with the cube root of q.

a) Find the change in t when:
   i) both p and q are doubled,
   ii) q is doubled and p is halved.

b) State the connection between the changes of p and q that would leave t unaltered, and quote a particular instance when this will be true (not when both are unaltered!).

OUTLINE ANSWERS TO EXAM QUESTIONS

A1

a) $n = 2$

b) Let the diameter of the first piece of wire be called d_1, then the diameter of the second piece of wire will be $3d_1$. So, for the first piece of wire we can state

$$5 = K\left(\frac{1}{d_1{}^2}\right) \rightarrow K = 5\,d_1{}^2$$

Hence for the second piece of wire $R = K\left(\frac{1}{(3d_1)^2}\right) = 5\,d_1{}^2 \times \frac{1}{9d_1{}^2}$

$$R = \frac{5}{9}\ \text{ohms.}$$

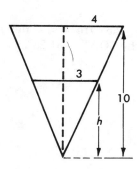

Fig. 5.12

A2

Draw a simple sketch as in Fig. 5.12 to illustrate a pair of similar triangles. Then we can write down $\dfrac{h}{3} = \dfrac{10}{4}$

$$\to h = \frac{30}{4} = 7.5 \text{ cm.}$$

A3

From the question $p \propto r^3$; hence $p = Kr^3$

When $r = 5, p = 80$, so $80 = K \times 125 \to K = \dfrac{80}{125} = 0.64$.

a) When $r = 15, p = 0.64 \times 15^3 = 2160 \text{ g/cm}^2$

b) When $p = 640, 640 = 0.64 \times r^3$
hence $r^3 = 640 \div 0.64 = 1000$
$r = \sqrt[3]{1000} = 10$
$r = 10 \text{ cm.}$

A4

a) i) Volume of A $= \pi r^2 h = \pi \times 16 \times 12 = 192\pi$
Volume of B $= \pi r^2 h = \pi \times 64 \times 6 = 384\pi$
Hence volume A : volume B $= 192\pi : 384\pi$

$$= 1 \quad : \frac{384\pi}{192\pi}$$

$$= 1 \quad : \quad 2$$

ii) Total surface area of A $= 2 \times \pi r^2 + 2\pi rh = (2 \times \pi \times 16) + (2 \times \pi \times 4 \times 12)$
$= 32\pi + 96\pi \qquad = 128\pi$
Total surface area of B $= 2\pi r^2 + 2\pi rh \quad = (2 \times \pi \times 64) + (2 \times \pi \times 8 \times 6)$
$= 128\pi + 96\pi \quad = 224\pi$
ratio of surface area of A : surface area of B $= 128\pi : 224\pi$

$$= 1 : \frac{224\pi}{128\pi}$$

$$= 1 : 1.75$$

b) Volume $= \pi r^2 h$.
So if another cylinder of same volume, yet radius $2r$, let h be h_1,
then $\pi r^2 h = \pi(2r)^2 h_1$
$\to \quad \pi r^2 h = 4\pi r^2 h_1$

$$\to \quad \frac{\pi r^2 h}{4\pi r^2} = h_1 \to h_1 = \frac{h}{4}.$$

A5

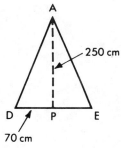

Fig. 5.13

a) i) $\dfrac{XY}{140} = \dfrac{75}{250} \to \quad XY = \dfrac{75 \times 140}{250} = 42 \text{ cm.}$

ii) Sketch the triangle ADE as shown in Fig. 5.13 with P the foot of the perpendicular from A.

Then $\tan D\hat{A}P = \dfrac{70}{250} = 0.28$

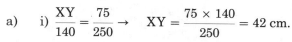

$\to D\hat{A}P = 15.64$

Hence $D\hat{A}E = 2 \times D\hat{A}P = 31°$ (to two significant figures).

iii) In Fig. 5.14, since $\hat{BAC} = 2 \times \hat{DAE}$, then $\hat{BAC} = 62.57$ (to 4 sig. figs.). So when T is the foot of the perpendicular from A, then $\hat{CAT} = 31.28°$.

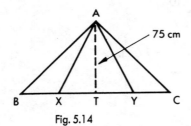

Fig. 5.14

Hence $\dfrac{TC}{75} = \tan 31.28$

$\to TC = 75 \tan 31.28° = 45.57$.
Hence $BC = 2 \times TC = 91$ cm (to 2 sig. figs.)

iv) Find area of three triangles ABX, ACY (which are the same area) and ADE.
Area of ABX $= \frac{1}{2}$base × height $= \frac{1}{2} \times (TC - TY) \times 75$
$= \frac{1}{2} \times (24.57) \times 75 = 921.5$ (4 sig. figs.)
Hence $ABX + ACY = 921.5 \times 2 \quad = 1843$ cm^2 (4 sig. figs.)
Area of ADE $= \frac{1}{2} + 140 \times 250 \qquad = 17\,500$ cm^2
Total area $= ABX + ACY + ADE = 19\,000$ cm^2 (2 sig. figs.)

b) i) Volume for each sign will be a) iv) × 3 mm, which is $19\,343 \times 0.3 = 5802.9$ cm^3, which is 5800 cm^3 (2 sig. figs.)

ii) Volume of cylinder up to height 40 cm will be given by
$30 \times$ b) i) $= 174\,087$ cm^3 (as accurately as possible).
Volume of cylinder given by $\pi r^2 h$ then $\pi r^2 \times 40 = 174\,087$

$$\to r^2 = \frac{174\,087}{40\pi} = 1385.34$$

$$\to r = 37 \text{ cm (2 sig. figs.)}$$

A6

a) 3.90 m ÷ 20 = 0.195 m = 19.5 cm
b) length ratio = 1 : 20 hence area ratio = 1 : 400

$$\text{sail area on model} = \frac{6.80 \times 100^2}{400} \text{ (to convert to cm}^2\text{)}$$

$$= 170 \text{ cm}^2$$

A7

a) angle A is common, $\angle AXY = \angle ABC$ (corresponding angles)
$\angle AYX = \angle ACB$ (corresponding angles)
hence all the angles correspond with each other.

b) $\dfrac{2 + p}{2} = \dfrac{8}{5} \Rightarrow 5(2 + p) = \ 8 \times 2$

$10 + 5p = 16$

$\Rightarrow \qquad 5p = \ 6$

$p = \ 1.2$

A8

The ratio of the lengths is varicen by the heights 1 : 2

a) $\dfrac{XY}{20} = \dfrac{1}{2} \Rightarrow XY = 10$ cm

b) ratio of volumes $= \left(\dfrac{1}{2}\right)^3 = \dfrac{1}{8}$

c) Trigonometry!
   Consider the right angled triangle
   T is the centre of the square ABCD
   where $AC = \sqrt{(20^2 + 20^2)}$
   $\qquad\qquad = \sqrt{(800)} = 28.2$
   $\qquad AT = \frac{1}{2}AC \quad = 14.14.$

   angle A given by $\tan^{-1} A = \dfrac{30}{14.14} \Rightarrow A = 64.8°$

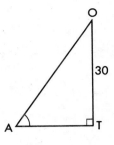

Fig. 5.15

A9

a) If $h \propto u$ then $h = ku$ then $\dfrac{h}{u} = k$ (a constant)

   hence consider the tables of ratios as:

u	1.4	1.7	2.2	2.4	
h	10	14	24	25	
(i) $\dfrac{h}{u^3}$	3.6	2.8	2.2	1.8	not constant
(ii) $\dfrac{h}{u^2}$	5.1	4.8	4.9	4.3	could well be constant
(iii) $\dfrac{h}{\sqrt{u}}$	8.5	10.7	16.2	16.1	not constant

   so (ii) best describes the variation, $h \propto u^2$

b) $k = 4.8$ (the average of the results)
   hence $h = 4.8\,u^2$
   when $u = 3$, $h = 4.8 \times 3^2 = 43.2$
   an approximate value of h will be 43

A10

$$F \propto \frac{1}{W} \Rightarrow F = \frac{K}{W} \Rightarrow K = FW$$

$$\Rightarrow K = 1053 \times 285$$

when $F = 909$

$$W = \frac{K}{F} = \frac{1053 \times 285}{909} = 330 \text{ m}$$

A11

a) Since $t \propto \dfrac{\sqrt[3]{q}}{p^2}$ then $t = \dfrac{K\sqrt[3]{q}}{p^2}$

   i) If $t_0 = \dfrac{K\sqrt[3]{q_0}}{p_0^2}$ then where p_0 and q_0 are both doubled

   $$t_1 = \frac{K\sqrt[3]{2q_0}}{(2p_0)^2} = \frac{K \cdot \sqrt[3]{2} \cdot \sqrt[3]{q_0}}{4p_0^2} = \frac{\sqrt[3]{2}}{4} \cdot \frac{K\sqrt[3]{q_0}}{p_0^2} = \frac{\sqrt[3]{2}}{4}\,t_0$$

   $t_1 = 0.315\,t_0$

   so t has been reduced by $(100 - 31.5)\%$, which is a reduction of 68.5%.

   ii) If $t_0 = \dfrac{K\sqrt[3]{q_0}}{p_0^2}$ then where q_0 is doubled, and p_0 is halved,

   $$t_1 = \frac{K\sqrt[3]{2q_0}}{(\frac{1}{2}p_0)^2} = \frac{\sqrt[3]{2}}{\frac{1}{4}} \cdot \frac{K\sqrt[3]{q_0}}{p_0^2} = 5.04\,t_0$$

   so t has been increased by $(504 - 100)\%$ which is an increase of 404%.

b) Let increase in $q = x\%$ and increase in $p = y\%$

then where $t_0 = \dfrac{K\sqrt[3]{q_0}}{p_0^2}$, $t_1 = \dfrac{K\sqrt[3]{\left(1 + \dfrac{x}{100}\right)q_0}}{\left(\left(1 + \dfrac{y}{100}\right)p_0\right)^2} = \dfrac{\sqrt[3]{\left(1 + \dfrac{x}{100}\right)}}{\left(1 + \dfrac{y}{100}\right)^2} \cdot \dfrac{K\sqrt[3]{q_0}}{p_0^2}$

when $t_0 = t_1$, then $\sqrt[3]{\left(1 + \dfrac{x}{100}\right)} = \left(1 + \dfrac{y}{100}\right)^2$

hence $\left(1 + \dfrac{x}{100}\right) = \left(1 + \dfrac{y}{100}\right)^6$

so there is no change when the increase in q is $x\%$ and of p is $y\%$

and $\left(1 + \dfrac{x}{100}\right) = \left(1 + \dfrac{y}{100}\right)^6$

So, for example, if the increase in q is 50%, then

$1.50 = \left(1 + \dfrac{y}{100}\right)^6$

$1.0699 = 1 + \dfrac{y}{100} \rightarrow y = 7\%$ increase.

i.e. when q is increased by 50% and p is increased by 7%, then t is unaltered.

GRADE CHECKLIST

For a Grade B you should:

Be able to: Understand direct and inverse proportion.

For a Grade A you should also:

Be able to: Express general laws in symbolic form.
Understand the relationships between similar shapes.

For a Grade A* you should also:

Be able to: Understand joint and partial variation.

A STUDENT'S ANSWER WITH EXAMINER'S COMMENTS

Question

Jean and Bill use a set of scales to weigh some coins. They have four 50p coins whose total weight is 5 grams and two 20p coins whose total weight is 1 gram.

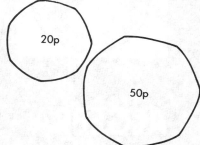

a)   i) Make an estimate of the weight of a 50p coin and of a 20p coin.

$$5 \div 4 = 1.25$$
$$1 \div 2 = 0.5$$

The 50p will weigh 1.25
the 20p will weigh 0.5

> ❝ Correct working, but no units given on the final answer, this will lose marks. ❞

ii) Which estimate is likely to be the more accurate and why?

the 50p because you used more coins.

> ❝ Correct answer, but answer is brief and more explanation is needed. ❞

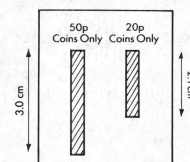

b)   A slot through which a 50p coin will just pass is 3.0 cm long. A 20p coin will just pass through a slot 2.1 cm long. The *faces* of the two coins have the same shape. Find the ratio of the areas of the faces of a 50p coin and a 20p coin in the form $n:1$.

ratio of lengths is 3.0 : 2.1

ratio of areas = $3.0 : 2.1^2$
= 9 : 4.41
= 2.04 : 1

> ❝ Living dangerously here, fortunately the next line shows the student's intent to square each part of the ratio, but this should have been made clear here. ❞

c)   The 50p coin is 2.5 mm thick. Assuming that both coins are made of the same metal, calculate an estimate of the thickness of a 20p coin.

We know that weight $\propto$ area $\times$ width, so weight = k area $\times$ width. let area of 50p = 2.04 and area of 20p = 1. For 50p then 1.25 = K $\times$ 2.04 $\times$ 2.5, K = 0.245 For 20p then 0.5 = 0.245 $\times$ 1 $\times$ width
width = 2.04 mm

> ❝ A good, sound method, but the final answer is too precise for an estimate. 2 mm would be the best answer. ❞

ALGEBRA

GETTING STARTED

Algebra and how you use it is perhaps the key 'thing' that makes mathematicians a grade A or a grade C! Up to grade C, algebra is informal and is mainly concerned with simple situations. At the higher grades and beyond, algebra is an integral part of many situations, as you will already have seen.

You must understand and be able to cope confidently with algebra. This chapter is about how you should be manipulating your algebraic terms and expressions.

USEFUL DEFINITIONS

Coefficient	The whole number next to a variable, e.g. the coefficient of x^2 in $3x^2$ is the 3.
Constant	Not changing.
Domain	The set of numbers from which a mapping or function is applied.
Expand	To multiply out brackets and simplify.
Factorise	Put into expressions containing brackets that multiply together to make the whole.
Function	An algebraic rule for changing one number to another, where each number will only have one unique image.
Generalise	Express in general terms, usually an algebraic formula.
Image	The number that is arrived at from another by some particular function.
Linear	An expression involving only single variables of power one, e.g. $x + y = 3$ or $2x = y + 7$.
Quadratic	An expression involving no power higher than a squared term, e.g. $5x^2 - 3x = 4$.
Range	The set of numbers to which a mapping or function form the image of a given domain.
Simplify	To make easier, usually in algebra means to collect like terms or cancel.
Transposition	To change the subject of a formula or equation.
Variable	A letter which may stand for various numbers.

ESSENTIAL PRINCIPLES

1 ⟩TRANSPOSITION

❝❝ This is your basic rule to follow, learn it and use it. ❞❞

All your manipulation of algebra lies in being able to understand the principle of:

If it's doing what it's doing to everything else on that side of the equation, then it can be moved to the other side and perform the opposite job.

Follow through the following changes of subject of formula and then try them yourself to make absolutely certain that you can confidently cope with this basic requirement of algebra.

WORKED EXAMPLE 1

Change $x = 5y - 7$ to make y the subject.

$$x + 7 = 5y$$
$$\rightarrow \frac{x + 7}{5} = y; \text{ hence } y = \frac{x + 7}{5}$$

WORKED EXAMPLE 2

Change $p = \dfrac{t}{4} + 7$ to make t the subject.

$$p - 7 = \frac{t}{4}$$

$$\rightarrow 4(p - 7) = t; \text{ hence } t = 4(p - 7)$$

WORKED EXAMPLE 3

Change $v = p(4t + 1)$ to make t the subject.

$$\frac{v}{p} = 4t + 1$$

$$\rightarrow \frac{v}{p} - 1 = 4t$$

$$\rightarrow \frac{v - p}{p} = 4t \text{ (easier to cope with if we simplify the LHS)}$$

$$\rightarrow \frac{v - p}{4p} = t$$

WORKED EXAMPLE 4

Change $t = \dfrac{3w + 4}{5 - w}$ to make w the subject.

$$t(5 - w) = 3w + 4$$
$$5t - wt = 3w + 4 \rightarrow 5t - 4 = 3w + wt$$
$$\rightarrow 5t - 4 = w(3 + t)$$
$$\rightarrow \frac{5t - 4}{3 + t} = w$$

hence $\quad w = \dfrac{5t - 4}{3 + t}$

WORKED EXAMPLE 5

Change $x = y^2 - 7$ to make y the subject.

$$x + 7 = y^2 \rightarrow \sqrt{(x + 7)} = y$$

hence $\quad y = \sqrt{(x + 7)}$

<table>
<tr><td>

2   **LINEAR EQUATIONS**

</td><td>

Linear equations are equations that involve single variables of power 1. They contain no expressions such as x^2, y^3, $\dfrac{1}{x}$, xy, etc.

</td></tr>
</table>

You should be familiar with linear equations and how to solve them. You move numbers around *until* you have the unknown as the subject, then do any necessary calculations.

WORKED EXAMPLE 6

Solve the equation $8 = \dfrac{x + 5}{5 - x}$

Change first to $8(5 - x) = x + 5$

$$\rightarrow 40 - 8x = x + 5$$
$$\rightarrow 40 - 5 = x + 8x = 9x$$
$$\rightarrow \frac{35}{9} = x$$
$$x = 3.9 \,(1 \text{ decimal place})$$

EXERCISE 1

Solve the equation $\dfrac{x - 3}{x + 3} = 3$

Quadratic equations are those that involve no higher power than a 2, nor any less than a 1. For example, $3x^2 + 6x - 1 = 0$.

3 **FACTORISATION**

You will often need to factorise other quadratic expressions such as this:

$$2x^2 + 12x + 18$$

which is of the general form:

$$ax^2 + bx + c$$

where a, b and c are the integers $+2$, $+12$ and $+18$ respectively, and x is a variable.

There are a number of different methods that can be used to help you to factorise quadratic expressions:

Method 1
Follow through this worked example to see how the method works.

WORKED EXAMPLE 7

Factorise $12x^2 + x - 35$

Factorise by trying to put this expression into two brackets ( )( ). The -35 indicates that the signs are different, hence (+)(−). Now the first numbers in each bracket (the coefficients of x) must multiply together to give 12, whilst the end two numbers in each bracket (constants) must multiply together to give 35. This gives us quite a few possibilities; e.g. $(6x + 7)(2x - 5)$, but the combination of the *outer two* and the *innter two* products (multiplications) must give us $+1x$. In effect we have the choices given by:

$$\begin{pmatrix} 12 \\ 1 \end{pmatrix} \times \begin{pmatrix} 35 \\ 1 \end{pmatrix}, \begin{pmatrix} 12 \\ 1 \end{pmatrix} \times \begin{pmatrix} 1 \\ 35 \end{pmatrix}, \begin{pmatrix} 12 \\ 1 \end{pmatrix} \times \begin{pmatrix} 5 \\ 7 \end{pmatrix}, \begin{pmatrix} 12 \\ 1 \end{pmatrix} \times \begin{pmatrix} 7 \\ 5 \end{pmatrix}, \begin{pmatrix} 6 \\ 2 \end{pmatrix} \times \begin{pmatrix} 35 \\ 1 \end{pmatrix}, \begin{pmatrix} 6 \\ 2 \end{pmatrix} \times \begin{pmatrix} 1 \\ 35 \end{pmatrix}$$

$$\begin{pmatrix} 6 \\ 2 \end{pmatrix} \times \begin{pmatrix} 5 \\ 7 \end{pmatrix}, \begin{pmatrix} 6 \\ 2 \end{pmatrix} \times \begin{pmatrix} 7 \\ 5 \end{pmatrix}, \begin{pmatrix} 3 \\ 4 \end{pmatrix} \times \begin{pmatrix} 35 \\ 1 \end{pmatrix}, \begin{pmatrix} 3 \\ 4 \end{pmatrix} \times \begin{pmatrix} 1 \\ 35 \end{pmatrix}, \begin{pmatrix} 3 \\ 4 \end{pmatrix} \times \begin{pmatrix} 5 \\ 7 \end{pmatrix}, \begin{pmatrix} 3 \\ 4 \end{pmatrix} \times \begin{pmatrix} 7 \\ 5 \end{pmatrix}$$

But here the *difference* in the diagonals must give us $+1$. This is done in the combination:

$$\begin{pmatrix} 3 & 5 \\ 4 & 7 \end{pmatrix} \text{ i.e. } (3 \times 7) - (4 \times 5) = 21 - 20 = 1$$

So the factorisation is $(3x - 5)(4x + 7)$, the positive product is the larger of the two products since the co-efficient of x is positive $(+1)$.

EXERCISE 2

Factorise   i) $x^2 + 10x + 24$
ii) $2m^2 - 5m - 3$
iii) $8t^2 + 14t - 15$

Method 2

Although it involves a certain amount of 'trial and error' we can follow a simple 'routine' to factorise this expression.

A useful routine for factorising quadratic expressions.

Routine

- Find the product ac
- Write down factor pairs of ac, remembering the signs
- Find the factor pair that adds up to b
- Rewrite the expression, with the middle term now expressed, using this factor pair
- Factorise by grouping

We now use this routine with a number of quadratic expressions.

WORKED EXAMPLE 8

Factorise $t^2 + 6t + 8$ $(a = +1, b = +6, c = +8)$

We can ignore negatives since there are no negative signs in the expression.

Working

Product ac: $1 \times 8 = 8$
Factor pairs of ac: $1 \times 8, 2 \times 4, (-1 \times -8, -2 \times -4)$
Which of these factor pairs adds up to 6?

Answer: (2, 4)

$t^2 + 2t + 4t + 8$ (*rewriting*)
$= t(t + 2) + 4(t + 2)$ (*factorise*
$= (t + 4)(t + 2)$ *by grouping*)

OR

$t \quad +2 \leftarrow$ factor
$t \quad +4 \leftarrow$ factor
$\overline{2t \quad + \quad 4t = 6t}$
$t^2 + 6t + 8 = (t + 2)(t + 4)$

WORKED EXAMPLE 9

Factorise $x^2 - 9x + 20$ $(a = +1, b = -9, c = +20)$

Working

Product ac: $1 \times 20 = 20$
Factor pairs of ac: $(1 \times 20, 2 \times 10, 4 \times 5, -1 \times -20, -2 \times -10, -4 \times -5)$
Which of these factor pairs adds upto -9?

Answer: $(-4, -5)$

$x^2 - 4x - 5x + 20$ (*rewriting*)
$= x(x - 4) - 5(x - 4)$ (*factorise*
$= (x - 5)(x - 4)$ *by grouping*)

OR

$x \quad +4 \leftarrow$ factor
$x \quad +5 \leftarrow$ factor
$\overline{-4x \quad - \quad 5x = -9x}$
$x^2 - 9x + 20 = (x + 4)(x + 5)$

WORKED EXAMPLE 10

Factorise $x^2 - 5x - 24$ $(a = +1, b = -5, c = -24)$

Working

Product ac: $1 \times -24 = -24$
Factor pairs of ac: $(-1 \times 24, -2 \times 12, -3 \times 8, -4 \times 6$
             and sign vice versa)
Which of these factor pairs adds up to -5?

Answer: (3, −8)

$x^2 + 3x - 8x - 24$ (*rewriting*)
$= x(x + 3) - 8(x + 3)$ (*factorise*
$= (x - 8)(x + 3)$ *by grouping*)

OR

$$x \diagdown \diagup +3 \leftarrow \text{factor}$$
$$x \diagup \diagdown -8 \leftarrow \text{factor}$$
$$3x \quad - \quad 8x = -5x$$
$$\overline{x^2 - 5x - 24 \ = (x + 3)(x - 8)}$$

WORKED EXAMPLE 11

Factorise $2x^2 + 11x + 12$ $(a = +2, b = +11, c = +12)$

Working

Product ac: $2 \times 12 = 24$
Factor pairs: $(1 \times 24, 2 \times 12, 3 \times 8, 4 \times 6)$
Which of these factor pairs add up to $+11$?

Answer: (3, 8)

$2x^2 + 3x + 8x + 12$ (*rewriting*)
$= x(2x + 3) + 4(2x + 3)$ (*factorise*
$= (x + 4)(2x + 3)$ *by grouping*)

OR

$$x \diagdown \diagup +4$$
$$2x \diagup \diagdown +3$$
$$8x \quad + \quad 3x = 11x$$
$$\overline{2x^2 + 11x + 12 \ = (x + 4)(2x + 3)}$$

WORKED EXAMPLE 12

Factorise $8x^2 - 14x - 15$ $(a = +8, b = -14, c = -15)$

Working

Product ac: $8 \times -15 = -120$
Too many factor pairs of -120, so only search until you find the sum of one factor pair is -14.
(i.e. $1 \times -120, 2 \times -60, 3 \times -40, 4 \times -30, 5 \times -24, 6 \times -20 \ldots$)
Stop, we have it!
$(6, -20)$ will add up to -14

$8x^2 + 6x - 20x - 15$ (*rewriting*)
$= 2x(4x + 3) - 5(4x + 3)$ (*factorise*
$= (2x - 5)(4x - 3)$ *by grouping*)

OR

$$2x \diagdown \diagup -5 \leftarrow \text{factor}$$
$$4x \diagup \diagdown +3 \leftarrow \text{factor}$$
$$-20x \quad + \quad 6x = -14x$$
$$\overline{8x^2 - 14x - 15 \ = (2x - 5)(4x + 3)}$$

WORKED EXAMPLE 13

Factorise $6x^2 - 17x + 5$ $(a = +6, b = -17, c = +5)$

Working

Product ac: $6 \times 5 = 30$
Search the factor pairs of 30 until you find the sum of -17
(i.e. $-1 \times -30, -2 \times -15, \ldots$ Stop since the factor pair adds up to -17.)

$6x^2 - 2x - 15x + 5$ (*rewriting*)
$= 2x(3x - 1) - 5(3x - 1)$ (*factorise*
$= (2x - 5)(3x - 1)$ *by grouping*)

OR

$$2x \diagdown \diagup -5 \leftarrow \text{factor}$$
$$3x \diagup \diagdown -1 \leftarrow \text{factor}$$
$$-15x \quad - \quad 2x = -17x$$
$$\overline{6x^2 - 17x + 15 \ = (2x - 5)(3x - 1)}$$

This routine method is very useful for completing the factorisation. There are, of course, times when you can see the answer without going through all this process.

Again the aim is that you become so familiar with the process that you are able to do the easier ones in your head!

EXERCISE 3

Try the method you are most comfortable with to factorise:
i) $4m^2 - 20m + 25$ ii) $4x^2 - 4x - 15$ iii) $18t^2 - 63t + 49$

QUADRATIC EQUATIONS

The hardest part of solving **quadratic equations** is to factorise them. Factorisation has been well covered earlier in this chapter. First, put the quadratic equation into the **general** form of:

$$ax^2 + bx + c = 0$$

We can then factorise, to give an equation in the form of:

$$(x + m)(x + n) = 0$$

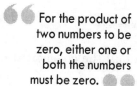 For the product of two numbers to be zero, either one or both the numbers must be zero.

Since both factors multiply to give zero, then one or both of the factors must be zero.
This then usually leads us to two simple linear equations to solve.

WORKED EXAMPLE 14

Solve $(x + 3)(x - 2) = 0$

Working

Either $(x + 3) = 0$ or $(x - 2) = 0$
hence $x = -3$ or $x = 2$

WORKED EXAMPLE 15

Solve $(2x + 3)(3x - 4) = 0$

Working

Either $(2x + 3) = 0$ or $(3x - 4) = 0$
hence $2x = -3$ or $3x = 4$

$$x = \frac{-3}{2} \quad \text{or} \quad x = \frac{4}{3}$$

WORKED EXAMPLE 16

Solve $4x^2 + 15x = -9$

Working

First, put the equation into the general form before factorising.

Rearrange to give $4x^2 + 15x + 9 = 0$
Factorise to give $(4x + 3)(x + 3) = 0$
hence $4x + 3 = 0$ or $x + 3 = 0$

$$x = \frac{-3}{4} \quad \text{or} \quad x = -3$$

WORKED EXAMPLE 17

Solve $x^2 - 6x + 9 = 0$

Working

You see, sometimes there is only *one* solution.

Factorise to give $(x - 3)(x - 3) = 0$
$$(x - 3)^2 = 0$$
hence $x - 3 = 0$
$$x = 3$$

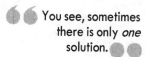

EXERCISE 4

Solve the equations:
  i) $18t^2 + 63t + 49 = 0$ ii) $25x^2 + 16 = 40x$
iii) $4x^2 - 12x + 9 = 0$ iv) $8y^2 - 6y = 9$

SOLVE BY COMPLETING THE SQUARE

You may have done that last exercise quite quickly, or you may have taken quite a time to solve it. It can be a quick method, but only if you *spot* the connection and even then only if it does give two nice brackets.

Another way of always finding a solution (if there is one) is the method of *completing the square*. This follows through the simple procedure:

$$ax^2 + bx + c = 0$$

Divide throughout by 'a' to give $x^2 + \dfrac{b}{a}x + \dfrac{c}{a} = 0$.

Move the constant term to the other side, to give $x^2 + \dfrac{b}{a}x = -\dfrac{c}{a}$

On the Left Hand Side (LHS) drop the square term add half the co-efficient of x, place within brackets, and square.

$$\text{LHS} = \left(x + \frac{b}{2a}\right)^2$$

On the Right Hand Side (RHS), add $\left(\dfrac{b}{2a}\right)^2$

$$\text{RHS} = -\frac{c}{a} + \left(\frac{b}{2a}\right)^2$$

This gives $\left(x + \dfrac{b}{2a}\right)^2 = -\dfrac{c}{a} + \left(\dfrac{b}{2a}\right)^2$, which will have given you an equation like

> 66 Don't give up yet, this really is a good method. 99

$$(x + d)^2 = e$$
$$\rightarrow x + d = +\sqrt{e} \text{ and } -\sqrt{e}$$
$$\rightarrow x = +\sqrt{e} - d \text{ and } -\sqrt{e} - d.$$

It looks worse than it actually is. Follow through worked example 18, then try this method in other exercises earlier in the chapter.

WORKED EXAMPLE 18

> 66 Halve the coefficient of x and follow the rule. 99

Solve the equation $3x^2 + 5x - 4 = 0$

Divide throughout by 3 to give $x^2 + \dfrac{5}{3}x - \dfrac{4}{3} = 0$

Move the constant term to the other side, to give $x^2 + \dfrac{5}{3}x = \dfrac{4}{3}$

$$\left[x + \frac{5}{6}\right]^2 = \frac{4}{3} + \frac{25}{36} \qquad \text{(look where numbers come from)}$$

hence $\left[x + \dfrac{5}{6}\right]^2 = 2.0278$ (use your calculator memory)

$$\Rightarrow x + \frac{5}{6} = 1.424 \text{ and } -1.424$$

$$x = (1.424 - 0.833) \text{ and } (-1.424 - 0.833)$$

$$x = 0.59 \text{ and } -2.26$$

EXERCISE 5

Solve the equations   i) $4x^2 + 12x + 5 = 0$ ii) $3d^2 - 5d - 4 = 0$

SOLVE BY THE FORMULA

There is a well known, loved and trusted *formula* which will also always work to solve equations of the type $ax^2 + bx + c = 0$.

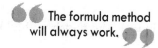 The formula method will always work.

This is $x = \dfrac{-b \pm \sqrt{b^2 - 4ac}}{2a}$

(it is the formal next stage to completing the square).

WORKED EXAMPLE 19

Solve the equation $2x^2 + 5x - 3 = 0$.

Using $x = \dfrac{-b \pm \sqrt{(b^2 - 4ac)}}{2a}$, where $a = 2$, $b = 5$ and $c = -3$

then $x = \dfrac{-5 \pm \sqrt{(25 + 24)}}{4} = \dfrac{-5 \pm \sqrt{(49)}}{4} = \dfrac{-5 \pm 7}{4}$

$x = \dfrac{-12}{4}$ and $\dfrac{2}{4}$

$x = -3$ and 0.5.

Try this method on the exercises 2, 3, 4 and 5 if you wish to compare. All three methods are good and useful. You need to use the method that you are most confident with, or which best suits the situation at the time.

SOLVE BY THE DIFFERENCE OF TWO SQUARES

When we have an expression that is made up of two square expressions (or numbers) and subtracted, then they can **always** be factorised as:

$A^2x^2 - B^2y^2 = (Ax + By)(Ax - By)$.

WORKED EXAMPLE 20

Factorise the equation $16x^2 - 9y^2$

$16x^2 - 9y^2 = (4x + 3y)(4x - 3y)$.

EXERCISE 6

Factorise the expressions   i) $9t^2 - 4p^2$;   ii) $4x^4 - 9y^2$.

PROBLEMS SOLVED BY QUADRATIC EQUATIONS

There are quite a few situations that can most easily be solved by the use of quadratic equations. The difficult part, usually, is putting the problem into the 'general' quadratic form in the first place. So go through the following examples carefully.

WORKED EXAMPLE 21

Two numbers have a product of 117 and a sum of 22. What are the numbers?

Working

Let one of the numbers be x, then the other must be $22 - x$, since they both add up to 22.

Then $x(22 - x) = 117$

so $22x - x^2 = 117$

i.e. $0 = x^2 - 22x + 117$

Factorising, we have $0 = (x - 9)(x - 13)$

hence $x - 9 = 0$ or $x - 13 = 0$

i.e. $x = 9$ or $x = 13$

The two numbers are 9 and 13.

WORKED EXAMPLE 22

A rectangular lawn has a perimeter of 42 m and an area of 68 m². Find the length and width of the lawn.

Working

Let the width be x, then since the perimeter is 42 m the length and width will add up to $\frac{1}{2}$ of $42 = 21$ m, so the length will be $21 - x$.

Hence area $= 68 \text{ m}^2 = x(21 - x) \qquad = 21x - x^2$

i.e. $\qquad\qquad\qquad\qquad x^2 - 21x + 68 = 0$

Factorise to give $\qquad (x - 17)(x - 4) = 0$

hence $\qquad\qquad\qquad\qquad x - 17 = 0 \quad$ or $\quad x - 4 = 0$

$\qquad\qquad\qquad\qquad\qquad\quad x = 17 \quad$ or $\quad x = 4$

Therefore the length $= 17$ m and the width $= 4$ m.

WORKED EXAMPLE 23

A picture measures 22 cm by 16 cm and the area of the uniform frame which surrounds it is 368 cm². Find the width of the frame.

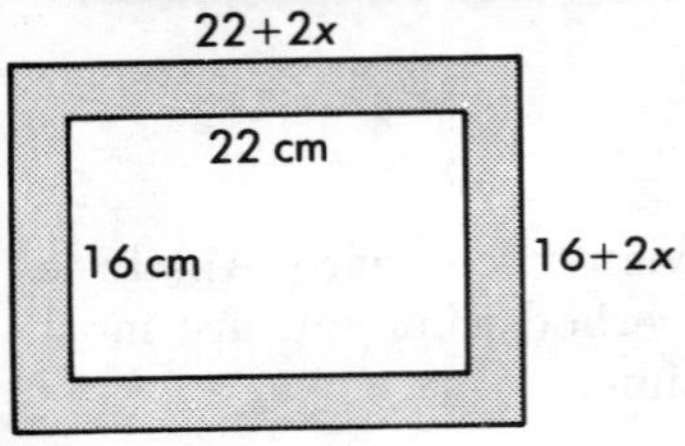

22+2x

22 cm

16 cm   16+2x

Fig. 6.1

Working

Let the frame be of width x, then the lengths of picture frame are $(22 + 2x)$ and $(16 + 2x)$. The total area of this rectangle is $(22 + 2x)(16 + 2x)$ which is equal to the area of the frame + area of picture $= 368 + (16 \times 22)$.

So, $(22 + 2x)(16 + 2x) = 368 + (16 \times 22)$

multiplying out to give

$\qquad 352 + 76x + 4x^2 = 720$

This re-arranges to give

$\qquad 4x^2 + 76x - 368 = 0$

which will divide by 4 to give

$\qquad x^2 + 19x - 92 = 0$

which factorises to give $\quad (x + 23)(x - 4) = 0$

which solves to give $\qquad x + 23 = 0 \quad$ or $\quad x - 4 = 0$

hence $\qquad\qquad\qquad\qquad x = -23 \quad$ or $\quad x = 4$

Clearly x cannot be negative, so our solution is $x = 4$.

EXERCISE 7

⇒ Read the questions carefully
⇒ Form your equations carefully
⇒ Find a suitable quadratic equation, and then solve it
⇒ Finally—don't forget to answer the question

1. A room was 4 m longer than its width. The area was 221 m². Find the dimensions of the room.
2. A swimming pool measures 12 m by 5 m, and a path of uniform width runs along one side and one end. The total area of the pool and path is 120 m². Find the width of the path.

5 ⟩ SIMULTANEOUS EQUATIONS

> These will often appear with equations in words instead of normal equations.

Simultaneous equations are pairs of equations that contain more than one variable and need solving at the same time. They are often linear, but they do not both need to be so. There are two basic techniques for solving them, the *elimination method* and the *substitution method*.

ELIMINATION METHOD

You eliminate one variable, solve the remaining equation then substitute back into one equation to find the final solution.

WORKED EXAMPLE 24

Solve simultaneously the equations: $4x - 2y = 11 \ldots (1)$
$$3x + y = 12 \ldots (2)$$

Multiply equation (2) through by 2 to enable us to eliminate y.

$$4x - 2y = 11 \ldots (1)$$
$$6x + 2y = 24 \ldots (3)$$

Adding the two equations eliminates y

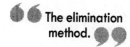 The elimination method.

hence $10x = 35$
$$\rightarrow \quad x = 3.5$$

Substitute $x = 3.5$ into equation (1)

$$14 - 2y = 11$$
$$\rightarrow 2y = 3$$
$$y = 1.5$$

It is usual to check the solution by substituting into the other equation, this time equation (2) to give $(3 \times 3.5) + 1.5 = 12$ which is correct; so the solution is $x = 3.5$, $y = 1.5$.

EXERCISE 8

Solve the pair of simultaneous equations

$$2x + 3y = 10$$
$$6x - y = 5$$

SUBSTITUTION METHOD

Let's use the same simultaneous equations as in the previous part

$$4x - 2y = 11 \ldots (1)$$
$$3x + y = 12 \ldots (2)$$

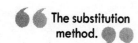 The substitution method.

Then from (2), $y = 12 - 3x$. Now substitute this into equation (1) to give

$$4x - 2(12 - 3x) = 11$$
$$\rightarrow 4x - 24 + 6x = 11$$
$$\rightarrow \qquad 10x = 35$$
$$\rightarrow \qquad x = 3.5$$

and we are where we arrived at before; we now need to substitute $x = 3.5$ into one of the equations to complete the solution.

This method really becomes more useful when only one equation is linear.

WORKED EXAMPLE 25

Solve the simultaneous equations $x^2 + y = 8 \ldots (1)$
$$x - 3y = 1 \ldots (2)$$

From equation (1), $y = 8 - x^2$, so substitute into equation (2) to give

$$x - 3(8 - x^2) = 1$$
$$x - 24 + 3x^2 = 1$$
$$3x^2 + x - 25 = 0$$

Which is a *quadratic* equation and can be solved by one of the previous methods to give $x = 2.72$ and $x = -3.06$ (2 decimal places). Substitute each into equation (1) which gives the final solution that

$$x = 2.72; \quad y = 0.60$$
$$\text{and } x = -3.06; \quad y = -1.36$$

EXERCISE 9

Solve the simultaneous equations $\quad x - y = 5 \ldots (1)$
$$x^2 + 2y = 24 \ldots (2)$$

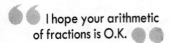

You really must be confident with normal fraction arithmetic to stand a chance of being successful with *algebraic fractions*. This is because you have to apply the normal fraction rules without being able to resort to 'common fractions'.

> I hope your arithmetic of fractions is O.K.

ADDING AND SUBTRACTING ALGEBRAIC FRACTIONS

To add or subtract **algebraic fractions** we still follow those same rules for adding:

- find the LCM of the denominator
- write each fraction with this LCM
- simplify the numerator

WORKED EXAMPLE 26

Simplify $\dfrac{x}{2} + \dfrac{(x-2)}{5}$

Recall how you would simplify $\dfrac{1}{2} + \dfrac{1}{5} = \dfrac{5+2}{10} = \dfrac{7}{10}$

The LCM of 2 and 5 is 10.

$$\frac{x}{2} + \frac{(x-2)}{5} = \frac{5x}{10} + \frac{2(x-2)}{10}$$

$$= \frac{(5x + 2x - 4)}{10}$$

$$= \frac{(7x - 4)}{10}$$

WORKED EXAMPLE 27

$$\frac{3x}{4} - \frac{2(x-3)}{5} = 2\tfrac{1}{4}$$

The LCM of 4 and 5 is 20.

> Solving fraction equations.

$$\frac{3x}{4} - \frac{2(x-3)}{5} = \frac{15x}{20} - \frac{8(x-3)}{20} = 2.25$$

$$= \frac{(15x - 8x + 24)}{20} = 2.25$$

$$= \frac{(7x + 24)}{20} \qquad = 2.25$$

$$7x + 24 = 2.25 \times 20 = 45$$

$$7x = 45 - 24 = 21$$

$$x = 3$$

WORKED EXAMPLE 28

$$\frac{1}{x-1} + \frac{3}{x+4} = 1$$

The LCM of the denominator is $(x-1)(x+4)$

so $\dfrac{1}{x-1} + \dfrac{3}{x+4} = \dfrac{1(x+4) + 3(x-1)}{(x-1)(x+4)} = 1$

$$= \dfrac{x+4+3x-3}{(x-1)(x+4)} = 1$$

$$= \dfrac{4x+1}{(x-1)(x+4)} = 1$$

$$4x + 1 = (x-1)(x+4) = x^2 + 3x - 4$$

hence $0 = x^2 - x - 5$

which solves to give $x = 2.79$ and $x = -1.79$

EXERCISE 10

Solve the equations   i) $5 + \dfrac{1}{x} = x$ ii) $\dfrac{1}{x-1} + \dfrac{2}{x+1} = 5$

MULTIPLYING

You must remember your cancelling technique, you can cancel any factor on the top with any factor on the bottom e.g.

$$\dfrac{\cancel{(x+1)}}{(x-3)\cancel{(x+1)}} = \dfrac{1}{x-3}$$

WORKED EXAMPLE 29

factorise and simplify $\dfrac{x^2 - 5x + 6}{x^2 - 4}$

factorise numerator and denominator: $\dfrac{\cancel{(x-2)}(x-3)}{(x+2)\cancel{(x-2)}} = \dfrac{x-3}{x+2}$

DIVIDING

Remember the rule to turn the second fraction upside down and multiply.

WORKED EXAMPLE 30

Solve $\dfrac{(x+1)}{3} \div \dfrac{4}{(x+1)} = 1$

Turn the second fraction upside down and multiply, which gives us

$$\dfrac{(x+1)}{3} \times \dfrac{(x+1)}{4} = 1$$

$$\rightarrow (x+1)^2 = 12$$
$$\rightarrow x+1 = \sqrt{12} = 3.46 \text{ and } -3.46$$
$$x = 3.46 - 1 \text{ and } -3.46 - 1$$
$$x = 2.46 \text{ and } -4.46$$

EXERCISE 11

Find   i) the product;   ii) the quotient of $\dfrac{x+1}{x-1}$ and $\dfrac{x^2-1}{x^2+1}$

The use of the *fractional index* is used to denote a root,

e.g. $9^{\frac{1}{2}} = \sqrt{9} = 3$ and -3

$8^{\frac{1}{3}} = \sqrt[3]{8} = 2$

NB. $8^{\frac{2}{3}} = (\sqrt[3]{8})^2 = 2^2 = 4$ or $\sqrt[3]{8^2} = \sqrt[3]{64} = 4$

Do work all these out on the calculator with the correct buttons ... it's so much easier.

Use the $x^{1/y}$ button on your calculator to calculate the answers. For example, to calculate $9^{\frac{1}{5}}$, just press 9 followed by $x^{1/y}$, followed by 5 = , this should give you 1.55.

Similarly, if you need to calculate a cube root, maybe from a similar shape situation, then use the $x^{1/y}$ button on your calculator followed by a 3.

WORKED EXAMPLE 31

Which is the larger? $18^{\frac{2}{3}}$ or $8^{\frac{3}{2}}$

$18^{\frac{2}{3}} = (\sqrt[3]{18})^2 = 6.868$

$8^{\frac{3}{2}} = (\sqrt{8})^3 = 22.63$

hence $8^{\frac{3}{2}} > 18^{\frac{2}{3}}$

EXERCISE 12

Calculate   i) $5^{\frac{2}{5}}$;   ii) $\sqrt[3]{11}$;   iii) $8^{-0.7}$

The only *functions* we are going to consider are *algebraic functions* which give a rule for changing one number to another.

For example $f: x \rightarrow 3x$ is the function f where any number is multiplied by 3 to obtain its image. Another way of denoting the same function is to say $f(x) = 3x$.

WORKED EXAMPLE 32

For the function $f: x \rightarrow \sin(2x)$ find f(40).

$f(40) = \sin(2 \times 40) = \sin 80 = 0.9848$.

EXERCISE 13

Where $f: x \rightarrow (x-1)^2$, what is   i) f(1);   ii) f(0);   iii) f(-1).

DOMAIN AND RANGE

The set of numbers that the given function is applied to is called the *domain*. The set of numbers that the function takes numbers to is called the *range*.

WORKED EXAMPLE 33

If the domain of the function $f: x \rightarrow \dfrac{1}{x+1}$ is $\{x: 2 \leqslant x \leqslant 10\}$ find the range of the function.

We need to find all the possible images from x between 2 and 10 inclusive. Looking at the function tells us that as x gets bigger then so $f(x)$ gets gradually smaller.

Hence f(2) will give the upper limit of the range $f(2) = \dfrac{1}{3}$

and f(10) will give the lower limit of the range $f(10) = \dfrac{1}{11}$

so the range will be $\left\{ x : \dfrac{1}{11} \leqslant x \leqslant \dfrac{1}{3} \right\}$

WHEN IS A FUNCTION NOT A FUNCTION?

The question should really be 'when is an algebraic rule that looks like a function not really a function?'.

A mathematical function, f, must have for each x in the domain one, and only one, possible image $f(x)$.

For example $f: x \rightarrow \sqrt{x}$ is *not* a mathematical function since the $\sqrt{x}$ will have two possible values, the negative and the positive square root of x.

INVERSE FUNCTIONS

The inverse of a function is that function that will return each number from the range back to its origin in the domain. It can be thought of as the function 'the opposite way round'.

The notation of an inverse function of $f(x)$ is usually $f^{-1}(x)$.

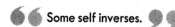 **Be familiar with inverse functions.**

There are a number of ways of finding an inverse to a function, some of these can quite readily be seen, for example:

$$\text{If } f(x) = x + 3 \quad \text{then } f^{-1}(x) = x - 3$$

$$\text{If } f(x) = 6x \qquad\qquad \text{then } f^{-1}(x) = \frac{6}{x}$$

Others, like $f(x) = \dfrac{3x + 1}{1 - x}$ are not quite so easily spotted, and we need a procedure to find them. But first we just need to look at *self inverses*.

A function has a self inverse when the same function will return each number in an image back to the original number in the domain. Try the following for yourself and see that they are *all* self inverses.

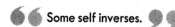 **Some self inverses.**

$$\text{If } f(x) = \frac{1}{x} \quad \text{then } f^{-1}(x) = \frac{1}{x}$$

$$\text{If } f(x) = \frac{24}{x} \quad \text{then } f^{-1}(x) = \frac{24}{x}$$

$$\text{If } f(x) = 10 - x \quad \text{then } f^{-1}(x) = 10 - x.$$

Hence the type of functions $f: x \rightarrow \dfrac{A}{x}$ and $f: x \rightarrow A - x$ when A is a real number are *all* self inverses.

A rule to find inverses

There are two ways of finding inverses, and each, at times, is better than the other. Look at both, and become familiar with both, so that when an inverse is needed, you are equipped to choose the best method for finding the inverse in that specific case.

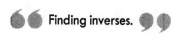 **Finding inverses.**

Flow diagram method

State the function as a *flow diagram*, or sequence of simple steps from x to $f(x)$, then write down the reverse process and put it into function form.

WORKED EXAMPLE 34

Find the inverse function of $f: x \rightarrow 5 + \dfrac{3}{(x - 1)}$

Write as a flow diagram starting with x.

Start $\rightarrow$ subtract 1 $\rightarrow$ divide into 3 $\rightarrow$ add on 5 $\rightarrow$ end

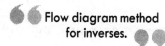 **Flow diagram method for inverses.**

$$x \quad \rightarrow \quad (x - 1) \quad \rightarrow \quad \frac{3}{(x - 1)} \quad \rightarrow 5 + \frac{3}{(x - 1)} = f(x).$$

Now the inverse will come back the other way, doing the inverse operations, starting with x

end $\leftarrow$ add 1 $\leftarrow$ divide into 3 $\leftarrow$ subtract 5 $\leftarrow$ start

$$f^{-1}(x) \leftarrow 1 + \frac{3}{(x-5)} \leftarrow \frac{3}{(x-5)} \leftarrow (x-5) \leftarrow x$$

hence inverse given by $f^{-1} : x \rightarrow 1 + \dfrac{3}{(x-5)}$

EXERCISE 14

Find the inverse of the following functions and state which inverse is not a function.

i) $f : x \rightarrow \dfrac{4-x}{5}$;   ii) $g : x \rightarrow \dfrac{6x-10}{3}$;   iii) $h : x \rightarrow x^2 + 1$

Transposition method

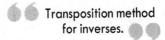

This method has the advantage over the previous one in that it will *always* work and is better suited to the more complicated functions.

It is dependent on rewriting the function as an algebraic equation and then transposing the equation to make x the subject. Follow through the worked example.

WORKED EXAMPLE 35

Find the inverse function of $f : x \rightarrow \dfrac{3x+1}{1-x}$

Rewrite as $y = \dfrac{3x+1}{1-x}$ then transpose to make x the subject.

$$\rightarrow y(1-x) = 3x + 1$$
$$\rightarrow y - yx = 3x + 1 \rightarrow y - 1 = 3x + yx$$
$$\rightarrow y - 1 = x(3+y) \rightarrow \frac{y-1}{3+y} = x$$

So the inverse function is $f^{-1} : x \rightarrow \dfrac{x-1}{3+x}$

(note that to write down the inverse function we need to replace the y with the x again).

EXERCISE 15

Find the inverse functions of   i) $f : x \rightarrow \dfrac{x}{4+x}$;   ii) $g(x) = \dfrac{x+1}{1-x}$

COMBINATION FUNCTIONS

When we combine two or more functions together we usually call them *composite functions*. For example, if we have two functions f and g such that $f : x \rightarrow 6x + 1$ $g : x \rightarrow \dfrac{x-2}{3}$ then fg(x) is the composite function of f and g together, where g is applied first, then f.

Hence $fg(x) = f\left(\dfrac{x-2}{3}\right) = 6\left(\dfrac{x-2}{3}\right) + 1 = 2(x-2) + 1 = 2x - 3.$

It should be noted that fg(x) and gf(x) are the different way round and will nearly always give a *different* composite function. For example, using the same f and g as above:

$$gf(x) = g(6x + 1) = \frac{(6x + 1) - 2}{3} = \frac{6x - 1}{3}$$

and so you see an example where gf(x) does not equal fg(x).

WORKED EXAMPLE 36

Where $f(x) = 2x + 1$ and $g(x) = x^2$, find the values of x such that $fg(x) = gf(x)$

$$fg(x) = f(x^2) = 2x^2 + 1$$

$$gf(x) = g(2x + 1) = (2x + 1)^2 = 4x^2 + 4x + 1.$$

When fg(x) = gf(x) then $2x^2 + 1 = 4x^2 + 4x + 1$

$$\rightarrow 0 = 2x^2 + 4x$$

$$\rightarrow 2x(x + 2) = 0$$

$$\rightarrow x = 0 \text{ and } x = -2.$$

Hence fg(x) = gf(x) when $x = 0$ and $x = -2$.

EXERCISE 16

Where $f : x \rightarrow \dfrac{1 + x}{x}$ and $g : x \rightarrow 1 + x$, find   i)   fg(x);   ii)   gf(x)

SOLUTIONS TO EXERCISES

S1

$$x - 3 = 3(x + 3) \rightarrow x - 3 = 3x + 9 \rightarrow -3 - 9 = 3x - x$$
$$\rightarrow -12 = 2x \qquad \rightarrow -6 = x \rightarrow x = -6$$

S2

i) $(x + 6)(x + 4)$ ii) $(2m + 1)(m - 3)$ iii) $(2t + 5)(4t - 3)$

S3

i) $(2x - 5)^2$ ii) $(2x + 3)(2x - 5)$ iii) $(6x - 7)(3x - 7)$

S4

i) $(6x + 7)(3x + 7) = 0 \Rightarrow 6x + 7 = 0$ and $3x + 7 = 0$
$$\Rightarrow x = \tfrac{-7}{6} \qquad \text{and} \qquad x = \tfrac{-7}{3}$$

ii) $25x^2 - 40x + 16 = 0 \Rightarrow (5x - 4)^2 = 0 \Rightarrow 5x - 4 = 0$
$$\Rightarrow x = \tfrac{4}{5}$$

iii) $(2x - 3)^2 = 0 \Rightarrow 2x - 3 = 0 \Rightarrow 2x = 3$
$$\Rightarrow x = \tfrac{3}{2}$$

iv) $8y^2 - 6y - 9 = 0$
$$\Rightarrow (4y + 3)(2y - 3) = 0 \Rightarrow 4y + 3 = 0 \qquad \text{and} \qquad 2y - 3 = 0$$
$$y = -\tfrac{3}{4} \qquad \text{and} \qquad y = \tfrac{3}{2}$$

S5

i) $x^2 + 3x + \frac{5}{4} = 0 \Rightarrow x^2 + 3x = \frac{-5}{4} \Rightarrow (x + \frac{3}{2})^2 = \frac{-5}{4} + \frac{9}{4}$

    $x + \frac{3}{2} = \pm 1 \Rightarrow x = -0.5$ and $x = -2.5$

ii) $d^2 - \frac{5}{3}d - \frac{4}{3} = 0 \Rightarrow d^2 - \frac{5}{3}d = \frac{4}{3} \Rightarrow (d - \frac{5}{6})^2 = \frac{4}{3} + \frac{25}{36}$

    $d - \frac{5}{6} = \pm \frac{73}{36} \Rightarrow d = \frac{73}{36} + \frac{5}{6}$ and $-\frac{73}{36} + \frac{5}{6}$

                   $= 2.86$ and -1.19

S6

i) $(3t + 2p)(3t - 2p)$ ii) $(2x^2 + 3y)(2x^2 - 3y)$

S7

1.   Let the width be x cm, then

    $x(x + 4) = 221 \Rightarrow x^2 + 4x - 221 = 0$

    this solves to give $x = 13$ or -17, we use the positive, hence the dimensions are 13 m, 17 m

2.   Let the width of the path be x, then

    $(2x + 5)(2x + 12) = 120 \Rightarrow 4x^2 + 34x + 60 = 120 \Rightarrow 4x^2 + 34x - 60 = 0$,

    this solves to give 1.5 and -10 hence the width of the path is 1.5·m.

S8

Eliminate y first to obtain $x = 1.25$, then substitute in one equation to give $y = 2.5$.

S9

From equation (1) $x = 5 + y$, substitute this into equation (2)
to give $(5 + y)^2 + 2y = 24$

    $\rightarrow 25 + 10y + y^2 + 2y = 24.$
    $\rightarrow y^2 + 12y + 1 \qquad = 0$

This will solve to give $y = -0.08$ and -11.9.
So from equation (1) we can now give the full solution of

      $x = 4.92, \quad y = -0.08$
  and $x = -6.9, \, y = -11.9$.

S10

i) $5x + 1 = x^2 \Rightarrow x^2 - 5x - 1 = 0$

              $\Rightarrow x = 5.19$ and $x = -0.19$

ii) $\dfrac{(x + 1) + 2(x - 1)}{(x - 1)(x + 1)} = 5$

      $x + 1 + 2x - 2 = 5x^2 - 5$

       $5x^2 - 3x - 4 = 0 \Rightarrow x = 1.24$ and -0.64

S11

i)   product $= \dfrac{(x + 1)}{(x - 1)} \times \dfrac{(x^2 - 1)}{(x^2 + 1)} = \dfrac{(x + 1)}{(x - 1)} \times \dfrac{(x + 1)(x - 1)}{(x^2 + 1)} = \dfrac{(x + 1)^2}{(x^2 + 1)}$

ii)   quotient $= \dfrac{(x + 1)}{(x - 1)} \div \dfrac{(x^2 - 1)}{(x^2 + 1)} = \dfrac{(x + 1)}{(x - 1)} \times \dfrac{(x^2 + 1)}{(x + 1)(x - 1)} = \dfrac{x^2 + 1}{(x - 1)^2}$

S12

i) Use calculator as $5 \to x^y \to 0.4$ (i.e. $\frac{2}{5}$) $= 1.9$
ii) Use calculator as $11 \to x^{1/y} \to 3 = 2.22$
iii) Use calculator as $8 \to x^y \to 0.7 \to {}^+/_- = 0.23$

Do try to become familiar with the use of x^y and $x^{1/y}$ buttons on your calculator.

S13

i) f(1) = 0; ii) f(0) = 1; iii) f(−1) = 4.

S14

i) $f^{-2}: x \to 4 - 5x$; ii) $f^{-1}: x \to \dfrac{3x + 10}{6}$; iii) $f^{-1}: x \to \sqrt{(x - 1)}$.

The last one is not a function since each image has two possibilities.

S15

i) $f^{-1}: x \to \dfrac{4x}{1 - x}$; ii) $f^{-1}: x \to \dfrac{x - 1}{x + 1}$

S16

i) $fg(x) = f(1 + x) = \dfrac{1 + (1 + x)}{(1 + x)} = \dfrac{2 + x}{1 + x}$

ii) $gf(x) = g\left(\dfrac{1 + x}{x}\right) = 1 + \left(\dfrac{1 + x}{x}\right) = \dfrac{x + 1 + x}{x} = \dfrac{2x + 1}{x}$

EXAM TYPE QUESTIONS

Q1

The ancient Babylonian stone tablet shown in Fig. 6.2 gives this formula for the length of the diagonal (d) of a rectangle. The longer side is l and the short w. The formula is only an approximation.

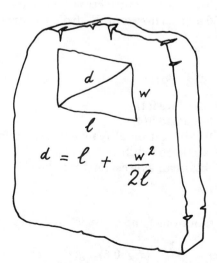

Fig. 6.2

a) What is the difference, to three decimal places, between the correct value of d and that given by the formula, when the rectangular measures i) 6 cm by 5 cm, and ii) 10 cm by 1 cm?
b) Re-arrange the formula to make w the subject (MEG)

Q2

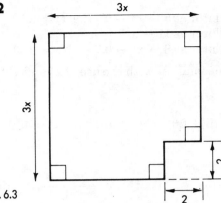

Fig. 6.3

a) Write down, in terms of x, an expression for the area of the shape in Fig. 6.3.
b) Multiply out $(3x + 2)(3x - 2)$, giving your answer in its simplest form.
c) By making one cut and reassembling, the shape in Fig. 6.3 can be made into a rectangle. Using your answers to a) and b), draw a diagram to show how this can be done. Mark the dimensions of the rectangle on your diagram.   (NEAB)

Q3

The cost, £C, of making n articles is given by the formula

$C = a + bn.$

where a and b are constants. The cost of making 4 articles is £20 and the cost of making 7 articles is £29.

a) Write down two equations in a and b.
b) Solve these equations to find the values of a and b.   (ULEAC)

Q4

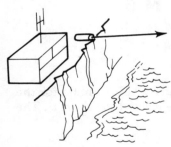

Fig. 6.4

A rescue harpoon is fired horizontally from a cliff top, as shown in Fig. 6.4. The horizontal distance, x metres, it has travelled after t seconds is given by $x = 250t$. The distance of the harpoon below the cliff top, y metres, is given by $y = 5t^2$.

a) i) Write t in terms of x.
   ii) Write an equation which connects y and x, but does not include t, in the form $y = \ldots$.
b) How many centimetres below the cliff top will the harpoon be when it is 50 metres horizontally from the firing gun?   (WJEC)

Q5

$f(x) = 3 - 2x$

a) Calculate $f(4)$
b) Calculate $ff(4)$
c) Obtain and simplify an expression for $ff(x)$
d) Calculate $f^{-1}(2)$
e) Obtain an expression for $f^{-1}(x)$ (MEG)

Q6

Two functions f and g are defined as follows:

$$f(x) = \frac{1}{2x - 1} \ (x \neq 0.5) \quad g(x) = x^2$$

a) Find the values of   i) $f(2)$;   ii) $gf(2)$
b) Find an expression for   i) $gf(x)$;   ii) $fg(x)$
c) Show that there is only one value of 'a' for which $fg(a) = gf(a)$ (NEAB)

Q7

0	1	2	3	4	5	6	7	8	9
10	11	12	13	14	15	16	17	18	19
20	21	22	23	24	25	26	27	28	29
30	31	32	33	34	35	36	37	38	39
40	41	42	43	....					

Fig. 6.5

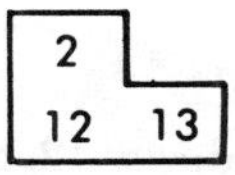

Fig. 6.6

Look at the number pattern in Fig. 6.5.

The section in Fig. 6.6 is called the **12L** because **12** is the middle number.

To find the value of 12L you multiply the end numbers and add the middle number, as follows: $(2 \times 13) + 12$. Therefore the value of 12L is 38.

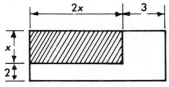

Fig. 6.7

a) What is the value of the 27L section?
b) i) Write down the numbers missing from this L in Fig. 6.7 in terms of x.
    ii) Find the value of this L in terms of x.
c) Which L has a value of 998?   (WJEC)

Q8

The outer rectangle shown in Fig. 6.8 measures $(2x + 3)$ by $(x + 2)$.

a) Express the area of the shaded rectangle in terms of x.
b) Express the area of the unshaded region in terms of x, in as simplified a form as possible.
c) Calculate the value of x when the area of the shaded region is 2 square units less than the area of the unshaded region.   (NEAB)

Fig. 6.8

Q9

Simplify a) $2x^4 \times 4x^{-3}$ b) $8x^2y \div 4x^4$ c) $x^{0.5} \times x^{2.5}$
          d) $(x^{\frac{1}{2}})^{-4}$ e) $\dfrac{1}{2x} - \dfrac{1}{2x + 1}$

Q10

a) Evaluate
    i) $8^{\frac{1}{3}}$
    ii) 3^{-4}
b) Solve the equation $16^x = \frac{1}{4}$

Q11

a) Solve the equation
    $x^5 = 0.002\,43$
b) Once a year a scientist measured the mass of a certain piece of a decaying radioactive element. His results are shown.

Time (years)	0	1	2	3
Mass (kg)	20	18	16.2	14.58

    i) Calculate the annual percentage decrease of the mass.
    ii) Calculate the mass after 10 years.
    iii) Estimate the half life of the element (i.e. the time it takes to lose half of its mass).

Q12

a) Work out $(a + b)(c + d)$.
b) Jhoti wanted to use her calculator to work out the exact value of $537\,142 \times 612\,304$.
    Work this out on your calculator. Write down the display.
    Explain why this is not an exact result.
c) Jhoti then wrote the problem as $(537\,000 + 142)(612\,000 + 304)$.
    i) Using the result obtained in part a), explain how she could find an exact answer to the problem.
    ii) What is the exact answer?

Q13

ABC is a right-angled triangle as shown. The total length of the sides is 12 cm. AC is 1 cm longer than AB, and $AB = x$ cm.

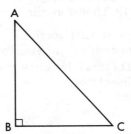

Fig. 6.9

a)   i) Using Pythagoras's Theorem for this triangle, show that $(11 - 2x)^2 + x^2 = (x + 1)^2$.
     ii) Show that this simplifies to $2x^2 - 23x + 60 = 0$.
b) The equation in a) ii) has two solutions, one of which is a whole number. Find this solution by any suitable means.
c) The second solution to the equation lies between $x = 7$ and $x = 8$. Explain why this is an unacceptable solution for the triangle given.

Q14

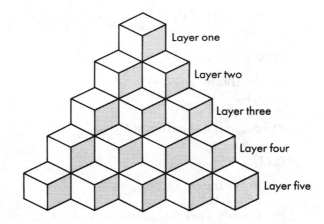

Fig. 6.10

The drawing shows a pile of bricks which are all the same size.
They have been carefully placed so as to produce a pattern.

a) Complete the table giving the number of bricks used to form the various layers.

Layer Number	1	2	3	4	5
Number of bricks	1	3			

b) This pattern of bricks is continued so as to have one more layer beneath those shown in the drawing. How many bricks will there be in this new layer?

c) The number of bricks, N, in a certain layer, L, is given by the formula
$$N = aL^2 + bL$$
where a and b are constants.
Use some of the information in the table above to form two simultaneous equations in a and b.
Solve your equations to find the exact formula.

Q15

A garden supplier regularly posts catalogues to his customers. There are two types of catalogue—a 'maxi' and a 'mini' version.

At the Post Office he is charged £2.20 for posting 3 'maxi' and 2 'mini' catalogues to five customers. Later he is charged £2.42 for posting 2 'maxi' and 5 'mini' catalogues to seven customers.

Work out the postal charge for sending each type of catalogue.

Q16

Three numbers x, y, z have the property that

$$(y - z) \times (z - x) \times (x - y) = 0.$$

a) From this, **one** of the following statements can be deduced. State which and give a reason for your answer.
 1. At least one of x, y, z is zero.
 2. At least two of x, y, z are zero.
 3. The numbers x, y, z are all zero.
 4. At least two of x, y, z are equal.
 5. The numbers x, y, z are all equal.

b) You are given that three numbers x, y, z satisfy the equations

$$(y - z)(z - x)(x - y) = 0$$

and $x + 1 = 2y + 3 = 3z + 6$.

There are three possible sets of values for x, y, z. Find them. (OCSEB)

Q17

The equation $a^2 + b^2 = c^2$ gives the relation between the lengths of the sides of a right angled triangle, c being the length of the hypotenuse and a and b the lengths of the other sides respectively. We wish to find integer values of a, b and c to satisfy the equation.

a) Show that the formulae $a = v^2 - u^2$, $b = 2uv$, and $c = u^2 + v^2$ may be used to find the required values.

b) How must u and v be chosen so that a, b and c have no common factor?
(WJEC)

Q18

Here are four consecutive numbers 13, 14, 15, 16.
If you multiply the middle pair, you get $14 \times 15 = 210$.
If you multiply the outer pair, you get $13 \times 16 = 208$.
 i) Do a calculation like this for a different set of four consecutive numbers of your own choice.
 ii) Repeat i) twice more. You should notice a general rule. State this clearly in words.
 iii) Use algebra to prove that your rule always works with any four consecutive numbers.
 iv) Find a similar rule which works if you start with four consecutive odd numbers (such as 17, 19, 21, 23). Use algebra to prove this rule. (OCSEB)

Q19

Two trains travel on parallel tracks towards each other at 60 mph and 80 mph respectively. At twelve o'clock they usually pass two points A and B respectively 80 miles apart.

a) Find where the trains pass each other.

b) One day, the slower train was late and passed the express train at a point 6 miles nearer to A than the usual passing point. Assuming the express train to be punctual and both trains to be travelling at the usual speeds, find how many minutes later than usual the slower train was that day. (WJEC)

OUTLINE ANSWERS TO EXAM QUESTIONS

A1

a) i) Actual value of $d = \sqrt{(6^2 + 5^2)} = 7.810\,25$.

Babylonian formula gives $d = 6 + \dfrac{25}{12} = 8.083\,333$. The difference is 0.273.

ii) Actual value of $d = \sqrt{(10^2 + 1^2)} = 10.049\,876$

Babylonian formula gives $d = 10 + \dfrac{1}{20} = 10.05$. The difference is 0.000\,123\,79, which to three decimal places is 0.000.

b) From $d = l + \dfrac{w^2}{2l} \rightarrow d - l = \dfrac{w^2}{2l} \rightarrow 2l(d - l) = w^2$

$\rightarrow w = \sqrt{2ld - 2l^2}$.

A2

a) $9x^2 - 4$

b) $9x^2 - 4$

c) See Fig. 6.11.

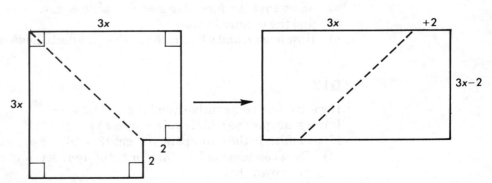

Fig. 6.11

A3

a) $20 = a + 4b \ldots (1)$ and $29 = a + 7b \ldots (2)$.

b) Solve the two simultaneous equations to give $b = 3$ and $a = 8$.

A4

a) i) $t = \dfrac{x}{250}$

    ii) $y = 5t^2 \to y = 5\left(\dfrac{x}{250}\right)^2 \to y = \dfrac{5x^2}{62\,500} = \dfrac{x^2}{12\,500}$

b) When $x = 50$, $y = \dfrac{50^2}{12\,500} = 0.2$ metres $= 20$ cm.

A5

a) $f(4) = 3 - 8 = -5$
b) $ff(4) = f(-5) = 3 + 10 = 13$.
c) $ff(x) = f(3 - 2x) = 3 - 2(3 - 2x) = 3 - 6 + 4x = 4x - 3$.
d) $f^{-1}(2) = 0.5$.

e) $f^{-1}(x) = \dfrac{3 - x}{2}$

A6

a) i) $f(2) = \tfrac{1}{3}$;   ii) $gf(2) = g(\tfrac{1}{3}) = \tfrac{1}{9}$

b) i) $gf(x) = g\left(\dfrac{1}{2x - 1}\right) = \left(\dfrac{1}{2x - 1}\right)^2$

    ii) $fg(x) = f(x^2) = \dfrac{1}{2x^2 - 1}$

c) When $gf(a) = fg(a)$ then $\dfrac{1}{(2a - 1)^2} = \dfrac{1}{2a^2 - 1}$

      $\to (2a - 1)^2 = 2a^2 - 1$
      $\to 4a^2 - 4a + 1 = 2a^2 - 1$
      $\to 2a^2 - 4a + 2 = 0$ $\to a^2 - 2a + 1 = 0$
                                     $\to (a - 1)^2 = 0$
                                       $\to a = 1$

There is only the one solution.

A7

a) $(17 \times 28) + 27 = 503$.
b) i) $(x - 10)$ and $(x + 1)$.
    ii) $(x - 10)(x + 1) + x = x^2 - 9x - 10 + x$
                               $= x^2 - 8x - 10$.
c) When $L = 998$
     then $x^2 - 8x - 10 = 998$
       $\to x^2 - 8x - 1008 = 0$
    which will solve to give $x = 36$ and $x = -28$.
    Here we need the positive solution of 36.

A8

a) $2x^2$
b) $(2x + 3)(x + 2) - 2x^2 = 2x^2 + 7x + 6 - 2x^2$
                             $= 7x + 6$
c) This will be when $2x^2 + 2 = 7x + 6$.
       Hence $2x^2 - 7x - 4 = 0$.
    which will solve to give $x = -0.5$ and $x = 4$.
    Here we need the positive solution of $x = 4$.

A9

a) $8x$ b) $\dfrac{2y}{x^2}$ c) x^3 d) $\dfrac{1}{x^2}$ e) $\dfrac{1}{2x(2x+1)}$

A10

a) i) $\sqrt[3]{8} = 2$ ii) $\dfrac{1}{3^4} = \dfrac{1}{81}$

b) $16^x = \frac{1}{4} \Rightarrow 4^{2x} = 4^{-1} \Rightarrow 2x = -1 \Rightarrow x = -\frac{1}{2}$

A11

a) $(0.002\,43)^{\frac{1}{3}} = 0.3 \Rightarrow x = 0.3$

b) i) $\dfrac{2}{20} \times 100 = 10\%$

   ii) $20 \times (0.9)^{10} = 6.97\,\text{kg}$

   iii) find x where $20 \times (0.9)^x = 10$
   $$\Rightarrow (0.9)^x = \tfrac{10}{20} = \tfrac{1}{2} = 0.5$$
   by trial and improvement $x = 6.58$ years (6.6 is acceptable)

A12

a) $ac + ad + bc + bd$

b) $3.288\,942 \times 10^{11}$, not enough room on the calculator display to show all the figures.

c) i) substitute the given values for a, b, c and d then add by 'long addition'.

   ii) where $a = 537\,000$ $b = 142$ $c = 612\,000$ $d = 304$
   $ac + ad + bc + bd$
   $= 328\,644\,000\,000 + 163\,248\,000 + 86\,904\,000 + 43\,168$
   $= 328\,894\,195\,168$

A13

a) i) $AB = x$, $AC = x + 1$, $BC = 12 - (x + x + 1) = 11 - 2x$
   since $BC^2 + AB^2 = AC^2$
   then $(11 - 2x)^2 + x^2 = (x + 1)^2$

   ii) this expands to $121 - 44x + 4x^2 + x^2 = x^2 + 2x + 1$
   $\Rightarrow 4x^2 - 46x + 120 = 0$ (divide through by two)
   $\Rightarrow 2x^2 - 23x + 60 = 0$

b) $(2x - 15)(x - 4) = 0 \Rightarrow x = 4$ is the whole number.

c) since then AC would be between 8 and 9. Yet the total perimeter has to be equal to 12, thus giving BC a negative value.

A14

a)

Layer Number	1	2	3	4	5
Number of bricks	1	3	6	10	15

b) by looking at how the table builds up you can now predict adding 6 onto 15 to give 21.

c) the simplest equations will be from layers 1 and 2.
   $\Rightarrow a + b = 1 \ldots \text{①}$ (layer 1)
   $\quad\; 4a + 2b = 3 \ldots \text{②}$ (layer 2).

multiply ① by ② then eliminate b to give $a = \frac{1}{2}$
substitute $a = \frac{1}{2}$ into ① to give $b = \frac{1}{2}$

hence the formula is $N = \frac{1}{2}l^2 + \frac{1}{2}l$.

A15

Set up a pair of simultaneous equations:

$$3 \max + 2 \min = 220 \dots ①$$
$$2 \max + 5 \min = 242 \dots ②$$

multiply ① by 2 and ② by 3 to give:

$$6 \max + 4 \min = 440 \dots ③$$
$$6 \max + 15 \min = 726 \dots ④$$

eliminate 'max' by subtracting ③ from ④ to give:

$$11 \min = 286$$
$$\min = 26$$

substitute into ① to give:

$$3 \max = 220 - 52 = 168$$
$$\max = 56$$

solution is max cost 56p and min cost 26p.

A16

a) Conditions 1, 2, 3 and 5 are all special cases where the equation is satisfied. Since $(y - z)(z - x)(x - y) = 0$, then all we can deduce is that one of the brackets is zero, hence either $y = z$ **or** $z = x$ **or** $x = y$, hence at at least two of x, y, z are equal. Condition 4 is satisfied.

b) There are three possibilities for $(y - z)(z - x)(x - y) = 0$.
These are that $y = z$, $z = x$ or $x = y$.
First, consider $y = z$
then where $x + 1 = 2y + 3 = 3z + 6$
$$x + 1 = [2y + 3 = 3y + 6]$$
$$[2y + 3 = 3y + 6] \rightarrow -3 = y$$
hence $x + 1 = -6 + 3 = -3 \quad \rightarrow x = -4$.
So $-4, -3, -3$, is a possible solution.
Next, consider $z = x$
then where $x + 1 = 2y + 3 = 3z + 6$
$$[x + 1] = 2y + 3 = [3x + 6]$$
$$[x + 1 = 3x + 6] \rightarrow -5 = 2x \rightarrow x = -2.5$$
hence $-2.5 + 1 = 2y + 3$
$$\rightarrow -4.5 = 2y \rightarrow y = -2.25$$
So $-2.5, -2.25, -2.5$ is another solution.
Lastly, consider $x = y$
then where $x + 1 = 2y + 3 = 3z + 6$
$$[x + 1 = 2x + 3] = 3z + 6$$
$$[x + 1 = 2x + 3] \rightarrow -2 = x$$
hence $ -2 + 1 = 3z + 6 \rightarrow z = \dfrac{-7}{3}$
So $-2, -2, \dfrac{-7}{3}$ is the third solution.

The three possible solutions to x, y, z are $(-4, -3, -3)$
$$(-2.5, -2.25, -2.5)$$
$$\left(-2, -2, \dfrac{-7}{3}\right)$$

A17

a) From $a^2 + b^2 = c^2$, take the left hand side where $a = v^2 - u^2$ and $b = 2uv$

$$\text{then } a^2 + b^2 = (v^2 - u^2)^2 + (2uv)^2$$
$$= v^4 - 2u^2v^2 + u^4 + 4u^2v^2$$
$$= v^4 + 2u^2v^2 + u^4.$$

Take the right hand side where $c = u^2 + v^2$

$$\text{then } c^2 = (u^2 + v^2)^2 = u^4 + 2u^2v^2 + v^4.$$

It can now be seen that $a^2 + b^2 = u^4 + 2u^2v^2 + v^4 = c^2$

$$\rightarrow a^2 + b^2 = c^2.$$

So the equations do hold on to the validity of $a^2 + b^2 = c^2$. Also, if we choose values of u and v to be integers, then so too will be v^2, u^2 and $2uv$, hence so too will be $v^2 - u^2$, $2uv$ and $v^2 + u^2$. So a, b and c will be integers in value.

b) If a, b and c have a common factor, say x, then when $a = Ax$, $b = Bx$, $c = Cx$, A, B and C are integers and so we will have $Ax = v^2 - u^2$, $Bx = 2uv$, $Cx = u^2 + v^2$.

Hence, since A, B and C are integers then

$$\frac{v^2 - u^2}{x}, \frac{2uv}{x}, \frac{u^2 + v^2}{x} \text{ are also all integers.}$$

Hence $(v^2 - u^2)$, $2uv$ and $(u^2 + v^2)$ are all multiples of x

$\rightarrow$ that both v^2 and u^2 are multiples of x

$\rightarrow$ both v and u are multiples of x.

So if we are to avoid a, b and c having common factors we must choose values of u and v that do not have common factors.

A18

i) You could choose **any** four consecutive numbers, for example, 3, 4, 5, 6 is a simple one to start with, which gives

$$\text{middle pair} = 4 \times 5 = 20$$
$$\text{outer pair} = 3 \times 6 = 18$$

ii) Choose two more sets (no need to choose large numbers, but you can if you wish). The general rule you should find is this—the product of the middle pair is always 2 more than the product of the outer pair.

iii) If we let x be the first number, then the next three after that will be $x + 1$, $x + 2$, $x + 3$, to give the consecutive numbers:

$$x, x + 1, x + 2, x + 3.$$

The product of the middle pair $= (x + 1)(x + 2) = x^2 + 3x + 2$.
The product of the outer pair $\;= x(x + 3) \qquad = x^2 + 3x$.
The difference is $(x^2 + 3x + 2) - (x^2 + 3x) = 2$.
So for all x, the difference is still 2.

iv) Let x be the first odd number, then the four consecutive odd numbers will be:

$$x, x + 2, x + 4, x + 6.$$

The product of the middle pair $= (x + 2)(x + 4) = x^2 + 6x + 8$.
The product of the outer pair $\;= x(x + 6) \qquad = x^2 + 6x$.
So the difference is 8, giving the rule that 'the product of the middle pair of consecutive odd numbers is 8 more than the product of the outer pair.'
P.S. This also works for consecutive even numbers.

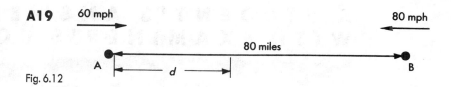

Fig. 6.12

a) In Fig. 6.12 let distance, *d,* be the point where the trains pass. Then $t = $ time travelled in hours. The slower train will satisfy the equation $d = 60t$, while the faster train will satisfy the equation $d = 80 - 80t$.
So if *d* is when they pass, then $60t = 80 - 80t$

$$\rightarrow 140t = 80 \quad \rightarrow t = 0.5714 \text{ hours}$$

gives the time on passing at 34 minutes and the distance from A given by $60 \times 0.5714 = 34.3$ miles.

b) If the trains passed 6 miles nearer to A, then they passed at a distance of 28.3 miles from A. As the express train was punctual, to find out how long it took that train to cover a distance of $(80 - 28.3)$ miles, we evaluate

$$\text{time} = \frac{\text{distance}}{\text{speed}} = \frac{51.7}{80} = 0.646\,25 \text{ hours} = 38.8 \text{ minutes}.$$

The slower train took $\dfrac{28.3}{60} = 0.4667 = 28$ minutes to reach that point. The difference in time tells how late the first train was, which was 10.8, rounded off to 11 minutes late.

GRADE CHECKLIST

For a Grade B you should:

Be able to: Evaluate formulae, including the use of fractions or negative numbers.
Manipulate algebraic formula, equations and expressions.
Factorise quadratic expressions.
Solve simultanous equations.

For a Grade A you should also:

Be able to: Use rules of indices for negative and fractional values.
Solve quadratic equations.

For a Grade A* you should also:

Be able to: Manipulate algebraic expressions in a variety of contexts.

A STUDENT'S ANSWER
WITH EXAMINER'S COMMENTS

Question

A road tanker carries 30 tonnes of oil. When cold, the oil can be pumped out at a rate of x tonnes per minute.

a) Write down an expression for the time, in minutes, taken to empty the tanker.

Answer $\dfrac{30}{x}$

" Good, clear and correct answers. "

If the oil is heated then an extra 0.5 tonnes cann be pumped out per minute.

b) Write down an expression for the time taken to empty the tanker when the oil is heated.

Answer $\dfrac{30}{x+0.5}$

If the oil has been heated then the time taken to empty the tanker is reduced by two minutes.

" Could have been better laid out, but it is correct and we can see what you have done. "

c) Show that the equation for x can be expressed in the form
$$2x^2 + x - 15 = 0$$

$\dfrac{30}{x} - \dfrac{30}{x+0.5} = 2 \qquad \dfrac{30(x+0.5)-30x}{x(x+0.5)} = 2$

$30x + 15 - 30x = 2x^2 + x$

$15 = 2x^2 + x$ So $2x^2 + x - 15 = 0$

" Good to *see* how you are trying to solve the equation. "

Solve this equation for x, and hence find the time taken to empty the tanker when the oil is cold.

$2 \quad 5$
$1 \quad 3$ $(2x-5)(x+3)=0$
So $x = 2.5$ and -3

Answer $x = 2.5$

" Correct final answer, but no mention has been made of *why* the negative answer of $x = -3$ has been rejected. This would lose a mark. "

" A good answer showing algebraic manipulation has been clearly understood. You will get high marks for this answer. "

CHAPTER 7

GRAPHS

- DRAWING GRAPHS FROM EQUATIONS
- GRAPHS AND THEIR 'STORIES'
- DISTANCE – TIME GRAPHS
- VELOCITY – TIME GRAPHS AND ACCELERATION
- AREA UNDER A CURVE
- CURVED VELOCITY – TIME GRAPHS
- LINEAR PROGRAMMING

GETTING STARTED

For the highest grades of GCSE you must be able to draw a good graph from any of the equations given, and to recognise the type of equation a given graph will have. You will be expected to sort out your own sensible scales and to draw your graphs with accuracy. The accuracy needed in examinations is usually to the nearest millimetre.

Graphs will generally be drawn in order to find an algebraic solution, or a gradient or an area beneath the graph. Sometimes a graph will be drawn as an end in itself.

USEFUL DEFINITIONS

Cubic	A cubic equation is one which has a cube as the highest power, e.g. $y^3 + 6y^2 + y = 5$.
Gradient	The 'steepness' of a line. It is the tangent of the angle made with the horizontal.
Intercept	Where a line crosses an axis.
Linear	A linear *equation* is one which involves only single variables of power one, e.g. $2x + y = 5$. A linear *graph* will be a straight line.
Quadratic	A quadratic *equation* is one which has a square as the highest power, e.g. $2x^2 + 4x = 3$. A quadratic *curve* is the graph of a quadratic equation and it is a symmetrical **U** shape.
Average Speed (Velocity)	Gradient of the *chord* joining the points on a distance-time graph.
Instantaneous Speed (Velocity)	Gradient of the *tangent* to a point on a distance-time graph.
Acceleration	Gradient to a velocity-time graph. The rate of change of velocity (speed).
Distance Travelled	Area under a velocity-time graph.

ESSENTIAL PRINCIPLES

> **DRAWING GRAPHS FROM EQUATIONS**

There are four main types of equation for which you should be able to draw graphs.

LINEAR EQUATIONS

A *linear equation* is of the form $y = mx + c$ where m and c are constants. This will always give a straight line, and the minimum number of points to plot is three. The easiest way to sketch or draw this type of equation is to find the x and y intercepts and one other point. Then draw the straight line that goes through all these points.

> **WORKED EXAMPLE 1**

Sketch the graph of $5x + 2y = 7$.

Find the x axis intercept by substituting $y = 0$, which gives $5x = 7$, $x = 1.4$. So one point is found as (1.4, 0). Find the y axis intercept by substituting $x = 0$, which gives $2y = 7$; $y = 3.5$. So another point is found as (0, 3.5). Find another by substituting, say, $y = 2$, which gives $5x + 4 = 7 \rightarrow 5x = 3 \rightarrow x = 0.6$, hence the third point is found as (0.6, 2). These can now be plotted and a straight line drawn through them, as shown in Fig. 7.1.

> **You need to be able to sketch it then draw it accurately.** 99

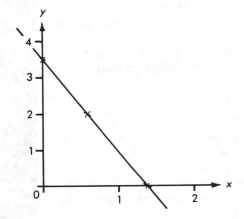

Fig. 7.1

EXERCISE 1

Sketch the graphs of $x + y = 8$ and $2x - y = 3$, stating the co-ordinate of intersection.

QUADRATIC EQUATIONS

A *quadratic equation* is of the form $y = ax^2 + bx + c$, where a, b and c are constants. This will always give you a curved graph, and the interesting part usually asked for is this part that does a **U** turn. See the two possible shapes in Fig. 7.2:

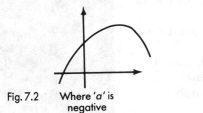

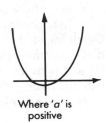

Fig. 7.2   Where '*a*' is negative   Where '*a*' is positive

You will need quite a few points for plotting, especially round the 'dip' or 'hill top'. In an examination it is most likely that you will be told the range of values to plot and hence the 'dip' will be among that range if the question requires it.

The main use of the 'dip' is to tell you the least possible value that the function has, or if it is the 'top of a hill' then the greatest possible value the function has.

WORKED EXAMPLE 2

Neil, a bit of a mathematician, reckoned that when he played golf and teed off with a 'one iron' then the path of the ball was given by the following equation:
$y = \dfrac{3x(95 - x)}{200}$ where y is the vertical distance above the tee and x is the horizontal distance from the tee. With a 'one iron', Neil usually managed to hit the ball about 100 metres. Draw a graph of the path of the ball and find out its greatest height.

A table needs to be built up of values of x from 0 to 100. If we start with x going up in 20s to start with, we get the table in Fig. 7.3.

x	0	20	40	60	80	100
$3x$	0	60	120	180	240	300
$95 - x$	95	75	55	35	15	−5
$y = \dfrac{3x(95 - x)}{200}$	0	22.5	33	31.5	18	−7.5

Fig. 7.3

This now lets us plot the points as in Fig. 7.4.

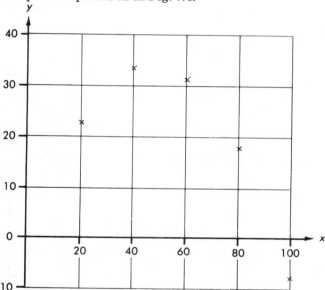

Fig. 7.4

> Notice that I chose a scale that will fit the points on but not be too big.

We could do with finding a few more points near the top of the hill. This seems around $x = 50$. Hence, find the y ordinate at $x = 42, 45, 48$ and 50. Evaluating these gives us (42, 33.4), (45, 33.75), (48, 33.84), (50, 33.75). When we plot these points we get a much better picture of the solution and can now draw the graph as in Fig. 7.5, and the maximum height can be seen to be 33.8 metres.

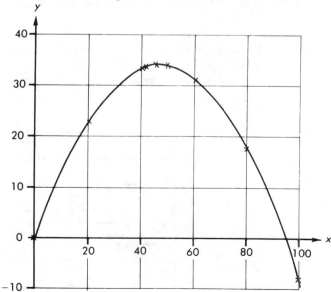

Fig. 7.5

EXERCISE 2

Draw the graph of $y = x^2 + 3x + 4$ and find the least possible value of y. (Use values of x where $-3 \leqslant x \leqslant 1$.)

Solutions to quadratic equations

These can be made from their graphs. For example, the solutions of $ax^2 + bx + c = 0$ will be where the graph of $y = ax^2 + bx + c$ cuts the x axis (i.e., where $y = 0$).

In general, the solution of $ax^2 + bx + c = d$ is where the graph of $y = ax^2 + bx + c$ cuts the line $y = d$.

WORKED EXAMPLE 3

Draw the graph of $y = x^2 + x - 4$ where $-3 \leqslant x \leqslant 3$ and hence find the solution to the equation $x^2 + x = 5$.

Construct the table of values for $-3 \leqslant x \leqslant 3$ as in Fig. 7.6.

x	-3	-2	-1	0	1	2	3
x^2	9	4	1	0	1	4	9
-4	-4	-4	-4	-4	-4	-4	-4
$y = x^2 + x - 4$	2	-2	-4	-4	-2	2	8

Fig. 7.6

This will give you the **U**-shaped curve as in Fig. 7.7.

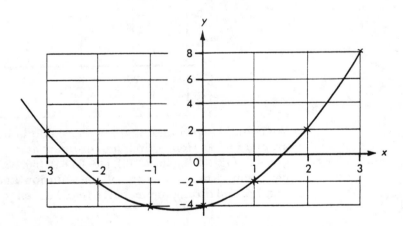

Fig. 7.7

The solution to $x^2 + x = 5$ is given by $x^2 + x - 4 = 1$. (Check that this is the same equation.) Hence where the graph of $y = x^2 + x - 4$ crosses $y = 1$, as in Fig. 7.8. The solutions are where $x = -2.8$ and $x = 1.8$.

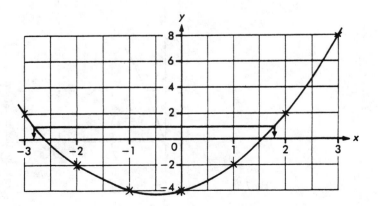

Fig. 7.8

RECIPROCAL EQUATIONS

A reciprocal equation is of the form $y = \dfrac{A}{x}$ where A can be any constant value not equal to zero. This will give a curved shape that has symmetry about the origin as you will see in the worked example.

WORKED EXAMPLE 4

Draw the graph of $y = \dfrac{6}{x}$ between $x = -3$ and $x = 3$ and fully describe all its symmetry.

First, construct the table of values for $-3 \leqslant x \leqslant 3$ as in Fig. 7.9. These points can now be plotted, as in Fig. 7.10. There are two symmetries of the drawn graph, for it has a line symmetry $y = -x$ and rotational symmetry of order 2. (If I had made the scale identical on both axes then $y = x$ would be another line of symmetry.)

x	-3	-2	-1	0	1	2	3
$y = \dfrac{6}{x}$	-2	-3	-6	∞	6	3	2

Fig. 7.9

Graph of a reciprocal equation.

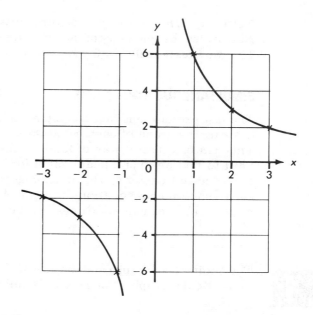

Fig. 7.10

EXERCISE 3

Draw the graphs of $y = \dfrac{12}{x}$ and $y = x^2 - 2x + 1$ where $0 < x < 5$, and so state a solution of the equation $x^3 - 2x^2 + x = 12$.

GRAPHS OF RECIPROCAL EQUATIONS IN THE FORM $Y = \dfrac{A}{x^2}$

WORKED EXAMPLE 5

Draw a graph of the reciprocal equation $y = \dfrac{12}{x^2}$.

Solution

To draw the graph of $y = \dfrac{12}{x^2}$ you need to find some values of x and y that fit the equation. Follow through the construction of the table of values below. (Notice we still cannot use $x = 0$.)

x	-4	-3	-2	-1	1	2	3	4
x^2	16	9	4	1	1	4	9	16
$y = \dfrac{12}{x^2}$	0.75	1.33	3	12	12	3	1.33	0.75

Plot the values of x and y and join up the points with a smooth curve (Fig. 7.11).

 Graph of a reciprocal equation involving a square term in the denominator.

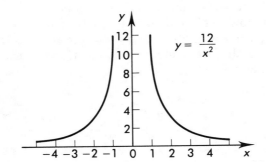

Fig. 7.11

Notice again how the curve does not cross any axes.
Notice also the symmetry of the two 'branches'.
The two axes namely $x = 0$ and $y = 0$ are the *asymptotes* of the curve.

SIMULTANEOUS EQUATIONS

The last exercise had you solving a simultaneous equation by graph, by simply drawing the graph of each equation and then finding where both graphs cross. This can be a useful way of finding an approximate solution (especially if you need to find an approximate value for starting an *iterative solution*, which we looked at in Chapter 4). However, in general terms, it is always better to try and solve simultaneous equations by an algebraic method rather than by graph if you can, unless an examination question specifically says 'by graph'.

2 ▷ GRAPHS AND THEIR 'STORIES'

The gradients of graphs and the area underneath them can have special meanings for particular graphs. You need to be fully aware of these.

GRADIENTS OF STRAIGHT LINES

The **gradient** of a straight line is a measure of its steepness. The gradient is defined as the vertical distance divided by the horizontal distance between any two points on that straight line. The gradient is often expressed as a fraction.

For example:
The gradient of the line AB in Fig. 7.12 is given by:

 Gradient of a straight line.

$$\frac{\text{vertical distance}}{\text{horizontal distance}} = \frac{3}{6} = \frac{1}{2}$$

Fig. 7.12

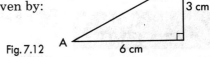

We need to make a clear difference between the gradients of lines 'sloping' in *opposite directions*.
Both AB and PQ in Fig. 7.13 have a gradient of $\frac{2}{3}$, yet they are clearly different.
We define a line sloping down from left to right (e.g. AB) as having a *negative*

gradient. We define a line sloping up from left to right (e.g. PQ) as having a *positive gradient.*

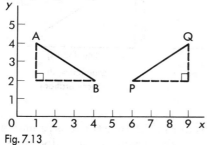

Negative and positive gradients.

Fig. 7.13

The gradient of AB is $-\dfrac{2}{3}$.

The gradient of PQ is $+\dfrac{2}{3}$ or $\dfrac{2}{3}$.

It will help if we can find a *rule* which will allow us to calculate the gradient of a line, including its sign.
Consider the gradient between two points $A(x_1, y_1)$ and $B(x_2, y_2)$ in Fig. 7.14.

Fig. 7.14

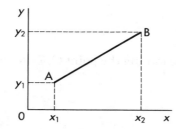
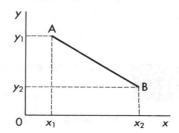

We can calculate the change in the *vertical distance* by the expression $(y_2 - y_1)$ and the change in the *horizontal distance* by the expression $(x_2 - x_1)$.

The gradient in each case would be $\dfrac{y_2 - y_1}{x_2 - x_1}$.

Notice the *negative gradient* in this case comes about when $(y_2 - y_1)$ is *negative.* Note that when you use this formula, you will get a negative gradient when either $(x_2 - x_1)$ or $(y_2 - y_1)$ is *negative.*

In Short

The gradient between two points (x_1, y_1) and (x_2, y_2) is given by the equation:

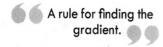

A rule for finding the gradient.

$$\text{gradient} = \frac{y_2 - y_1}{x_2 - x_1}$$

EXERCISE 4

Find the gradient of the straight line passing through
i) (1, 3) and (5, 5)   ii) (3, 2) and (5, −7)

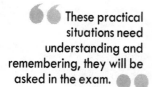

These practical situations need understanding and remembering, they will be asked in the exam.

Making sure your x_2 is always the biggest of the x co-ordinates will give you a *positive* denominator, so that when $y_2 > y_1$, your gradient is positive (uphill) and when $y_2 < y_1$, the gradient is negative (downhill).
Look through the examples of axes, lines and gradients shown in Fig. 7.15 to gain the feel for changing axis units to gradient units.

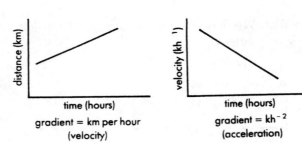
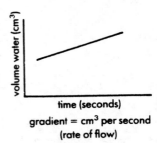

Fig. 7.15

The first two examples in Fig. 7.15 are the most common ones that you will meet in the examination, where the gradient of a distance, time graph is always the *velocity*, and the gradient of a velocity, time graph is always the *acceleration*.

If you have the equation of the straight line, which can always be put into the form of $y = mx + c$ where m and c are some constants, then the *coefficient of x*, namely m, will always be equal to the *gradient* of the graph of that equation.

THE EQUATION OF THE STRAIGHT LINE JOINING TWO POINTS

Given any two points, A and B, we can join them together with a straight line. We then find the gradient, m of this line and use the equation $y = mx + c$ to calculate c. We now have enough information to write down the equation of the line.

WORKED EXAMPLE 6

Find the equation of the line joining the point (2, 7) to the point (5, 16).

Working

The gradient of the line joining (2, 7) to (5, 16) is given by:

$$\text{gradient} = \frac{16 - 7}{5 - 2}$$

$$= \frac{9}{3} = 3$$

The equation of the line is $y = 3x + c$.
To find c we substitute into this equation the coordinates of any one of the two given points. For example we can substitute (2, 7) into the equation to give:

$$7 = 3 \times 2 + c$$
$$7 = 6 + c$$

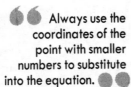 Always use the coordinates of the point with smaller numbers to substitute into the equation.

giving $c = 1$

Hence the equation will be $y = 3x + 1$.

WORKED EXAMPLE 7

Find the equation of the line joining the points A(-3, 4) and B(2, -1).

Working

The gradient is given by $\dfrac{-1 - 4}{2 - (-3)} = \dfrac{-5}{5} = -1$

Hence the equation of the line is $y = -x + c$

Now substitute $(2, -1)$ into this equation to give

$$-1 = -2 + c$$
$$2 - 1 = c = 1$$

hence $y = -x + 1$

EXERCISE 5

i) Find the equation of the straight line passing through the points $(7, 1)$ and $(1, 3)$

ii) Calculate the equation of the line parallel to $y = 3x - 1$ and passing through the point $(2, 4)$.

3 > DISTANCE-TIME GRAPHS

Many distance-time graphs you have met would have used straight lines, as in Fig. 7.16.

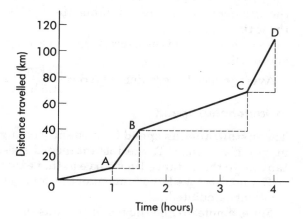

Fig. 7.16

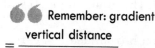 Remember: gradient
$$= \frac{\text{vertical distance}}{\text{horizontal distance}}.$$

The graph shows the journey of a coach in four stages.
The *GRADIENT* of each stage represents the *SPEED* of the coach.
From Fig. 7.16 we can work out these gradients.

EXAMPLE

From O to A; speed = gradient $= \dfrac{10 \text{ km}}{1 \text{ hour}} = 10 \text{ km/h}$

From A to B; speed = gradient $= \dfrac{30 \text{ km}}{\frac{1}{2} \text{ hour}} = 60 \text{ km/h}$

From B to C; speed = gradient $= \dfrac{30 \text{ km}}{2 \text{ hours}} = 15 \text{ km/h}$

From C to D; speed = gradient $= \dfrac{40 \text{ km}}{\frac{1}{2} \text{ hour}} = 80 \text{ km/h}$

In Fig. 7.16 the speed has only changed on 4 occasions, and is constant throughout each of the 4 stages of the journey.

When the speed of an object is *continually* changing, then the distance-time graph is a *curved line*.

We can still use the idea of a gradient to find the 'average speed' between any two times, and the speed at any particular instant of time.

Fig. 7.17 shows another coach's journey over a four-hour period from 12 noon to 4 pm. This time the graph is a curved line.

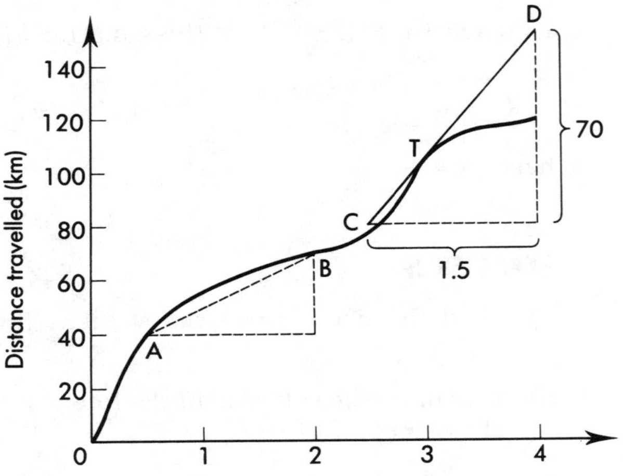

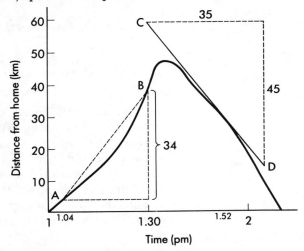

Fig. 7.17

Average speed

The **average speed** between time t_1 and time t_2 is found by calculating the *gradient of the chord* joining the points on the curve that correspond to those times.

For example, to find the average speed between 12.30 pm and 2.00 pm, we draw the chord AB.

$$\text{Average speed} = \text{gradient of AB} = \frac{33 \text{ km}}{1.5 \text{ h}} = 22 \text{ km/h}.$$

Instantaneous speed

The **instantaneous speed** is constantly changing along a curved line. However, at any given time, T, the instantaneous speed is given by the gradient of the tangent to the distance-time curve at that exact time, T.

To find this speed, the tangent of the curve at that point has to be drawn and the gradient calculated.

> For your tangent, always try to draw the largest possible right-angled triangle.

For example, to find the instantaneous speed at 3.00 pm, we draw the tangent to the curve at T = 3.00 pm. This is shown as CD in Fig. 7.17. The gradient of CD will give the instantaneous speed.

$$\text{Instaneous speed} = \text{gradient of CD} = \frac{70 \text{ km}}{1.5 \text{ hours}} = 47 \text{ km/h (rounded to nearest whole number)}$$

Note: The gradient can have a positive or negative sign. Here we can give the *absolute value* of the gradient and ignore any negative signs. For example, a 'negative' gradient (Fig. 7.18) simply means the speed on the *return* journey.

WORKED EXAMPLE 8

A woman drives to the airport to pick up her son, and then drives him back home. The graph in Fig. 7.18 shows her journey. Calculate:

a)   the average speed between 1.04 pm and 1.30 pm;
b)   the actual (instantaneous) speed at 1.52 pm.

Give your answers in km/h.

Fig. 7.18

Working

a) Find the gradient of AB, from 1.04 pm to 1.30 pm:

$$\text{Average speed} = \text{gradient} = \frac{34 \text{ km}}{26 \text{ min}}$$

$$= 1.308 \times 60 \text{ km/h}$$
$$= 78.5 \text{ km/h}.$$

> Remember to ignore the negative sign for the gradient. This is simply the speed at a particular time on the return journey.

b) Find the gradient of the tangent CD at 1.52 pm:

$$\text{Speed} = \text{gradient} = \frac{45 \text{ km}}{35 \text{ min}}$$

$$= 1.286 \times 60 \text{ km/h}$$
$$= 77.2 \text{ km/h}$$

EXERCISE 6

A stone was thrown off a cliff and out to sea. After t seconds, its height was h metres above the ground, as shown in the table below.

t	0	0.5	1	1.5	2	2.5	3	3.5	4	4.5	5
h	20	27	30	32	30	27	20	10	0	-14	-30

Draw the graph of h against t, and use your graph to help you calculate:

a) the average speed of the stone from:
    i) $t = 0.5$ to 2   ii) $t = 4.5$ to 5;

b) the speed of the stone when:
    i) $t = 1$ ii) $t = 3.5$.

4 ▷ VELOCITY-TIME GRAPHS AND ACCELERATION

> *Acceleration* is the rate of change of velocity (or speed) with respect to time.

When we plot the velocity of a moving object against the time taken, we can find two very useful pieces of information.

⇒ The GRADIENT of the velocity-time graph at any time T, will give the **acceleration** of the object.
⇒ The AREA under the graph between t_1 and t_2 (i.e. the area enclosed by the graph and the horizontal axis) will give the **distance travelled** between those times.

WORKED EXAMPLE 9

Look at the velocity-time graph in Fig. 7.19. Identify and describe the periods of constant velocity and of acceleration. Also work out the distance travelled over the various periods of time.

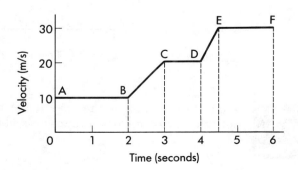

Fig. 7.19

Working

The graph shows the following:

⇒ Three periods of constant velocity; i.e.
  AB—10 m/s
  CD—20 m/s
  EF—30 m/s

⇒ Two periods of positive acceleration (increasing velocity)
  BC—acceleration = gradient

$$= \frac{10 \text{ m/s}}{1 \text{ s}} = 10 \text{ m/s/s}$$

  DE—acceleration = gradient

$$= \frac{10 \text{ m/s}}{\frac{1}{2}} = 20 \text{ m/s/s}$$

> 66 Note that the unit for acceleration m/s/s is written as m/s². 99

⇒ The distance travelled during various periods of time.
  The area under the section of the graph AB represents the distance travelled at 10 m/s for 2 seconds = 20 m.
  (Notice that the area under AB will also be 10 × 2 = 20 m.)

  The area under BC, which is a trapezium gives an area of $\frac{1}{2}(10 + 20) = 15$ m.

  The area under CD = 20 × 1 = 20 m.

> 66 Here area is the distance travelled. 99

  The area under DE = $\frac{0.5}{2}$ × (20 + 30) = 12.5 m.

  The area under EF = 30 × 1.5 = 45 m.

  The *total area* under the graph is therefore:
  20 + 15 + 20 + 12.5 + 45 = 112.5 m.

EXERCISE 7

1. Fig. 7.20 shows the speed of a bird over 12 seconds.

   a) Calculate the acceleration:
      i) over the first two seconds;
      ii) after 10 seconds.

   b) Calculate the total distance the bird has travelled in these 12 seconds.

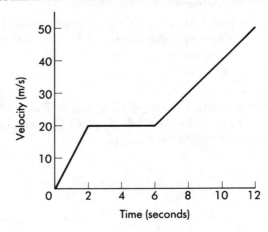

Fig. 7.20

---

5 ▷ THE AREA UNDER A CURVE

We can only *estimate* the **area** under most curves. The best way to do this is to split the region up into trapeziums and then find the area of each trapezium.

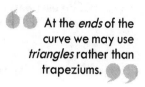

Find the area under the curve shown in Fig. 7.21.

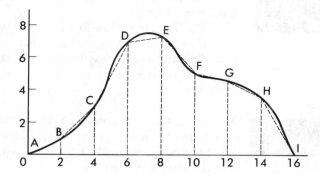

Fig. 7.21

> *At the ends of the curve we may use triangles rather than trapeziums.*

Notice that we split the area under the curve at regular intervals into

1. *triangles* at either end and
2. *trapeziums* in the middle.

Notice also that for some of these 'strips' we will get an area LESS than the actual area under the curve. On the other hand, some 'strips' will give us an area GREATER than the actual area under the curve.
These differences usually balance out when we make the *total* estimation of area under the curve.

In this example, the *total area* will be estimated by summing the areas under the following lines

> *The area of a trapezium is found by taking the average of the lengths of the two parallel sides and multiplying by the distance between them.*

AB + BC + CD + DE + EF + FG + GH + HI

$$= (\frac{2}{2} \times 1) + \frac{2}{2}(1 + 3.4) + \frac{2}{2}(3.4 + 7) + \frac{2}{2}(7 + 7.5) + \frac{2}{2}(7.5 + 5.2) + \frac{2}{2}(5.2 + 3.3)$$
$$+ (\frac{2}{2} \times 3.3)$$

$$= 1 + 4.4 + 10.4 + 14.5 + 12.7 + 8.5 + 3.3$$
$$= 54.8 \text{ sq. units}$$

We can also summarise this to the trapezium rule if we divide the area under the curve into strips of equal length as shown in Fig. 7.22, the total area is

$$\frac{1}{2}h(y_0 + y_1) + \frac{1}{2}h(y_1 + y_2) + \frac{1}{2}h(y_2 + y_3) + \frac{1}{2}h(y_3 + y_4)$$

$$= \frac{1}{2}h[(y_0 + y_4) + 2(y_1 + y_2 + y_3)]$$

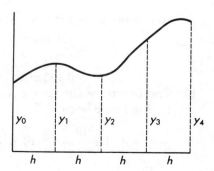

Fig. 7.22

In general, if you divide the area into *n* strips of equal width, then

$$\text{total area} = \frac{1}{2}h[(y_0 + y_n) + 2(y_1 + y_2 + y_3 + \cdots + y_{n-1})]$$

<table>
<tr><td>6 ></td><td>**CURVED VELOCITY-TIME GRAPHS**</td></tr>
</table>

To be realistic, more situations give us *curved* velocity-time graphs than straight ones. Hence more thought and care has to be taken when finding information from these curves.

⇒ The **acceleration** at any *point* will be found by first drawing a tangent *at that point* on the curve and then calculating the gradient.

⇒ The **distance travelled** over part (or all) of the journey will be estimated by calculating *the area under the curve*.

WORKED EXAMPLE 11

In a race, Graham's velocity was recorded at different times. The velocity-time graph for the race is given in Fig. 7.23. Calculate:
a) the acceleration after 15 seconds exactly;
b) the length of the race.

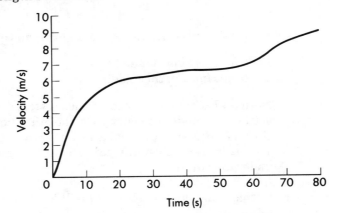

Fig. 7.23

Working

a) Acceleration after 15 seconds is found by first drawing the tangent to the curve at 15 s and then by calculating the gradient of the tangent.

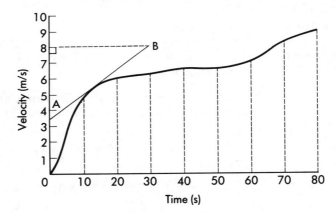

Fig. 7.24

Acceleration = gradient AB

$$= \frac{4.6 \text{ m/s}}{30 \text{ s}}$$

$$= 0.153 \text{ m/s}^2$$

b) The length of the race is the area under the whole curve. We have split the region into 8 'strips'. The areas under these strips are as follows:

$$\frac{1}{2}(10 + 4.5) + \frac{10}{2}(4.5 + 6) + \frac{10}{2}(6 + 6.3) + \frac{10}{2}(6.3 + 6.4) + \frac{10}{2}(6.4 + 6.6)$$

$$+ \frac{10}{2}(6.6 + 7.1) + \frac{10}{2}(7.1 + 8.3) + \frac{10}{2}(8.3 + 9)$$

$$= 22.5 + 52.5 + 61.5 + 63.5 + 65 + 68.5 + 77 + 86.5$$

$$= 497.$$

I would estimate that the race was a 500 m race.

EXERCISE 8

1. The speed of a cyclist is observed at 10-second intervals over one minute. The observations are as follows:

time (s)	0	10	20	30	40	50	60
speed (m/s)	0	5	14	26	34	38	40

a) Plot the points on a speed-time graph and join them together with a smooth curve.

b) Estimate the acceleration
   i) after 30 seconds   ii) when the speed is 35 m/s

c) Estimate the total distance covered by the cyclist over the minute.

2. Gillian, who was learning to drive, was practising by driving along quiet country lanes. Over the first 4 hours she drove with a speed v kilometres per hour, varying with time, t hours, given by the equation $v = t^3 - 4t^2 + 3t + 20$. Find the total distance covered in these 4 hours.

7 LINEAR PROGRAMMING

Linear Programming is a way of modelling real situations to enable you to see a possible range of solutions and then come to a most suitable solution to a particular problem.

Graphing linear inequalities

To draw the region $y \leqslant 3x + 1$ is best done in two parts.

⇒ i) draw the line $y = 3x + 1$.
   This is a linear equation and hence is a straight line. Three points will define this line.
   Check that $(0, 1)$, $(1, 4)$ and $(2, 7)$ are all points on the line $y = 3x + 1$.
   The line through these points can be drawn.

⇒ ii) Decide which side of the line to shade, by shading out the region we do *not* want.
   A simple way of doing this is to choose a simple point such as $(0, 0)$ or $(1, 1)$ and see if it is in the required region or not.

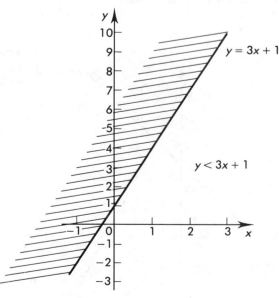

e.g. Try $(0, 0)$, substitute $x = 0$, $y = 0$ into $y \leqslant 3x + 1$ to get, $0 \leqslant 1$. This is *true*, hence the region with $(0, 0)$ in is the required region so we shade out the other region. The unshaded region is the region $y < 3x + 1$. The line is the region $y = 3x + 1$. Hence the unshaded region *AND* the line define the region $y \leqslant 3x + 1$.

Fig. 7.25

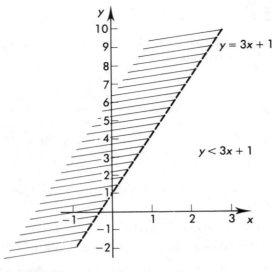

If the region $y < 3x + 1$ was to be shown we should show this where the dotted line indicates that the line itself is *not* part of the solution.

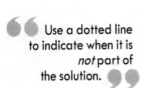

Use a dotted line to indicate when it is *not* part of the solution.

Fig. 7.26

EXERCISE 9

Draw diagrams to illustrate the following regions. (Shade out the region you do not want).

  a) $y \leqslant x$
  b) $y > x + 3$
  c) $y \leqslant 6 - x$

Solution Sets

When we are asked to find a region that satisfies two or more inequalities we call this the *solution set*.

WORKED EXAMPLE 12

Show on a graph the region which is the solution set of the inequalities

  $2x + y < 6$ and $y - x \leqslant 3$

We need to shade out the *unwanted regions* of both inequalities.
⇒ Draw the line $2x + y = 6$ (dotted since we do not want the line in the solution).
   Use the points $(0, 6)$, $(2, 2)$ and $(3, 0)$ to define the line.
⇒ Check if $(0, 0)$ fits the inequality $2x + y < 6$.
   Yes, it does, hence we shade out the region NOT including the origin (right hand side of line).
⇒ Draw the line $y - x = 3$ (continuous line, since the line is part of the solution).
   Use the points $(3, 6)$, $(2, 5)$ and $(0, 3)$ to define the line.
⇒ Check if $(0, 0)$ fits the inequality $y - x \leqslant 3$.
   Yes, it does, hence we shade the region NOT including the origin. (Left hand side of line).

Finding a solution set, involving two or more inequalities.

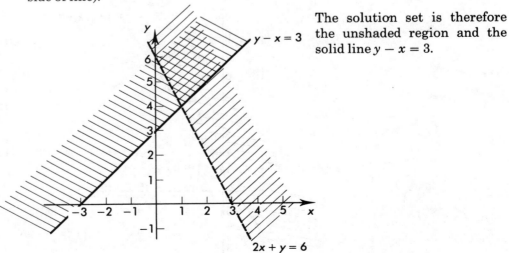

The solution set is therefore the unshaded region and the solid line $y - x = 3$.

Fig. 7.27

EXERCISE 10

Illustrate the solution sets of the inequalities by shading out the unwanted regions.

$3x + 2y \geqslant 15$ and $4x - 3y \geqslant 12$.

WORKED EXAMPLE 13

Show on a graph the region which gives the solution set of the inequalities

$y - x \leqslant 2$, $2x < 5$ and $3y > -2x$

⇒ Draw the solid line $y - x = 2$ (solid because the line contains solutions).
$0 - 0 \leqslant 2$ is correct, hence $(0, 0)$ is IN the region $y - x \leqslant 2$, so shade out the left hand side of $y - x = 2$.

⇒ Draw the dotted line $2x = 5$, i.e. $x = 2.5$
(dotted because the line is not part of the solution).
Shade out the right hand side of $x = 2.5$.

⇒ Draw the dotted line $3y = -2x$, i.e. $y = -\dfrac{2}{3}x$

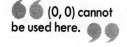 (0, 0) cannot be used here.

Test the point $(1, 1)$ is $3 \times 1 > -2 \times 1$. Yes, so $(1, 1)$ is in the region we want, so shade out the left hand side of $y = -\dfrac{2}{3}x$.

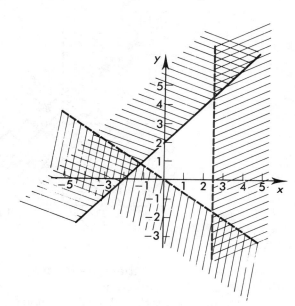

Fig. 7.28

The unshaded region gives the solution set for all points which satisfy all three inequalities.

EXERCISE 11

Draw diagrams to illustrate the solution sets for the following.
(Shade out the unwanted regions).

$x + y < 5$, $y - x \leqslant 3$, $x \geqslant 0$, $y \geqslant 0$

Linear Programming in practice

Problems involving inequalities often occur in industry and in ordinary life. Many of these problems can be solved by drawing graphs to show solution sets and, from these, possible answers can be determined.

WORKED EXAMPLE 14

For a party, it is decided to spend £1 on small prizes. The choice of suitable prizes at a local shop is:

small lollipops 6p each or candy sticks 8p each.

There must be at least 6 of each type, and each of the 13 children at the party must get at least one prize. How can the £ be spent?
(The first thing is to sort out the information and write down some inequalities).

Let the number of lollipops be   L
Let the number of candy sticks be   K

then
    since there is 100p to be spent and each lollipop is 6p with each candy stick 8p

$$\Rightarrow 6L + 8K \leqslant 100$$

since there must be at least six of each type

$$\Rightarrow L \geqslant 6 \quad \text{and} \quad K \geqslant 6$$

since each of the 13 children must get a prize

$$\Rightarrow L + K \geqslant 13.$$

These can now be drawn on a graph as Fig. 7.29.

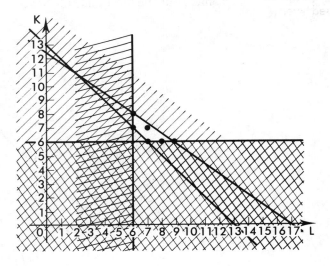

Fig. 7.29

Notice the possible solutions are the *integer values* in the solution set, shown by the heavy dots in the diagram.
So the possible prizes that can be bought are:

Lollipops		Candy sticks
6	and	7
6	and	8
7	and	6
7	and	7
8	and	6

Often a further piece of information is required, such as what is the least cost or the greatest number of prizes that can be bought. These answers can either be found by intelligent trial and error on the values in the solution set, or by using what can be called a solution line.

WORKED EXAMPLE 15 From the party above what is the greatest number of prizes that can be won?

$\Rightarrow$ (Yes, we can see the solution is 14 by intelligent trial and error, but follow through this method of solution as it is useful when you have a lot more possibilities).

⇒ The number of prizes bought is L + K, hence we want the largest value of N where L + K = N.

From the diagram Fig. 7.30 you will see that all the lines L + K = N will be parallel to each other.

Our solution is found by using a ruler parallel to the lines L + K = N and finding the solution line which is as far to the right as possible on our diaagram Fig. 7.29. This is in our solution set.

You will find on Fig. 7.29 that this solution line is L + K = 14 which gives the three possible solutions on it:

Lollipops	Candy sticks
6	8
7	7
8	6

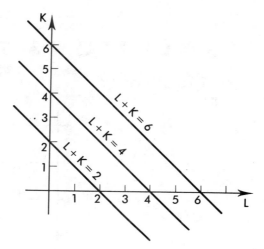

Fig. 7.30

WORKED EXAMPLE 16

A market stall holder is to spend up to £1100 buying up to 500 T shirts. He has the choice of two kinds:

One at £1 each, the other at £3 each.

The profit on the dearer type is twice that on the cheaper.
How many of each kind should he buy to give himself the greatest possible profit?

Let him buy x of the cheaper T shirts
   and y of the expensive T shirts.

The inequalities to be satisfied then are:

$$x + y \leqslant 500 \qquad x + 3y \leqslant 1100 \qquad x \geqslant 0 \qquad y \geqslant 0$$

The fig. 7.31 shows the solution set.

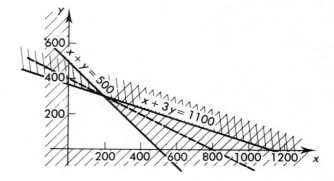

Fig. 7.31

The profit line is $x + 2y = P$ (P = profit).

Find a line in this family; say $x + 2y = 400$, then find the line parallel to this but as far to the right as possible.
This solution line is the dotted line on Fig. 7.31.
This gives the greatest profit at (200, 300)

The solution of greatest profit then is

　　　200 of the cheaper T shirts
　and 300 of the expensive T shirts.

EXERCISE 12

A manager buys two types of printer, a 'dot matrix' and an 'ink injection'. The 'dot matrix' would need a working space of 3000 cm² and costs £200. The 'ink injection' would need a working space of 2000 cm² and costs £600. The manager has only 40 000 cm² of working space available, and can spend up to £4500. What is the greatest number of printers he can buy?

S O L U T I O N S   T O   E X E R C I S E S

S1

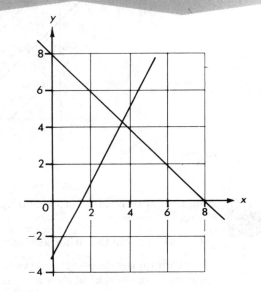

Fig. 7.32

The point of intersection is the point (3.7, 4.3), as shown in Fig. 7.32.

S2

You should have a table of values and a graph, as shown in Fig. 7.33.

x	-3	-2	-1	0	1
x^2	9	4	1	0	1
$3x$	-9	-6	-3	0	3
4	4	4	4	4	4
$y = x^2 + 3x + 4$	4	2	2	4	8

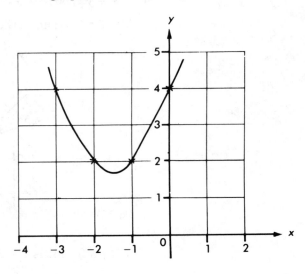

Fig. 7.33

The 'dip' looks to be about $x = -1.5$. We can then find this value substituted into $y = x^2 + 3x + 4$ to get $y = 1.75$, which seems to be confirmed by the graph. So the least possible value of y is 1.75.

S3

You should have tables as shown in Fig. 7.34.

x	1	2	3	4	5
$y = \dfrac{12}{x}$	12	6	4	3	2.4

x	0	1	2	3	4	5
x^2	0	1	4	9	16	25
$-2x$	0	-2	-4	-6	-8	-10
1	1	1	1	1	1	1
$y = x^2 - 2x + 1$	1	0	1	4	9	16

Fig. 7.34

You should then see which 'gaps' needed filling in. These would be chiefly on the $y = x^2 - 2x + 1$ graph around the dip, at $x = \frac{1}{2}$ and $x = 1\frac{1}{2}$. The solution of the equation $x^3 - 2x^2 + x = 12$ is given by the intersection of the two curves as from

$$y = \frac{12}{x} = x^2 - 2x + 1 \rightarrow 12 = x^3 - 2x^2 + x.$$

This point of intersection is at the point $x = 3$ (which you can see from the tables).

S4

i) gradient $= \dfrac{5 - 3}{5 - 1} = \dfrac{2}{4} = \dfrac{1}{2}$

ii) gradient $= \dfrac{-7 - 2}{5 - 3} = \dfrac{-9}{2} = -4.5$

S5

i) gradient $= \dfrac{3 - 1}{1 - 7} = \dfrac{2}{-6} = \dfrac{-1}{3}$

it passes through (1, 3), hence $3 = -\dfrac{1}{3} \times 1 + c \Rightarrow c = \dfrac{10}{3}$

hence equation is $y = -\dfrac{1}{3}x + \dfrac{10}{3}$ which simplifies to $3y = 10 - x$

ii) gradient $= 3$, c given by: $4 = 3 \times 2 + c$

$$\Rightarrow c = -2$$

equation is $y = 3x - 2$

S6

a) i) find the gradient of the line from $t = 0.5$ to 2 on the graph. 3 m/s
    ii) similarly 32 m/s

b) find the gradients of the tangents at each point to give
    i) 5 m/s
    ii) 20 m/s

S7

a) i) the gradient of the line is 10 m/s²
    ii) the gradient at $t = 10$ is the same as the line it is on; 5 m/s²

b) The total area under the graph adds up to 310 m.

S8

1. b) i) the gradient of the tangent at $t = 30$ is 1.15 m/s^2

   ii) and at speed $= 35$ is 0.65 m/s

   c) The total area under the graph adds up to 1370 m.

2. You need to draw the graph then find the area underneath. You should end up with a table of values as in Fig. 7.35.

t	0	1	2	3	4
v	20	20	18	20	32

Fig. 7.35

As you see, you would really need to know what value v has when $t = \frac{1}{2}$. This is $v = 20.625$. The graph can now be drawn as in Fig. 7.36, and can be split into the four strips as shown. Using the trapezium rule we would end up with:

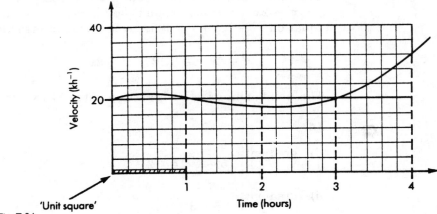

Fig. 7.36

total area $= \frac{1}{2}\{20 + 2(20 + 18 + 20) + 32\} = 84$.

The unit 'square' has been 1 kh^{-1} for 1 hour, which is a distance of 1 kilometre. So the total distance covered by Gillian while practising her driving would be 84 kilometres.

S9

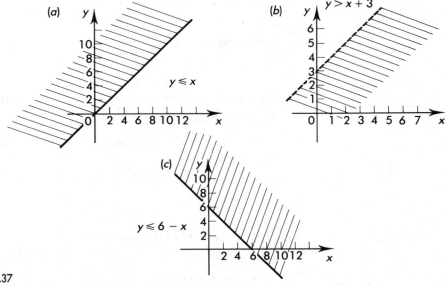

Fig. 7.37

S10

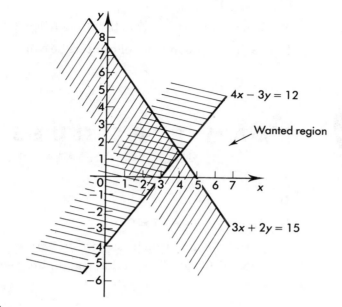

Fig. 7.38

S11

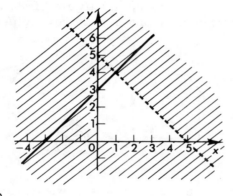

Fig. 7.39

S12

From the floor space, we get the equation:

$$3000d + 2000i \leqslant 40\,000 \Rightarrow 3d + 2i \leqslant 40$$

from the cost, we get the equation

$$200d + 600i \leqslant 4500 \Rightarrow 2d + 6i \leqslant 45$$

These two give the solution set:

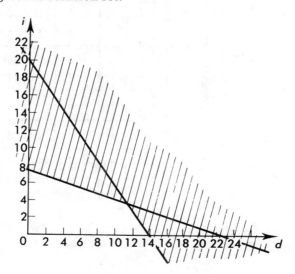

Fig. 7.40

The biggest value of $d + i$ in that region is $d + i = 14$ (to nearest whole number)

Hence the largest number of printers he can buy is 14.

EXAM TYPE QUESTIONS

Q1

Given that $3x + 4y + 7 = 0$

i)   Write this equation in the form $y = mx + c$.

ii) What is the gradient of the straight line represented by this equation?

(NEAB)

Q2

Huw observes a bird flying directly away from a bird box. He starts his watch and finds out how far the bird is from the box at different times.

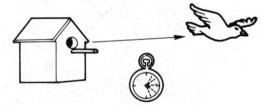

Fig. 7.41

The graph shown in Fig. 7.42 was drawn from his results.

a)   How far is the bird from the box when Huw starts his watch?

b)   How fast is the bird flying?

c)   Write down a formula for the distance, d, the bird is from the box in terms of time, t.

(WJEC)

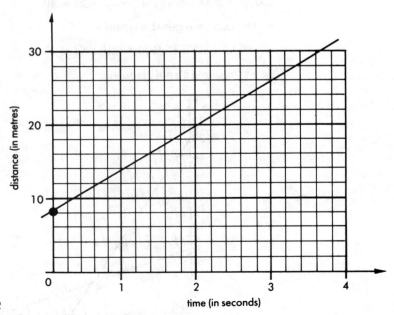

Fig. 7.42

Q3

A school inspector uses his own car to visit schools. He can claim travel expenses each week on one or other of two schemes.

Scheme A: For distances up to 100 miles, 40 pence per mile. For distances over 100 miles, 40 pence per mile for the first 100 miles then 10 pence per mile for each mile after the first 100 miles.

Scheme B: A basic allowance of £10 plus 20 pence per mile travelled.

a) Copy and complete the table for scheme A: shown in Fig. 7.43.

Miles travelled (x)	0	50	100	150	200	250	300	350	400
Expenses claimed (£y)	0		40		50			65	

Fig. 7.43

b) On graph paper, using scales of 2 cm to 50 miles travelled and 2 cm to £10 expenses claimed, draw a graph for scheme A for distances travelled up to 400 miles in one week.

c) On the same axes, draw a graph for scheme B for distances travelled up to 400 miles in one week.

d) i) Use your graphs to find the two values of x (miles travelled) for which scheme A and scheme B produce equal values of £y (expenses claimed).

  ii) For what range of values of x (miles travelled) does scheme A produce the greater value of £y (expenses claimed)?

  iii) When the distance travelled is 400 miles, find how much more can be claimed using scheme B than using scheme A.

  iv) Find the values of x for which the amount claimed using one scheme is £10 more than the amount claimed using the other scheme.   (ULEAC)

Q4

On the grid in Fig. 7.44, indicate, by shading out the region not required, the solution of the inequality $2x + 3y \geqslant 6$.   (MEG)

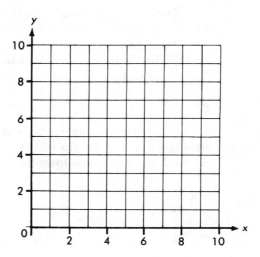

Fig. 7.44

Q5

The values in Fig. 7.45 are based on the performance figures for a Datsun Bluebird car as it accelerates from rest.

Time (seconds), t	0	2	4	6	8	10
velocity (metres per second), v	0	10	18	23.5	27.5	31

Fig. 7.45

a) Draw the graph of v against t.
b) By drawing the tangent to the curve at (4, 18), estimate the gradient of the curve at this point, and state the significance of this value.
c) Estimate the area of the region bounded by the curve, the t-axis and the line $t = 10$ by approximating this area to a triangle and four trapezia. State the significance of this value.   (NEAB)

Q6

The graph in Fig. 7.46 is of $y = x^2 - 2x - 5$.

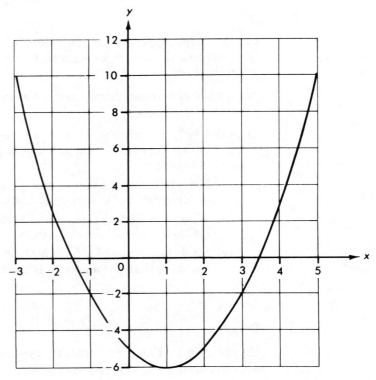

Fig. 7.46

a) Using the same axes, draw the line whose equation is $y = x - 1$.
b) Write down the solution set to $x^2 - 2x - 5 = x - 1$.
c) Show that $x^2 - 2x - 5 = x - 1$ can be written as $x^2 - 3x - 4 = 0$.
d) By drawing a suitable line, using the same axes, solve the equation $x^2 - x - 11 = 0$.   (WJEC)

Q7

A pebble is thrown upwards from the edge of a seaside cliff and eventually falls into the sea. The height of the pebble above the sea after t seconds is h metres, where h is given by the formula $h = 24 + 8t - 2t^2$.

t	0	1	2	3	4	5	6
h							

Fig. 7.47

a) Copy and complete the table in Fig. 7.47 for the values of h.

b) Using a scale of 2 cm for 5 m on the h-axis and 2 cm for 1 second on the t-axis, draw a graph of h against t for $0 \leqslant t \leqslant 6$.

c) Find i) the height of the cliff; ii) how high the pebble rises above the level of the cliff-top; iii) after how many seconds the pebble lands in the sea; iv) by drawing a suitable line, an estimate for the speed of the pebble after 5 seconds. (ULEAC)

Q8

A rectangular block shown in Fig. 7.48 has a square base of side x cm and a height of h cm. The total surface area of the block is 72 cm².

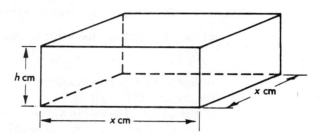

Fig. 7.48

a) Express h in terms of x.

b) Show that the volume, V cm³, of the block is given by $V = 18x - \dfrac{x^3}{2}$.

c) Copy and complete the table in Fig. 7.49 to show corresponding values of x and V.

x	0	1	2	3	4	5	6
V	0			40.5	40		0

Fig. 7.49

> **Use the scale they've given you or you will lose marks.**

d) Using a scale of 2 cm to represent 1 unit on the x-axis and 2 cm to represent 10 units on the V-axis, draw the graph of $V = 18x - \dfrac{x^3}{2}$ for values of x from 0 to 6 inclusive.

e) A block of this type has a volume of 30 cm³. Given that $h > x$, find the dimensions of the block. (MEG)

Q9

The number of bacteria in a colony doubles every 30 minutes.

a) Complete the table in Fig. 7.50 to show the number of bacteria for the first four hours. The colony starts with 25 bacteria.

Time (hours)	0	½	1	1½	2	2½	3	3½	4
No. of bacteria	25	50							

Fig. 7.50

b) i) Draw a graph to represent these figures, forming the points with a smooth curve.

ii) From the graph find the time when there will be 2500 bacteria.

c) If the number continues to double every 30 minutes, calculate how many bacteria there would be after 10 hours. (MEG)

Q10

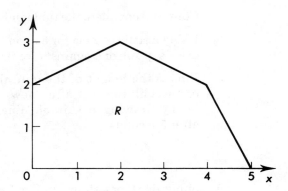

Fig. 7.51

The region R shown in the diagram is bounded by five straight lines.

a) R is defined by five inequalities, three of which are

$$x \geqslant 0, \qquad y \geqslant 0, \qquad x + 2y \leqslant 8.$$

Find the other two inequalities.

b) For the points (x, y) in R, find
   i) the greatest possible value of $x + y$ and the coordinates of the point at which this greatest possible value occurs,
   ii) the least possible value of $x - 2y$ and the coordinates of one point at which this least possible value occurs.   (MEG)

Q11

On each of the grids below, the graph of $y = x^2$ is drawn.

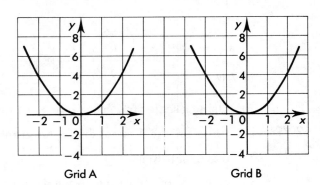

Fig. 7.52   Grid A   Grid B

a) On grid A, sketch the graph of $y = x^2 - 1$.
b) On grid B, sketch the graph of $y = (x - 1)^2$.

Q12

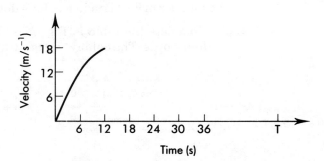

Fig. 7.53   Time (s)

The diagram represents part of a velocity time graph for a car moving between two sets of traffic lights.

a) Calculate an estimate of the maximum acceleration during the first 12 seconds of the motion.

After the first 12 seconds, the car maintains a constant velocity of 18 m/s^{-1} for the next 20 seconds.

b) Continue the velocity time graph to show this stage of the journey

It then slows down with constant deceleration until it comes to rest at time T seconds.
The total distance travelled is approximately 630 m.

c) Find the value of T. (ULEAC)

Q13

On the graph shown, the line *PQ* has the equation $y = ax + b$.

a) Write down the value of b.
b) Find the value of a.
c) Write down the three inequalities which together define the region shaded.

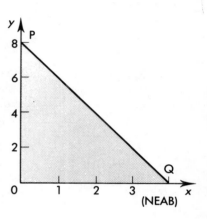

Fig. 7.54

(NEAB)

(NEAB)

Q14

The diagram below shows the graph of $y = x^2 - \dfrac{1}{x}$.

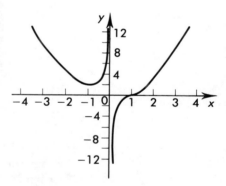

Fig. 7.55

a) From this graph write down (correct to the nearest integer) the solutions of the equation

$$x^2 - \frac{1}{x} = 10.$$

The solutions of $x^2 - \dfrac{1}{x} = 10$ may also be found by iteration.

b) One method is to re-write the equation as $x = \sqrt{10 + \dfrac{1}{x}}$, and use the iteration

$$u_{n+1} = \sqrt{10 + \frac{1}{u_n}}.$$

i) Using this iteration with $u_1 = 3$ find u_2 and u_3, writing down all the figures shown on your calculator.
ii) Hence write down, correct to 2 decimal places, one solution of the equation.

c)   i) Show that the equation may also be re-written as

$$x = \frac{1}{x^2 - 10}.$$

   ii) Use the iteration $u_{n+1} = \dfrac{1}{u_n^{\,2} - 10}$ to find a second solution, correct to 2 decimal places, of the equation.

d)   Use a modification of the iteration in b) to find the third solution, correct to 2 decimal places, of the equation.

Q15

The consumption of electricity in a house is measured by the number of rotations of the disc in the electricity meter. One unit of electricity is equivalent to 150 revolutions of the disc.

a)   When an immersion heater is switched on, the disc rotates at a constant rate of 12 revolutions every minute. Calculate the number of units of electricity used in one hour.

b)   The graph below shows the speed of rotation of the disc, ω, in revolutions per minute (r.p.m.) over a three hour period, where t is the time in hours after 7 p.m.

The curved part of the graph is given by the equation $\omega = \dfrac{15}{t} - t.$

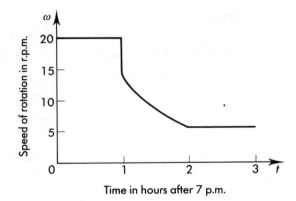

Fig. 7.56

   i) From the graph, estimate the value of t when the disc is rotating at 8 r.p.m.

   ii) Use this estimate and the iterative formula

$$t_{n+1} = \tfrac{1}{8}(15 - t_n^{\,2})$$

   to calculate this time to the nearest minute.

c)   i) Estimate, as accurately as possible, the area of the region between the graph and the t-axis from $t = 0$ to $t = 3$.

   ii) Electricity is charged at 6p per unit. Use your answer to part c) i) to estimate the cost of electricity used between 7 p.m. and 10 p.m.   (MEG)

Q16

   $f(x) = x^2$ and $g(x) = x^2 - 2x + 3.$

a) $g(x) = f(x - a) + b$, where a and b are constants. Find the values of a and b.

b)   Hence sketch the graphs of f and g, indicating clearly the relationship between the two graphs.

Q17

A fish tank of dimensions 40 cm × 40 cm × 90 cm contained two types of tropical fish; Dwarf Gourami (which have average length of 5 cm) and Climbing Perch (which have average length 20 cm). The Dwarf Gourami require 0.1 g of fish food each day whereas the Climbing Perch need 0.5 g each day.

a) To exist in harmony it is assumed that each fish needs a volume equal to the cube of twice the average length. The number of Dwarf Gourami is x and the number of Climbing Perch is y. Show that x and y satisfy the inequality.

$$x + 64y \leqslant 144$$

b) Each day 2 g of fish food is available. Show that

$$x + 5y \leqslant 20$$

c) i) Using x axis from 0 to 30. Draw the lines whose equations are

$$x + 5y = 20 \quad \text{and} \quad x + 64y = 144$$

   ii) In each case clearly identify which side of the line corresponds to the required inequalities.

d) There must be at least one of each type of fish in the tank.
   What is the maximum possible number of fish in the tank? (SEG)

Q18

The graph shows how the speed of a car changes as it comes to rest.

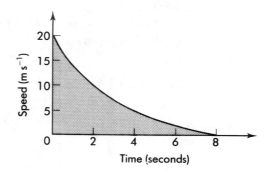

Fig. 7.57

a) Calculate, in kilometres per hour, the speed of the car when $t = 0$.

b) The area under the curve gives the distance travelled by the car in coming to rest. This area is shaded on the graph.
   Divide the area into four strips of equal width. Calculate an estimate of the distance travelled by the car as it comes to rest. (NEAB)

Q19

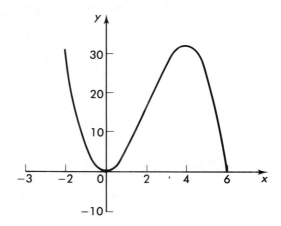

Fig. 7.58

The diagram shows the graph of $y = x^2(6 - x)$ for $-2 \leqslant x \leqslant 6$.

a) Making your method clear, find the gradient of this graph at the point $(-1, 7)$.

b) Using the given graph together with a straight line which is to be drawn in the diagram, solve the equation

$$x^2(6 - x) = 8(2 - x)$$

for x in the range $-2 \leqslant x \leqslant 6$.

(MEG)

Q20

a) An open-air swimming pool is filled through a pipe. The rate of flow is 10 000 litres per hour from noon until 7 pm, and it is increased to 15 000 litres per hour from 7 pm until 9 pm. This is shown on the graph in Fig. 7.59.

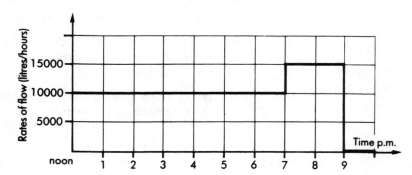

Fig. 7.59

Show that the total amount of water put into the pool is measured by the area under the graph.

b) At midnight it starts to rain. The graph in Fig. 7.60 shows the rate at which the rain falls on the pool.

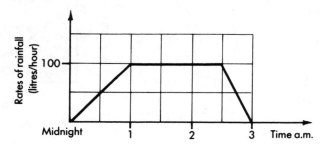

Fig. 7.60

i) Describe in words how the rainfall varies between midnight and 3 am.

ii) Assuming that the total amount of rain that falls into the pool is measured by the area under the graph, calculate this amount in litres.

iii) When the pool was filled through the pipe the previous day, the average depth of the water was 2 metres. How much does the water level rise as a result of the rain?

c) Between 8 am and 9 am there is a thunderstorm. The graph in Fig. 7.61 shows the rate at which rain falls on the pool during the storm.

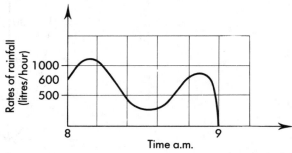

Fig. 7.61

Use an approximate method to estimate how much rain falls on the pool during the storm.

(OCSEB)

Q21

John is trying to design a more efficient speedboat. He has designed the hull of the boat and tested it. He recorded the drag d (the resistance of the water), measured in Newtons at various velocities (V).

Fig. 7.62

Velocity, V (m/s)	0.50	1.00	1.50	2.00	2.50	3.00
Drag d (Newtons)	0.52	1.15	2.41	4.07	5.88	8.53

a) Explain how John can tell from the table of values in Fig. 7.62 that the graph of (V, d) is not a straight line.

b) He wanted to test whether the drag would satisfy a formula of the type $d = aV^2 + b$ where a and b are constants. He made a new table to show the values of V^2 and d.
Complete the new table in Fig. 7.63 to show the values of V^2 and d obtained from the table above.

Fig. 7.63

V^2	0.25	1.00				
d	0.52	1.15	2.41	4.07	5.88	8.53

c) i) When John graphed this table, why do you think he would be satisfied?

   ii) Deduce the formula that John is likely to declare satisfies the performance of his speedboat.

OUTLINE ANSWERS TO EXAM QUESTIONS

A1

a) $3x + 4y + 7 = 0 \rightarrow 4y = -3x - 7$

$$\rightarrow y = -\frac{3}{4}x - \frac{7}{4}$$

b) The gradient is the co-efficient of x which is $-\frac{3}{4}$.

A2

a) 8 metres. (It is the point on the graph where $t = 0$.)

b) The gradient of the line which is found from two points (0, 8) and (3, 26) to give $\dfrac{26 - 8}{3 - 0} = \dfrac{18}{3} = 6 \text{ m s}^{-1}$.

c) The equation is of the form $y = mx + c$ where m is the gradient and c the y-axis intercept. So here it will be $d = 6t + 8$.

A3

a) See Fig. 7.64.

Fig. 7.64

Miles travelled (x)	0	50	100	150	200	250	300	350	400
Expenses claimed (£y)	0	20	40	45	50	55	60	65	70

b) See Fig. 7.65.

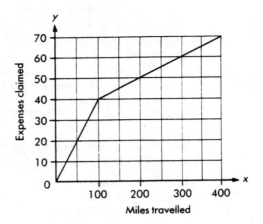

Fig. 7.65

c) See Fig. 7.66.

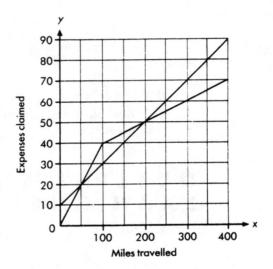

Fig. 7.66

d) i) Where the graphs intersect is $x = 50$ and $x = 200$.
    ii) $50 < x < 200$.
    iii) £90 − £70 = £20.
    iv) Look at the graph to see where the vertical difference is worth just £10. This happens when $x = 0$, $x = 100$, $x = 300$, although I don't think the school inspector would claim when $x = 0$. So the two values would be just $x = 100$ and $x = 300$.

A4

Draw the line $2x + 3y = 6$ first, which is a straight line as illustrated in Fig. 7.67.

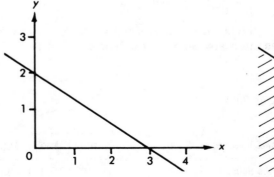

Fig. 7.67

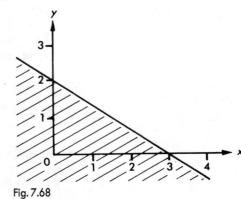

Fig. 7.68

Then consider any point, say, (0, 0), substitute it into the inequality and you get $0 + 0 \geqslant 6$. This is not true hence this is the region we do *not* want, and therefore in this question the one that needs shading out (see Fig. 7.68). Do not *touch* the line $2x + 3y = 6$, as this line is included in the region wanted.

A5

a) Your graph should look like that in Fig. 7.69.

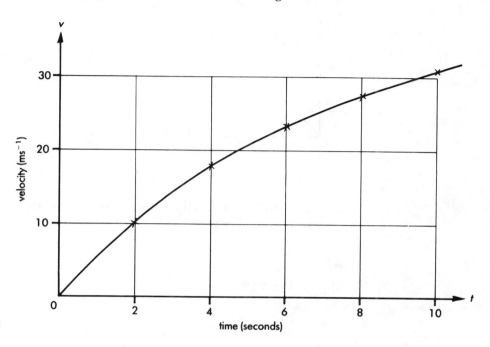

Fig. 7.69

b) The gradient of the straight line in Fig. 7.70 is $28 \div 8 = 3.5$ and the significance of this is that this represents the actual acceleration of the car after 4 seconds.

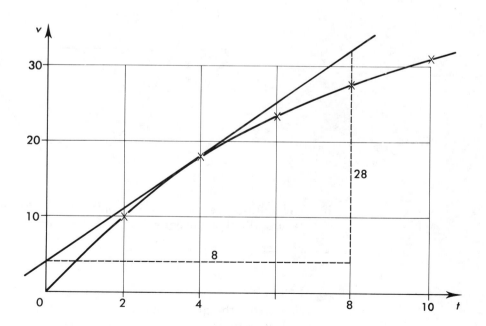

Fig. 7.70

c) In Fig. 7.71, estimating the area by the trapezium method gives us

$$-\text{area} = \frac{2}{2}\{0 + 2(10 + 18 + 23.5 + 27.5) + 31\}$$

$$\text{area} = 189.$$

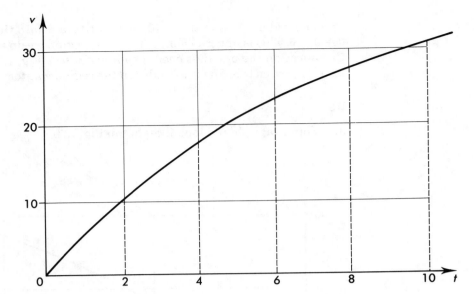

Fig. 7.71

The significance of this is that it represents the total distance covered over the 10 seconds which will be 189 metres.

A6

a) See Fig. 7.72.

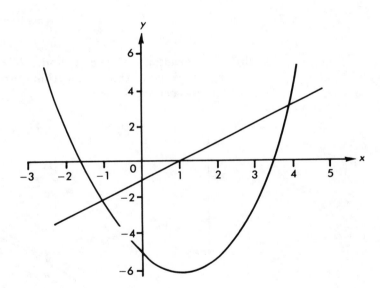

Fig. 7.72

b) The solution set is found at points where the intersection of these curves occurs, which is the point where $x = -1$ and the point where $x = 4$.

c) $x^2 - 2x - 5 = x - 1 \rightarrow x^2 - 2x - x - 5 + 1 = 0$
$$\rightarrow x^2 - 3x - 4 = 0.$$

d) You need to evaluate $(x^2 - 2x - 5) - (x^2 - x - 11) = -x + 6 = 6 - x$.

Now, from the given equation $x^2 - x - 11 = 0$, we see that adding $6 - x$ to both sides gives $(x^2 - x - 11) + (6 - x) = 6 - x$
$$\rightarrow x^2 - 2x - 5 = 6 - x.$$

You now need to draw the line $y = 6 - x$ and find its point of intersection with $y = x^2 - 2x - 5$. Doing this will give you the solutions $x = 3.9$ and $x = -2.8$.

A7

a) The missing heights are 24, 30, 32, 30, 24, 14, 0, respectively.
b) Your graph should look something like Fig. 7.73.

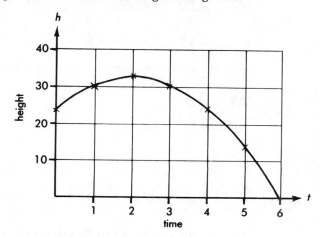

Fig. 7.73

c)   i) Height of the cliff is where the graph starts on the y-axis, 24 metres.
    ii) Up to 32 metres, 8 metres higher than the cliff-top.
    iii) Hits the sea when $h = 0$, this is when $t = 6$, i.e. after 6 seconds.
    iv) You need to draw a tangent to the curve at $t = 5$, which will give you a straight line of gradient $= \dfrac{-36}{4} = -9$ metres per second, but this is velocity, and the speed is the velocity with no sign, so the speed is 9 metres per second.

A8

a) Surface area given by $2 \times (hx + hx + x^2) = 4hx + 2x^2$, and since the total surface area is 72 cm^2, then $4hx + 2x^2 = 72 \rightarrow 4hx = 72 - 2x^2$

$$h = \frac{72 - 2x^2}{4x} = \frac{18}{x} - \frac{x}{2}$$

b) Volume = length × breadth × height
    $= x \times x \times h$
    $= x^2\left(\dfrac{18}{x} - \dfrac{1}{2}x\right) = 18x - \dfrac{1}{2}x^3.$

c) The table should be completed as in Fig. 7.74.

x	0	1	2	3	4	5	6
v	0	17.5	32	40.5	40	27.5	0

Fig. 7.74

d) The graph will look like Fig. 7.75.

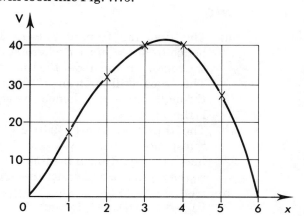

Fig. 7.75

e)   Read from the graph above when V = 30 metres. There are two values, $x = 1.8$ and 4.8; but since we are told that $h > x$, then from where

$$h = \frac{18}{x} - \frac{x}{2} \text{ then } \frac{18}{x} - \frac{x}{2} > x \rightarrow \frac{18}{x} > \frac{3x}{2}$$

$$\rightarrow 12 > x^2 \rightarrow x < 3.5.$$

So the solution we seek is $x = 1.8$ cm (from the graph), hence $h = 9.1$ cm.

A9

a)   See Fig. 7.76.

Fig. 7.76

Time (hours)	0	½	1	1½	2	2½	3	3½	4
Number of bacteria	25	50	100	200	400	800	1600	3200	6400

b)   i) The graph will be like that in Fig. 7.77.

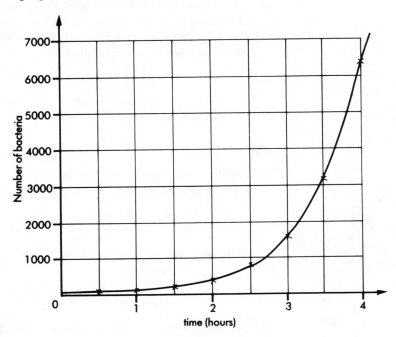

Fig. 7.77

time (hours)

ii) Read from the graph when the bacteria reach 2500 — it is after 3.3 hours (3 hours 18 minutes).

c)   After 10 hours the number has doubled 20 times, hence 25×2^{20}, which will be 26 214 400 or 26 million.

A10

a)   The 'first line' from (0, 2) to (2, 3), has gradient $\frac{1}{2}$ and passes through (0, 2) hence from $y = mx + c$ where $m = \frac{1}{2}$ and $c = 2$ the equation is $y = \frac{1}{2}x + 2$. So the region on and under the line is $y \leqslant \frac{1}{2}x + 2$.
The 'second line' from (2, 3) to (4, 2) has gradient $-\frac{1}{2}$ and will pass through y axis at 4, hence the equation is $y = -\frac{1}{2}x + 4 \Rightarrow 2y = 8 - x$ which is the one given.
The 'third line' from (4, 2) to (5, 0) has a gradient -2.
Substitute (5, 0) into $y = -2x + c \Rightarrow c = 10$
hence the equation of the line is $y = -2x + 10$
so the region on and under the line is $y \leqslant 10 - 2x$.

b)   i)   6 at (4, 2)
ii) -4 at (0, 2) or (1, $1\frac{1}{2}$) or (2, 3).

A11

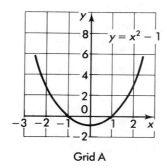

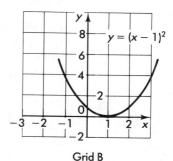

Fig. 7.78   Grid A   Grid B

A12

a) The steepest slope is at the beginning, the gradient of this line is $\frac{18}{8} = 2.25$ m/s².

b) You should draw a straight line for 20 seconds horizontal at $V = 18$.

c) The area under the graph up to 32 seconds is 474 m, which leaves 156 m to cover. The last part of the journey is a triangle where $\frac{1}{2} \times t_1 \times 18 = 156 \Rightarrow t_1 = 17.3$, hence T will be $32 + 17 = 49$.

A13

a) the y axis intercept, 8

b) the gradient, $\dfrac{-8}{4} = -2$

c) $x > 0, \quad y > 0, \quad y < 8 - 2x$.

A14

a) Where $y = 10$; $x = -1$ $x = 3$ $x = -3$ (to the nearest integer)
                                                                                (note that 0 is not an integer)

b) i) $u_2 = \sqrt{10 + \dfrac{1}{3}} = 3.214\,550\,3$

      $u_3 = \sqrt{10 + \dfrac{1}{u_2}} = 3.211\,087\,9$

   ii) the solution is $x = 3.21$

c) i) from $x^2 - \dfrac{1}{x} = 10 \Rightarrow x^2 - 10 = \dfrac{1}{x} \Rightarrow x = \dfrac{1}{x^2 - 10}$

   ii) Start with $u_1 = -1$

      then $u_2 = \dfrac{1}{(-1)^2 - 10} = -0.111\,111\,11$

                 $u_3 = \dfrac{1}{(u_2)^2 - 10} = -0.100\,123\,6$

                 $u_4 = \dfrac{1}{(u_3)^2 - 10} = -0.100\,100\,3$

      hence solution is $x = -0.10$.

d) let $u_1 = -3$

      then $u_2 = \sqrt{10 + \dfrac{1}{-3}} = -3.109\,126\,4$ (note we use the negative)

            $u_3 = \sqrt{10 + \dfrac{1}{u_2}} = -3.111\,007\,3$

      the solution is $x = -3.11$

A15

a) $12 \times 60 \div 150 = 4.8$ units

b)   i) 1.575

ii) $t_2 = \dfrac{1}{8}(15 - 1.575^2) = 1.5649219$

$t_3 = \dfrac{1}{8}(15 - t_2{}^2) \quad = 1.5688774$

$t_4 = \dfrac{1}{8}(15 - t_3{}^2) \quad = 1.5673279$

solution is 1.57 (two decimal places)
which is 1 hour 34 minutes.

c)   i) Area $= (20 \times 60) + \dfrac{30}{2}(14 + 8.5) + \dfrac{30}{2}(8.5 + 5.5) + (5.5 \times 60)$

$= 2077.5$ (note we used minutes as our unit)

ii) 2077.5 represents the number of revolutions in the 3 hours.

Cost $= \dfrac{2077.5}{150} \times 6 = 83.1$

estimated cost $= 83p$.

A16

a) $x^2 - 2x + 3 = (x - a)^2 + b$
$\qquad\qquad\qquad = x^2 - 2ax + a^2 + b$
$\Rightarrow a = 1, \quad a^2 + b = 3 \Rightarrow b = 2.$

b)

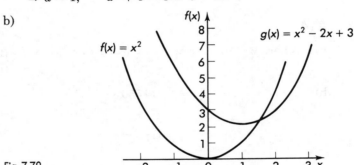

Fig. 7.79

The two graphs are parallel, $g(x)$ is $f(x)$ after a translation $\begin{pmatrix} 1 \\ 2 \end{pmatrix}$.

A17

a) $(2 \times 5)^3 x + (2 \times 20)^3 y \leqslant 40 \times 40 \times 90$
$\qquad \Rightarrow 1000x + 64\,000y \leqslant 144\,000$ (divide through by 1000)
$\qquad \Rightarrow \quad x + \quad 64y \quad \leqslant 144$

b) $\qquad 0.1x + \quad 0.5y \quad \leqslant 2$ (multiply through by 10)
$\qquad\qquad x + \quad 5y \quad \leqslant 20$

c)

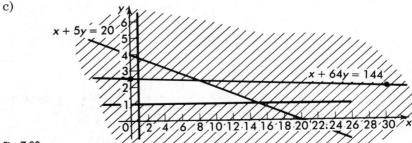

Fig. 7.80

d)   the maximum number of fish is 16, one Perch and 15 Gourami.

A18

a) Read from the graph, speed = 20 m/s

b) Area $= \dfrac{2}{2}(20 + 10) + \dfrac{2}{2}(10 + 5) + \dfrac{2}{2}(5 + 2) + \dfrac{1}{2}2 \times 2$

$\qquad = 54$ m.

A19

a) Find the gradient of the tangent at $(-1, 7)$; $-\dfrac{21}{7} = -3$

b) Draw the line $y = 8(2 - x)$
and the solutions are the x ordinates of the intersections;
$x = -2$ and $x = 1.2$.

A20

a) 10 000 litres per hour for 7 hours = 70 000 litres.
15 000 litres per hour for 2 hours = 30 000 litres
giving a total of 100 000 litres.
Looking at the graph, if we calculate the area of the two rectangles as in Fig. 7.81, the area = (10 000 × 7) + (2 × 15 000) = 100 000, the same as above. So the area beneath the graph is the amount of water put into the pool.

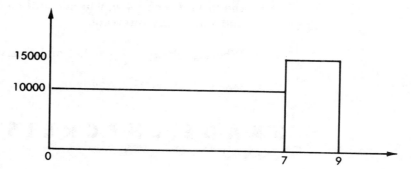

Fig. 7.81

b) i) From midnight the rainfall steadily increased until 1 am. From 1 am to 2.30 am, it was a continuous downpour, then it gradually decreased until at 3 am it had stopped raining.

 ii) The shape is a trapezium of area $\dfrac{100}{2}(1\tfrac{1}{2} + 3) = 225$ litres.

iii) Height of water, h metres $\propto$ amount of water put in, w litres, i.e. $h \propto w$.
Hence $h = kw$ (k being a constant).
When $w = 100\,000$, $h = 2 \rightarrow 2 = 100\,000\,\text{k} \rightarrow \text{k} = 0.000\,02$.
So when $w = 225$, representing the extra water put in, the rise in height will be given by
$\qquad h = 0.000\,02 \times 225$ metres
$\qquad\quad = 0.0045$ metres $= 0.45$ cm.

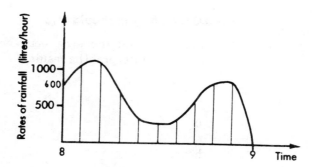

Fig. 7.82

c) Split the shape up into trapeziums as in Fig. 7.82, then using the trapezium rule width of $2\frac{1}{2}$ little squares, which will represent a time of 0.1 hour. The area will be given by:

$$\text{area} = \frac{0.1}{2}[600 + 2(1050 + 1100 + 700 + 300 + 250 + 300 + 600 + 800 + 850) + 0]$$

$$= 625 \text{ litres.}$$

A21

a) Since the differences of V are all the same (0.50), then if the relationship between V and d gave a straight line the differences between d would also be constant. Here they are 0.63, 1.26, 1.66, 1.81, 2.65, gradually increasing and *not* constant. So the graph of (V, d) is *not* going to be a straight line.

b) See Fig. 7.83.

V^2	0.25	1.00	2.25	4.00	6.25	9.00
d	0.52	1.15	2.41	4.07	5.88	8.53

Fig. 7.83

c) i) Because if you draw the graph V^2 against d you do get points that look as if they lie in a straight line, and so this shows that the relationship is of the form $d = aV^2 + b$, where a will be the gradient of that straight line, and b the d-axis intercept.

ii) Where gradient $= \dfrac{8.75}{8.01} = 1.09$ and d-axis intercept $= -0.32$.

Hence $d = 1.09 \, V^2 - 0.32$.

GRADE CHECKLIST

For a Grade B you should:

Be able to: Locate regions given by linear inequalities.
Interpret graphs which describe real life situations and contexts.

Know: The shapes of simple functions:
e.g. quadratic, cubic, reciprocal.

For a Grade A you should also:

Be able to: Solve equations using graphical methods.
Calculate gradients of curves.

Understand: What distance/time graphs tell us.
What speed/time graphs tell us.

For a Grade A* you should also

Be able to: Find the area between a curve, the axis and two limits, and interpret the result.

A STUDENT'S ANSWER
WITH EXAMINER'S COMMENTS

a) Copy and complete the table for values of y where

$$y = 2x - 7 + \frac{10}{x}$$

Good, correct answers, rounded off to a suitable degree of accuracy.

x	1	1.5	2	2.5	3	3.5	4
y	5	2·7	2	2	2·3	2·9	3·5

b) Draw an x-axis, using a scale of 4 cm to 1 unit. Draw a y-axis using a scale of 2 cm to 1 unit.
Plot the points from your table and draw the graph of

$$y = 2x - 7 + \frac{10}{x}$$

Points plotted correctly, but the curve is rubbish! Here is a bump! It should be a smooth curve.

A poor flat bottom! This should have been rounded to give a smooth curved bottom.

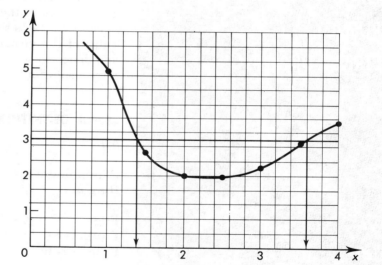

c) Use the graph to find the minimum value of $2x - 7 + \frac{10}{x}$ for values of x between 1 and 4.

Answer wrong because of the flat bottom. Unlikely to be given any credit here at all.

answer 2

d) By drawing a suitable straight line on your graph parallel to the x-axis, find the approximate solutions of

$$2x + \frac{10}{x} = 10.$$

Excellent, well done, drawn in the correct line of $y = 3$ *and* found the intersection with the curve accurately from your graph.

$x = 1·35$ $x = 3·59$

You are obviously a good student, but have thrown marks away with a sloppy curve. Would still score well with this answer.

GEOMETRY

ANGLES

INTERSECTING CHORD
THEOREM

CONGRUENCY

GEOMETRICAL DRAWING

LOCI

GETTING STARTED

At the Higher Level of mathematics, the knowledge of *geometrical facts* is expected. These will often have been explored during coursework in school or college, but they do need *learning* for the examination. In the exam it is how you *apply* your knowledge of geometrical facts that gains you marks. So be familiar with the 'rules of the geometrical game'. These will then give you the confidence to search through a geometrical problem to find the correct solution.

USEFUL DEFINITIONS

Allied	Supplementary angles on one side of a transversal, facing each other.
Complementary	Angles that add up to 90°.
Diagonal	A line joining two corners of a geometrical shape.
Edge	The line where two faces meet.
Equilateral	Having same lengths.
Euler's rule	$V + F - E = 2$, i.e. the number of vertices + the number of faces − the number of edges = 2, in a polygon.
Face	The surface of a solid shape bounded by edges.
Polygon	A plane shape with many straight lines.
Rhombus	A parallelogram with all its sides the same length.
Subtend	Two lines that meet and form an angle.
Supplementary	Angles adding up to 180°.
Tessellation	A plane shape that will fill a complete plane and leave **no** spaces.
Transversal	A straight line that crosses through at least two parallel lines.
Vertex	A point where two lines or edges meet.

ESSENTIAL PRINCIPLES

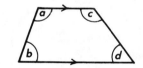

There are a lot of geometrical facts involving *angles*. You are advised to learn them all. This will then arm you with the weapons necessary for problem solving and for recognising the different situations that these geometrical facts apply to.

POLYGONS (having N sides)

The total of the exterior angles is **always** 360°.
The total of the interior angles is 180 (N − 2)°.

REGULAR POLYGONS (having N sides)

A *regular polygon* is one that has all its sides the same length and where each exterior angle is equal.

Then: the size of each *exterior* angle is given by $\dfrac{360°}{N}$

the size of each *interior* angle is given by $180° - \dfrac{360°}{N}$

ISOSCELES TRIANGLE

An *isosceles triangle* has two sides the same length, and the angles opposite to these equal sides are always equal (see Fig. 8.1). The vertical angle bisector will also be the perpendicular bisector of the opposite side as shown here. This will give us two congruent triangles, as shown in Fig. 8.2.

Fig. 8.1

Fig. 8.2

TRAPEZIUM

Fig. 8.3

A *trapezium* is a quadrilateral that has two sides parallel as shown in Fig. 8.3. The pairs of angles made with each transversal are *allied* angles, that is they add up to 180° (e.g. $a + b = 180° = c + d$).

CIRCLES

From any chord in a *circle*, all the angles subtended on the same arc are equal (see Fig. 8.4).

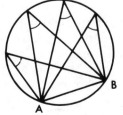

Fig. 8.4

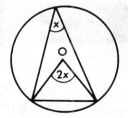

Fig. 8.5

From any chord in a circle, the angle subtended at the centre is double any angle subtended at the arc of the circle in the same segment (see Fig. 8.5).

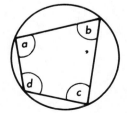

Fig. 8.6

Any quadrilateral drawn so that its four vertices touch the circumference of the same circle is said to be *cyclic*. The opposite angles will add up to 180°, e.g. in Fig. 8.6, $a + c = 180°$, $b + d = 180°$. Any quadrilateral that has its opposite angles adding up to 180 will be cyclic and so a circle can be drawn around the vertices.

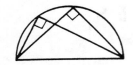

Fig. 8.7

If any triangle is drawn in a *semi-circle* with one side the diameter and its opposite angle on the arc (as in Fig. 8.7), then this angle made at the arc is a right angle.

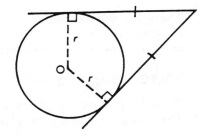

Fig. 8.8

Tangents to a circle will be perpendicular to the radius of the circle. Intersecting tangents form an isosceles triangle (see Fig. 8.8).

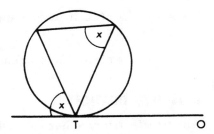

> Now see how many of these facts you've remembered, go on, test yourself.

Fig. 8.9

Where OT is a tangent at T, then the angles indicated (x) are equal, this being called the 'alternate segment' theorem (see Fig. 8.9).

This can quite easily be shown by drawing and measuring, and will probably have been part of your coursework.

2 > INTERSECTING CHORD THEOREM

INTERNAL INTERSECTING

In Fig. 8.10, chords AB and CD intersect each other at X, then $AX.XB = CX.XD$.

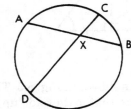

Fig. 8.10

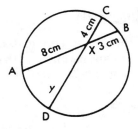

Fig. 8.11

WORKED EXAMPLE 1

In Fig. 8.11, find y.
We can use the intersecting chord theorem to say $AX.XB = CX.XD$,

hence $8 \times 3 = 4 \times y$

$\rightarrow \quad \dfrac{8 \times 3}{4} = y = 6$ cm.

EXTERNAL INTERSECTING

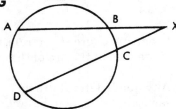

Fig. 8.12

In Fig. 8.12, the **same** rule works also, i.e. $AX.XB = CX.DX$

WORKED EXAMPLE 2	In Fig. 8.13, find y.

Using the theorem $AX.XB = CX.XD$, then $(5 + 2) \times 2 = 3 \times (y + 3)$

$$\rightarrow 14 = 3y + 9$$
$$14 - 9 = 3y = 5$$
$$y = \frac{5}{3} \text{ cm.}$$

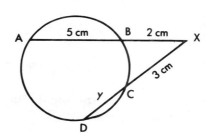

Fig. 8.13

TANGENTS

Where XT is a *tangent* to the circle at T then the intersecting chord theorem is $AX.XB = XT^2$.

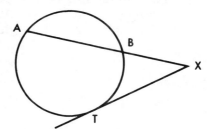

Fig. 8.14

EXERCISE 1

Where TC is the tangent to the circle, find the lengths of i) p, ii) q.

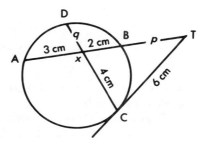

Fig. 8.15

3 > CONGRUENT TRIANGLES	*Congruent* triangles are exactly the same in shape, lengths and angles (although one may be a reflection of the other).

There are 4 possible conditions for two triangles which will determine whether both triangles are congruent. Meeting any *one* condition will result in the triangles being congruent.

> The conditions that will lead to congruent triangles are listed here. Any one condition will do.

- ■ All three sides are known.
- ■ Given two sides and the angle between them.
- ■ Given all the angles and a particular side.
- ■ Given a right angle, the longest side and one other length.

It is **impossible** to draw more than one triangle if we know any of the facts in the situations above.

Hence, if we are given two triangles and **any** of the above situationns fit **both** triangles, then we can say that these triangles are **congruent**.

The four rules can be abbreviated to help us remember them:

1. **The corresponding sides of both triangles are equal**
    Side, Side, Side — SSS
    Triangle ABC ≡ Triangle XYZ

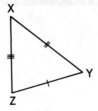
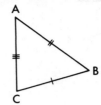

Fig. 8.16

2. **The two sides and the included angle of both triangles are equal**
    Side, Angle, Side — SAS
    Triangle ABC ≡ Triangle DEF

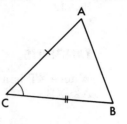
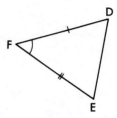

Fig. 8.17

3. **Two angles and a corresponding side of both triangles are equal**
    Angle, Angle, Side — AAS or Angle, Side, Angle — ASA
    Triangle ABC ≡ Triangle PQR

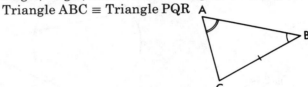
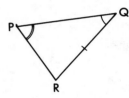

OR

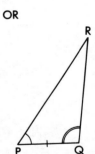

Fig. 8.18

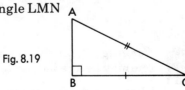
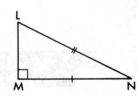

4. **Both triangles have a right angle with equal hypotenuse and corresponding side**
    Right angle, Hypotenuse, Side — RHS
    Triangle ABC ≡ Triangle LMN

Fig. 8.19

WORKED EXAMPLE 3

The triangles in Fig. 8.20 are congruent: triangle ABC ≡ triangle MLN.
Reason: SSS.
    Notice how we say ABC ≡ MLN
    since   angle A matches up with angle M
            angle B matches up with angle L
            angle C matches up with angle N

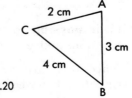
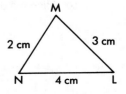

Fig. 8.20

WORKED EXAMPLE 4

The triangles in Fig. 8.21 are congruent: triangle ABC ≡ triangle PQR.
Reason: ASA
[Note that you are expected to be able to find the third angle if you are given the first two!]

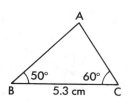 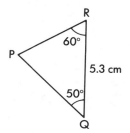

Fig. 8.21

WORKED EXAMPLE 5

The triangles in Fig. 8.22 are *not* congruent since we cannot match the triangles with each other *and* since we cannot fit any one of the four rules to the situation. *[Note: If we know that two sides of two triangles are the same then the known angle must be in between them if we are to identify them as congruent.]*

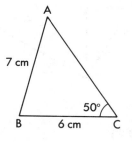 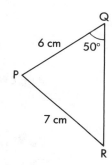

Fig. 8.22

EXERCISE 2

a) Draw a rectangle (not a square!) ABCD. Draw in the diagonals AC and BD. Let the diagonals intersect at X. Which triangles are congruent?
b) Draw an equilateral triangle ABC. Draw in the angle bisectors AM, BN and CP. Which triangles are congruent?

 **GEOMETRICAL DRAWING**

Even at the highest level of GCSE mathematics you are quite likely to be asked to draw or construct a particular plane shape. It could be to find out a result or to solve some problem by a scale drawing.

You need to be confident about drawing to scale information about a particular bearing by the use of a protractor, remembering always to start by drawing in your *North* line.

WORKED EXAMPLE 6

From home, Jenny flew a plane 30 km on a bearing of 150°, then flew at a bearing of 060° until landing at Cleethorpes Airport. She flew straight back on a bearing of 260°. How far is her home from Cleethorpes Airport?

If we use a scale drawing of 1 cm to represent 10 km then we can easily drawn Jenny's journey to Cleethorpes in Fig. 8.23, except as yet we do not know where she stopped.

Now, since home is a bearing of 260° from Cleethorpes, then Cleethorpes must be on a bearing of $260 - 180 = 80°$ from home. Draw this line in to give us the situation in Fig. 8.24. We can now see where Cleethorpes Airport is and measure the distance. It will be 8.9×10 km = 89 km.

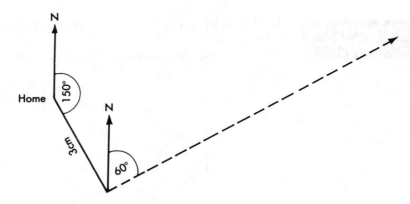

Fig. 8.23

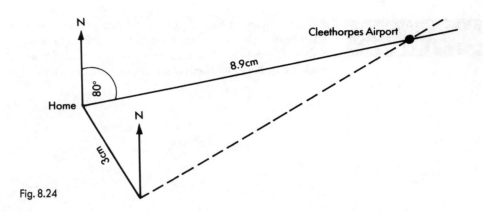

Fig. 8.24

CONSTRUCTIONS

You need to confidently perform the following constructions:

Line bisector

By making two arcs from either end of the line and draw a straight line through the points of intersection. Figure 8.25 illustrates this method of bisecting the line CD. It is worth noting that this line is properly called the 'perpendicular bisector'.

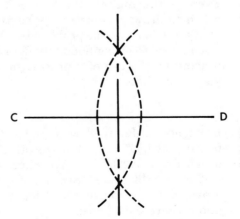

Fig. 8.25

Angle bisector

From the vertex of the angle, draw an arc through both sides of the angle. Then from these points of intersection, arc into the middle of the space between the angles. Where these two arcs cross over join to the vertex of the angle for the angle bisector. This is illustrated in Fig. 8.26.

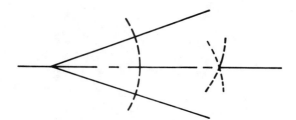

Fig. 8.26

Right angle at a point

From the point P where the right angle needs to be drawn, arc on both sides. (You may need to extend the line to be able to do this.) From these two arcs just construct a line bisector. This will be a perpendicular line at the point where you want it. This is illustrated in Fig. 8.27.

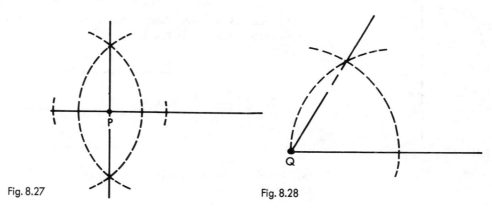

Fig. 8.27   Fig. 8.28

60° angle

From the point Q where you want the 60°, arc a quarter turn to just intersect with the line where you want the angle. Then from that intersection, with the same size arc, arc a quarter turn to go from your original point to intercept with the previous quarter turn. Join this point of intersection with the original point to give 60°. This is shown in Fig. 8.28.

Perpendicular from a point, R, to a line

From the given point, R, draw an arc big enough to cut the line twice. Then from these cuts, construct on the other side of the line, a perpendicular bisector between them; join this up to the given point R and you have your perpendicular. This is illustrated in Fig. 8.29.

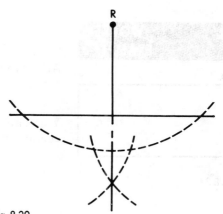

Fig. 8.29

5 ⟩ **LOCI**

Loci are the paths of moving points that usually have some pattern to them. You are quite likely to be asked to find the locus of a point, but there are some locus situations with which you ought to be familiar to start off with.

The *locus* of a point moving so that it is a constant distance from:

1   a point A; is a circle (see Fig. 8.30).

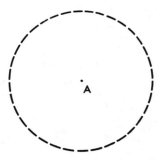

Fig. 8.30

2   two fixed points, A and B; is the perpendicular bisector of the line joining those two points (see Fig. 8.31).

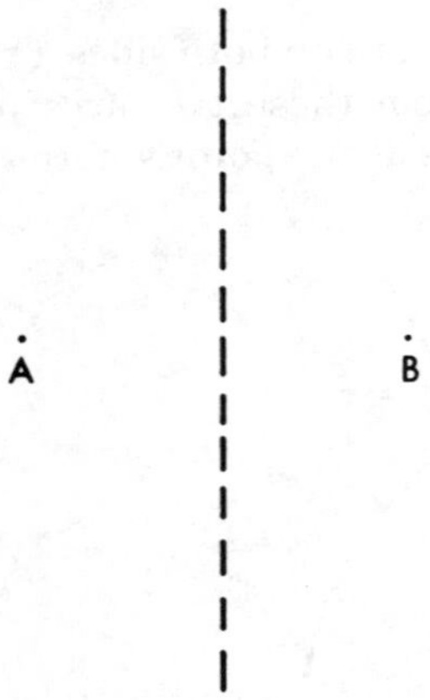

3   a line AB; is a 'racetrack' shape, made up of two parallel lines and two semi-circles (see Fig. 8.32).

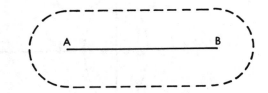

Fig. 8.32

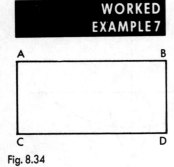

Fig. 8.31

4   two lines AB and DC; is the angle bisector of the angle that both lines subtend to (see Fig. 8.33).

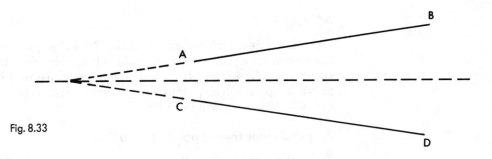

Fig. 8.33

WORKED EXAMPLE 7

Draw the locus of the point P which is always 1 cm away from the rectangle ABCD in Fig. 8.34

You can see from Fig. 8.35 that the distances easily worked out are those vertically perpendicular 1 cm from the straight edges.

A   B

C   D

Fig. 8.34

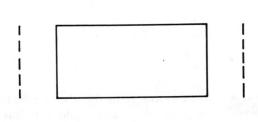

Fig. 8.35

We then need to consider the point, P, 1 cm away from each vertex A, B, C and D. These will be quarter circles joining the given straight lengths already to give the final locus as in Fig. 8.36.

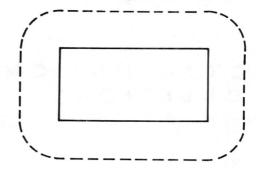

Fig. 8.36

EXERCISE 3

Construct an equilateral triangle of side 4 cm, then draw the locus of the point, P, which is 1 cm away from the triangle (and not inside it).

S O L U T I O N S   T O   E X E R C I S E S

S1

i) To find p, use $AT.TB = TC^2$ → $(5 + p) \times p = 36$
   → $5p + p^2 = 36$ → $p^2 + 5p - 36 = 0$
   which solves to give $p = 4$ and $p = -9$, the negative answer here has no use to us, so we take the solution $p = 4$.

ii) To find q, use $AX.XB = XC.XD$ → $3 \times 2 = 4 \times q$

$$→ 6 = 4q → q = \frac{3}{2}$$

S2

a)   There are three different sets:
   a)   ABC, DCB, CDA and BAD
   b)   ABX, DCX
   c)   ADX, BCX.
b)   There are two different sets:
   a)   AXC, AXB, BXC
   b)   the six little triangles AXN, CXN, CXM, BXM, BXP, and AXP

S3

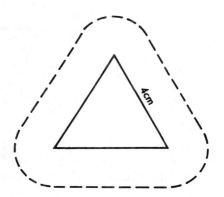

Fig. 8.37

You will have a shape looking something like Fig. 8.37. With three straight sides of length 4 cm, each parallel to one side of the equilateral triangle, then the curved parts are each arcs of circles with radius 1 cm having the centres the vertices of the triangle.

EXAMINATION TYPE QUESTIONS

Q1

In Fig. 8.38 angle EAD = 40° and angle AFB = 60°. Calculate the size of angle AED, giving reasons for each step of your calculation. (NEAB)

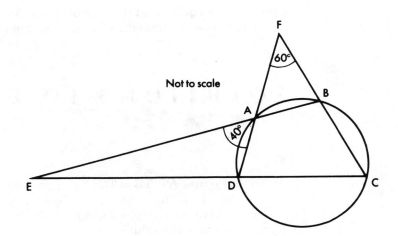

Fig. 8.38

Q2

In this question you must give valid reasons for your answers. Numbers on their own will not be sufficient. Figure 8.39 shows the cross section of a tunnel. The tunnel is circular with a platform DC in it. The platform is held by five rods AB, AD, BC, BD and AC. Rods AB, AD and BC are all the same length. The angle between AC and BC is 30°.

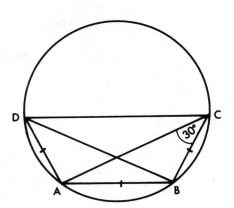

Fig. 8.39

a) Find   i) $\angle$ADB;   ii) $\angle$ABD;   iii) $\angle$DBC;   iv) $\angle$BDC.
b)   i) Explain how you know that platform DC must be parallel to rod AB.
     ii) What does the answer to a) iii) tell you about DC? (WJEC)

Q3

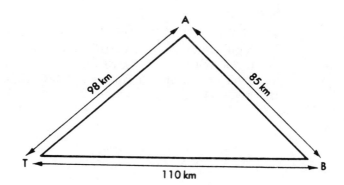

Fig. 8.40

Figure 8.40 shows the location of a television transmitter (T) in relation to two towns Amburg (A) and Beetown (B).

a) Using a scale of 1 cm to represent 10 km, draw an accurate scale diagram of the triangle TAB.

b) The transmitter has a range of 80 km. Draw accurately, on your scale drawing, the curve which represents the limiting range of the transmitter.

> Use your pair of compasses for the curve to be accurate.

It is planned to build a repeater station, R, which is an equal distance from both Amburg and Beetown.

c) On your drawing, construct accurately the line on which the repeater station must be built.

The repeater station is to be built at the maximum range of the transmitter.

d) i) Mark with the letter R the position of the repeater station on your diagram.

   ii) Find the minimum transmitting range of the repeater stations so that programmes can be received in Amburg. Give your answer in km, to the nearest km.

(ULEAC)

Q4

Figure 8.41 shows the outline of a 50p piece. O is the centre.

a) i) Work our the sizes of the angles marked x and y.

   ii) Correct your answers to the nearest $\frac{1}{2}$ degree.

b) Work out $x + 2y$ using your answers to a) ii).

c) Explain why the answer to b) is not 180°.

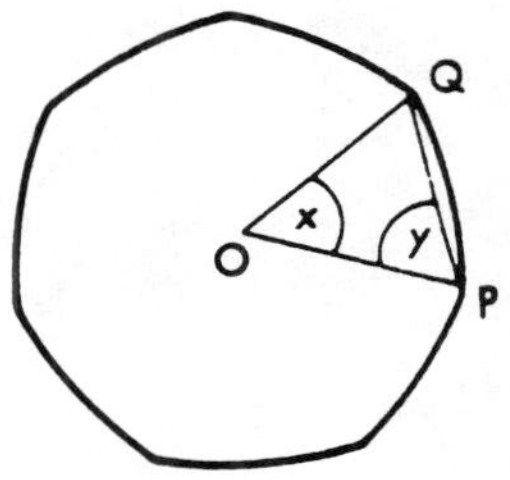

Fig. 8.41

(MEG)

Q5

Figure 8.42, which is drawn to scale, shows a wheel, centre A, of radius 25 cm which rolls along the ground and then mounts a step of height 15 cm. Draw the resulting locus of A as the wheel approaches the step, mounts it and then moves on.

(NEAB)

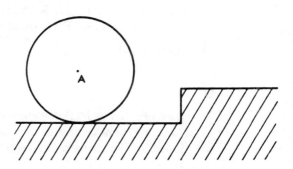

Fig. 8.42

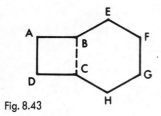

Fig. 8.43

Q6

a) The tile ABEFGHCD in Fig. 8.43 is made up of a square ABCD attached to a regular hexagon BEFGHC along their common side BC. What is the size of
i) $\angle ABC$; ii) $\angle EBC$; iii) $\angle ABE$?

b) Tiles of the same shape as ABEFGHCD are placed in the pattern shown in Fig. 8.44

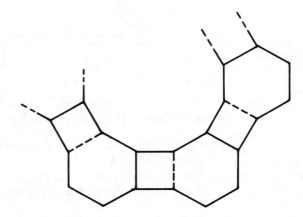

Fig. 8.44

i) Without drawing the completed figure, explain why the tiles will form a closed shape if the pattern is continued.

ii) The completed shape encloses a regular polygon. How many sides has this polygon? (WJEC)

Q7

Figure 8.45 shows a cyclic quadrilateral ABCD with AB parallel to DC. The line TAS is the tangent to the circle at A. Angle DAT = 47° and angle BAS = 52°.

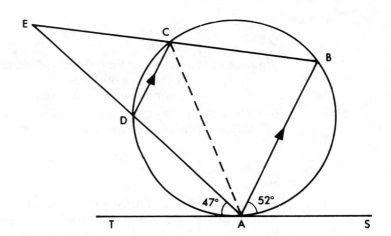

Fig. 8.45

a) Find the size of i) angle ACB; ii) angle DCA; iii) angle CBA.

The lines BC and AD are produced to meet at E.

b) Show that the triangle EBA is isosceles.

The triangles ECD and EBA are similar such that EC : CB = 2 : 3.

c) Calculate the value of $\dfrac{\text{area of triangle ECD}}{\text{area of triangle EBA}}$ (ULEAC)

Q8

Two rods pivoted at P (Fig. 8.46) are touching a cylinder at points A and B.

a) Use congruent triangles to show that $PA = PB$.

b) Show that the angle between the radii OA and OB is equal to the angle θ. (MEG)

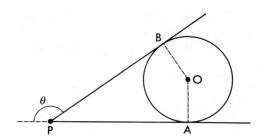

Fig. 8.46

Q9

a) The country of Futuria is one vast horizontal plain. As part of its national defences, a straight electronic strip, 20 km long and of negligible width, is built along the ground. This emits delta-rays, which causes radio jamming anywhere within 10 km of any point of the strip. Draw, on a scale of 1 cm to 4 km, the region on the ground that is affected by the jamming.

b) The influence of the strip also extends into the atmosphere, so that there is a region above the ground affected by the radio jamming. Describe the shape of this region in words, using the names of mathematical figures.

c) Foreign aircraft are required to fly across Futuria horizontally at a height of 8 km above the ground. The Ministry of Aviation issues charts showing the region affected by the jamming at this height. Draw, on the same scale as a), the shape of this region.

d) In another part of the country there is a strip with similar properties in the shape of a letter L, each arm of the L being 10 km long. Draw, on the same scale as a), the region on the ground affected by jamming from this strip.

(OCSEB)

Q10

a) Figure 8.47 shows the proposed vertices of a planar network (that is, a network in which no edges cross over one another). Also, each vertex is to be joined to each other vertex by one edge (but not more than one). Draw this network, and answer the following questions about it:

   i) What are the values of V, R and E, the numbers of vertices, regions and edges? (Do not forget to count the outside region.)

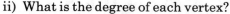

· Fig. 8.47

   ii) What is the degree of each vertex?

   Euler's rule.

   iii) Check that V + R − E = 2. (This is called Euler's rule.)

   iv) How many edges are there on the boundary of each region?

b) The problem in this part of the question is to draw a different planar network: each vertex is to be joined to exactly three other vertices, and there are to be four edges on the boundary of each region.

   i) Give a reason why E must be equal to $\frac{3}{2}V$.

   ii) Give a reason why E must be equal to 2R.

   iii) Use Euler's rule to calculate the values of V, R and E.

   iv) Make a drawing of this network.

c) Now consider the problem of drawing a planar network in which each vertex is joined to exactly four other vertices, and in which there are five edges on the boundary of each region.

i) Write down equations connecting E with V, and E with R.
ii) Use Euler's rule to calculate the values of V, R and E.
iii) What do you deduce about this network?

Fig. 8.48

d) Figure 8.48 shows how a doodler marked five points on a sheet of paper, and tried to join each vertex to each other vertex by one edge, in such a way that no edges crossed over one another. Prove that, however, he tried to do it, he would not be successful. (OCSEB)

Q11

a) Mark two points A and B on your paper, 8 cm apart. By choosing various pairs of numbers (not necessarily both whole numbers) which multiply together to give 20, plot a number of points P on your paper with the property that $PA \times PB = 20$, (where both PA and PB are measured in centimetres). Hence draw as accurately as you can, the locus of points with this property.

b) Starting again with a new pair of points A and B, still 8 cm apart, draw the locus of points with the property $PA \times PB = 16$.

c) Repeat b) with the property $PA \times PB = 15$.

d) The three loci which you have drawn should all look different, but they all have the same kinds of symmetry. Name, with reference to the points A and B,
  i) any lines of reflective symmetry,
  ii) the centre and order of any rotational symmetry, for all three loci.
     Describe a simple shape which has the same symmetry as these loci.

e) All the loci in a), b) and c) have a property of the form $PA \times PB = K$, where K is a number. For some values of K, there are points where the locus cuts the line between A and B. Suppose that it does this at a point P where $PA = x$ cm.
  i) What is the length PB in terms of x?
  ii) Show that x satisfies the quadratic equation $x^2 - 8x + K = 0$.
  iii) For the values $K = 16$ and $K = 15$, solve this equation for x.
  ix) Show that, if $K = 20$, the equation has no solution for x.
  v) Use these results to explain why the loci have different forms for these three values of K. (OCSEB)

OUTLINE ANSWERS TO EXAM QUESTIONS

A1

You should work it out on the diagram first, then state the route that gets you to the answer in the shortest (but correct) way.

BAF = 40° . . . opposite angles equal.
BAD = 140° . . . angles on a line add up to 180°.
BCD = 40° . . . cyclic quadrilateral, opposite angles add up to 180°.
FDC = 80° . . . angles in a triangle add up to 180°.
ADF = 100° . . . angles on a line add up to 180°.
AED = 40° . . . angles in a triangle add up to 180°.
Hence AED = 40°.

A2

a)   i) ADB = 30°. From the same chord AB that angle ACB is from, hence ADB = ACB.

ii) ABD = 30° since triangle ABD is isosceles and so ABD = ADB.

iii) Since DAB = 120°, angles in a triangle add up to 180°, then DCB = 60°, because opposite angles in a cyclic quadrilateral add up to 180°.
Also BAC = 30°, since ABC is an isosceles triangle where BAC = BCA.
Hence CDB = 30°, it is from the same chord BC that angle BAC is from.
Finally DBC = 90° since DBC, BCD and CDB add up to the angles of a triangle and hence 180°.

iv) BDC = 30°, having found it on the way to DBC.

b)   i) Because the angles DCB and CBA add up to 180° and in their position are allied angles, meaning that BC is the transversal so DC and AB are parallel.

ii) That DC is the diameter of the circle.

A3

Your final diagram should look like Fig. 8.49.

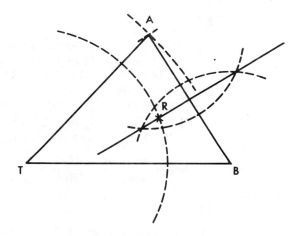

Fig. 8.49

d)   ii) The minimum range is the distance from A to the point R which is 45 km.

A4

a)   i) $x = 360 \div 7 = 51.43°$ $y = \frac{1}{2}(180 - 51.43) = 64.29°$

ii) $x = 51.5°$ $y = 64°$

b) $x + 2y = 51 + 2 \times 64 = 179$.

c)   Due to both x and y having been rounded down.

A5

The locus will follow the dotted line shown in Fig. 8.50.

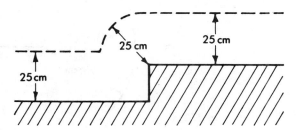

Fig. 8.50

You do need to find the centre when the wheel has just touched the step for the first time, since that is where the locus changes from the straight line to the curve, of the centre top vertex of the step.

A6

a)   i) $90°$ ii) $180 - \left(\dfrac{360}{6}\right) = 120°$

 iii) $360° - (90 + 120) = 150°$.

b)   i) Because they fit together forming a regular shape where the inside edges are a regular polygon of exterior angles shown in Fig. 8.51, and thirty is a factor of 360, hence they will all fit together with $\dfrac{360}{30} = 12$ so 12 edges are needed, hence 6 tiles are being used.

 ii) The polygon has $\dfrac{360}{30} = 12$ sides.

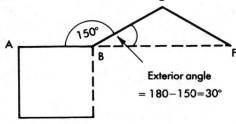

Fig. 8.51

A7

a)   i) $52°$ (alternate segment theorem).
 ii) $47°$ (alternate segment theorem).
 iii) $180 - (52 + 47) = 81°$ (CBA and BCD being allied angles).

b)   Angle $DAB = 180 - (52 + 47) = 81°$ (angles on a line add up to 180). Hence angle $DAB =$ angle CBA, and triangle EBA is isosceles.

c)   If $EC:CB = 2:3$ then $EC:(EC + CB) = 2:5$. So the ratio of the lengths of $\triangle ECD$ and $\triangle EBA$ is $2:5$, and the ratio of the triangles is $2^2:5^2 = 4:25$,

 hence $\dfrac{\text{area of } \triangle ECD}{\text{area of } \triangle EBA} = \dfrac{4}{25}$

A8

a)   Consider triangles POB and POA.
 both $\angle B$ and $\angle A$ are right angles (PB and PA being perpendicular to radii)
 both OB and OA are radii, hence equal.
 PO is common to both triangles.
 hence Right Angle, Side, Side illustrate congruent triangles.
 Hence $PA = PB$ (corresponding sides).

b) $\angle BPA + \theta = 180°$ (angles on a line); $\angle BPA + \angle BOA = 180$ ($360° - 90 - 90$)
 hence $\angle BPA + \theta = \angle BPA + \angle BOA \Rightarrow \angle BOA = \theta$.

A9

a)   See Fig. 8.52.

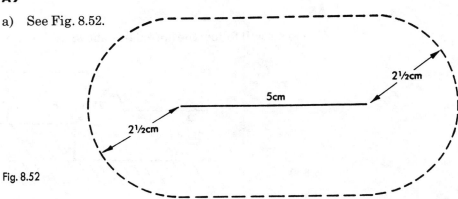

Fig. 8.52

b)   At each end the shape will be one half of a hemisphere of radius 10 km, then between them will be half a cylinder with regular cross section being a semicircle of radius 10 km.

c) Consider the semicircle cross section of the middle, shown in Fig. 8.53. The dotted line represents the limit of the unsafe area.

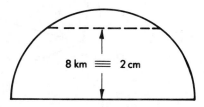

Fig. 8.53

8 km ≡ 2 cm

Consider the front elevation of the atmospheric 'shape' shown in Fig. 8.54. Again the dotted line indicates the limit of the unsafe area.

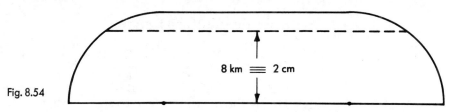

Fig. 8.54

8 km ≡ 2 cm

So on the plan of the shape, by using the end and front elevations, you can fix the bounds of this region, as shown in Fig. 8.55.

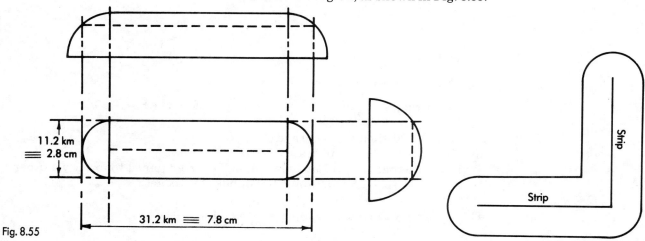

11.2 km ≡ 2.8 cm

31.2 km ≡ 7.8 cm

Fig. 8.55

Strip

Strip

d) See Fig. 8.56.   Fig. 8.56

A10

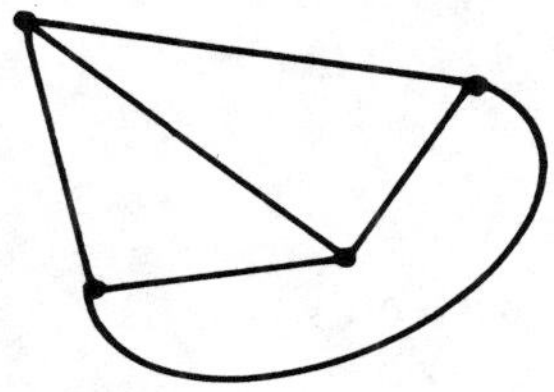

a) See Fig. 8.57
   i) $V = 4, R = 4, E = 6$.   ii) 3
   iii) $4 + 4 - 6 = 2$. Yes.   iv) 3

b) i) Each vertex has 3 edges coming from it, so you would have $E = 3V$, but each edge is joined to 2 edges, hence you halve the total number of edges, so $E = \dfrac{3V}{2}$ (see Fig. 8.58).

Fig. 8.57

ii) Since 4 edges bound each region, then this would give $E = 4R$, but each edge is used to form two regions, hence $E = \dfrac{4R}{2}$ which gives $E = 2R$.

iii) Using $V + R - E = 2$ and $E = \dfrac{3V}{2} \rightarrow V = \dfrac{2E}{3}$

and $E = 2R \rightarrow R = \frac{1}{2}E$.

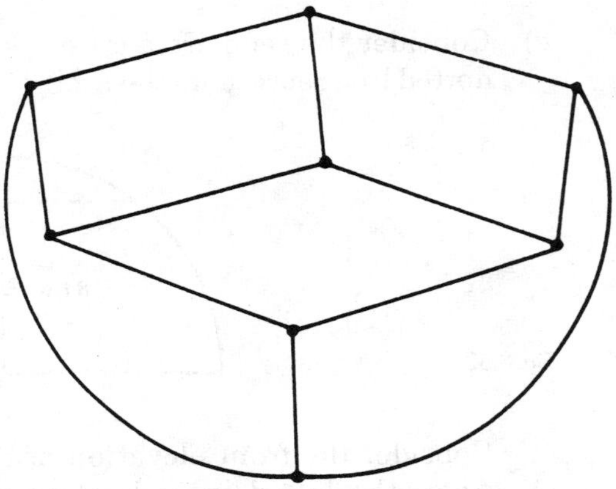

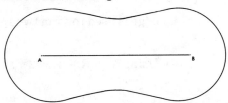

Fig. 8.58

Substitute for V and R gives

$$\frac{2E}{3} + \frac{1E}{2} - E = 2 \rightarrow \frac{7E}{6} - E = 2 \rightarrow \frac{E}{6} = 2 \rightarrow E = 12.$$

If E = 12, then V = 8 and R = 6.

iv) This is the drawing given to start with, which is possibly the best way to start the problem!

c) i) By following the pattern found in the last part, here you would get

$$E = \frac{4V}{2} \rightarrow E = 2V$$

and $E = \frac{5R}{2}$

ii) From Euler's rule V + R − E = 2.

Substitute $V = \frac{E}{2}$ and $R = \frac{2E}{5} \rightarrow \frac{E}{2} + \frac{2E}{5} - E = 2 \rightarrow E = -20.$

If E = −20, then V = −10 and R = −8.

iii) That it is impossible to draw.

d) Trying to do that is to try and make i) each vertex joined to exactly 4 other vertices and so each region would be bounded by 3 edges.

This will imply the relationship $E = \frac{4V}{2}$ and $E = \frac{3R}{2}$.

So solving V + R − E = 2 when E = 2V and $E = \frac{3R}{2}$

$$\rightarrow V = \frac{1E}{2} \text{ and } R = \frac{2E}{3}.$$

Substituting gives us $\frac{1E}{2} + \frac{2E}{3} - E = 2 \rightarrow \frac{7E}{6} - E = 2$

$$\rightarrow E = 12.$$

E = 12 → R = 8 and V = 6.

So you need 6 vertices to do this and so it is impossible with only 5.

A11

a) Using pairs of numbers like (2, 10), (10, 2), (4, 5), (5, 4), $(2\frac{1}{2}, 8)$, $(8, 2\frac{1}{2})$, etc. you should end up with a locus like Fig. 8.59.

Fig. 8.59

b) See Fig. 8.60.   c) See Fig. 8.61.

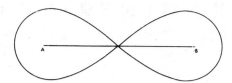   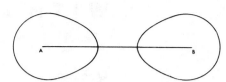

Fig. 8.60   Fig. 8.61

d)   i) All have 2 lines of symmetry, one along the line AB, the other along the perpendicular bisector of AB.
     ii) Rotational symmetry of order 2 about the midpoint of line AB.
         (All rectangles (that are not squares) have the same properties.)

e)   i) $8 - x$.
     ii) Since PA × PB = K, where PA = x and PB = $8 - x$
         then $x(8 - x) = K \rightarrow 8x - x^2 = K \rightarrow 0 = K - 8x + x^2$
         $\rightarrow x^2 - 8x + K = 0$.
    iii) When K = 16
         $$x^2 - 8x + 16 = 0 \rightarrow (x - 4)(x - 4) = 0$$
         $$\rightarrow x = 4.$$
         When K = 15
         $$x^2 - 8x + 15 = 0 \rightarrow (x - 3)(x - 5) = 0$$
         $$\rightarrow x = 3 \text{ and } x = 5$$
     iv) When K = 20
         $$x^2 - 8x + 20 = 0.$$

         If we tried to solve by using the formula $x = \dfrac{-b \pm \sqrt{b^2 - 4ac}}{2a}$

         where $a = 1, b = -8, c = 20,$

         then $x = \dfrac{8 \pm \sqrt{(64 - 80)}}{2}$

         But note $\sqrt{-16}$ is impossible, hence there is no solution.
      v) The solutions to $x^2 - 8x + K = 0$ are the possible distances AP where P is the point that the loci cross AB.
         Each different value of K here gives a different type of quadratic equation.
         When K = 16, the equation has only one solution, hence the loci only cross AB once.
         When K = 15, the equation has two solutions, hence the loci cross AB twice.
         When K = 20, the equation has no solutions, hence the loci do not cross AB at all.

GRADE CHECKLIST

For a grade B you should:

Be able to: Remember the angle rules and which equal which!
                 Recognise loci.

For a grade A you should also:

Understand: The intersecting chord theorem
                 Congruent triangles

For a grade A* you should also:

Know and use: Angle and tangent properties of circles.

A STUDENT'S ANSWER
WITH EXAMINER'S COMMENTS

Question

The diagram, which is drawn to a scale of 1 cm to represent 1 m shows a rod OA of length 3 m which is pivoted at a point O on a horizontal table so that it can rotate in a vertical plane. A light is positioned at L, 5 m vertically above O, as a result of which the rod casts a shadow OP on the table.

When the size of angle LOA is $x°$, the length of the shadow OP is y metres.

By drawing different positions of OA and measuring, construct a table of possible values of y against x for $0 \leqslant x \leqslant 90$. Draw a graph to show how y varies as x increases from 0 to 90 and hence determine the greatest possible value of y.

> Good to see the systematic approach of measuring every 10°

> The table confirms the correct approach to the problem, but the accuracy could be better as the graph indicates.

> From this graph the answer is correct and would gain credit.

> The points have been plotted correctly and the axes are just what was asked for — well done. The funny dip at $x = 50°$ should have indicated an error and this particular piece of data should have been checked.

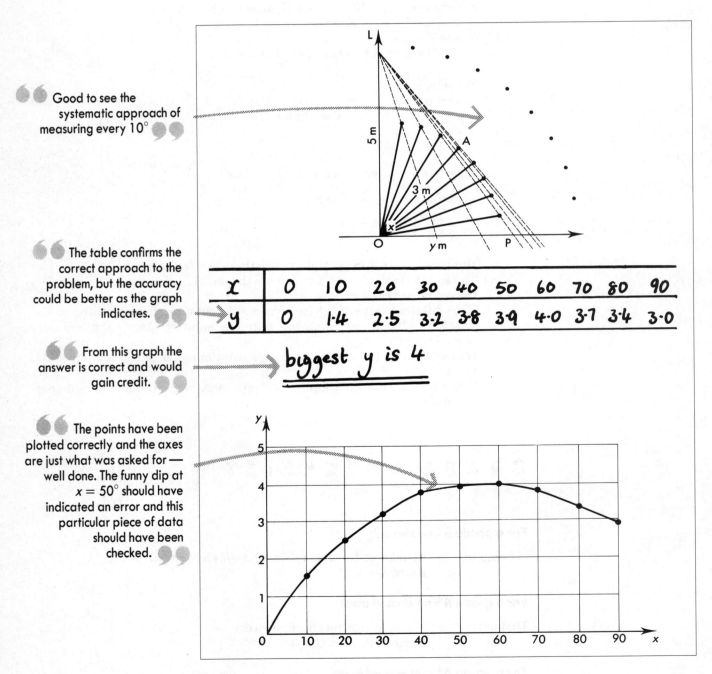

x	0	10	20	30	40	50	60	70	80	90
y	0	1·4	2·5	3·2	3·8	3·9	4·0	3·7	3·4	3·0

biggest y is 4

> Poor drawing resulted in wrong information being used and lost marks. (The correct answer should be 3.75 cm, try and show this to yourself.)

MENSURATION

GETTING STARTED

This topic is all about calculating lengths, areas and volumes of given shapes and solids, or even distances from one place to another. It is a vital link between arithmetic and algebra. In the vast majority of cases you will need a *formula* to substitute into. These formulae are best learned, then you will have the confidence that you are armed with the right equipment for problem solving. At the Higher Level of GCSE mathematics a lot of the problems to solve are 3D situations in which you have to think abstractly about the situation.

There will be many questions set in your mathematics examination that relate to this chapter.

USEFUL DEFINITIONS

Arc	Part of the circumference of a circle.
Area	Flat space included in a boundary.
Adjacent	The side of a triangle next to the angle concerned and the right angle.
Depression (angle of)	The angle measured below the horizon.
Elevation (angle of)	The angle measured above the horizon.
Hypotenuse	The longest side of a right angled triangle.
Opposite	The side of a triangle opposite the angle concerned.
Perimeter	The length around all the outside of a flat shape.
Sector	The area of a circle bounded by two radii and the circumference.
Volume	The space inside a 3 dimensional shape.

E S S E N T I A L   P R I N C I P L E S

| 1 | PERIMETER |

It is essential that you understand the meaning of *perimeter*; it is the total outside length of a flat shape. The one formula you must learn is the perimeter of a circle, which is given by:

circumference = π × diameter of circle   or   C = πD.

| 2 | AREA |

You must *learn* the following facts:

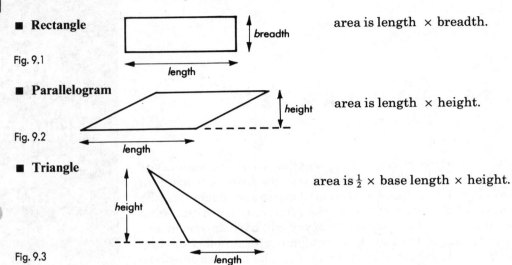

■ **Rectangle**   area is length × breadth.

Fig. 9.1

■ **Parallelogram**   area is length × height.

Fig. 9.2

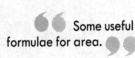

Some useful formulae for area.

■ **Triangle**   area is $\frac{1}{2}$ × base length × height.

Fig. 9.3

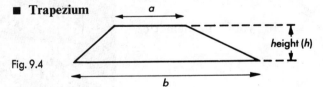

■ **Trapezium**   area is $\frac{1}{2}$ × height × sum of
                                 parallel lengths = $\frac{h}{2}(a + b)$.

Fig. 9.4

■ **Circle**   area is πr^2.

Fig. 9.5

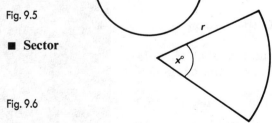

■ **Sector**   area is $\dfrac{x}{360}\pi r^2$

Do try to learn them, it saves a lot of time and helps you to see the solution more clearly.

Fig. 9.6

Although some of these will be on a formula sheet, it will give you much more confidence if you know them and are familiar with them all.

| 3 | VOLUME |

You should be familiar with the following two formulae for finding *volumes*. In an examination a formula might well be given, but it will help you to have more confidence and to see what is the appropriate method to use if you actually know these formulae yourself.

Prisms

Many of our regular mathematical shapes are *prisms*, and the volume of any prism is found by:

Volume = length × (regular cross sectional area)

In a prism the regular cross section is the same as the area of the end, hence the formula is perhaps better remembered as volume = length × end area.

Pyramids

The volume of any pyramid or cone is given by:

Volume = (height × base area) ÷ 3.

WORKED EXAMPLE 1

The cone shape in Fig. 9.7 is full of water. The water is poured into the cup shown next to it. What will be the depth of water in the cup?

Volume of water in the cone = $\frac{1}{3} \times 8 \times$ end area = $\frac{1}{3} \times 8 \times \pi \times 3^2 = 24\pi$ (I keep it in terms of π as I do not want to have to do any rounding off until the very end of the question). The volume of water inside the cup is given by

(end area) × height = $\pi \times 2.5^2 \times h$

but as the volume we are interested in is 24π then we can set up the equation

$\pi \times 2.5^2 \times h = 24\pi$

$$\to h = \frac{24\pi}{\pi \times 2.5^2} = 3.84$$

Hence the depth of water will be 3.8 cm.

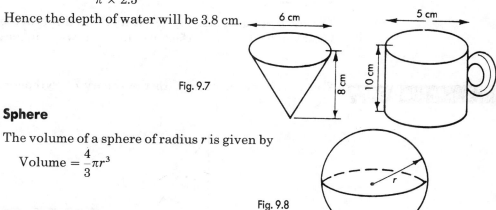

Fig. 9.7

Sphere

The volume of a sphere of radius r is given by

$$\text{Volume} = \frac{4}{3}\pi r^3$$

Fig. 9.8

EXERCISE 1

Into a cone shaped cornet of diameter 5 cm and a height of 12 cm, was placed a sphere of ice cream of diameter 5 cm. It melted, yet all stayed inside the cone. What depth of the cone was filled with the melted ice cream? (Assume the melted ice cream will have the same volume as the frozen ice cream.)

Fig. 9.9

4 ▷ SURFACE AREA

There is no regular pattern here to follow, so use your mathematical wits and common sense, being sure to remember the surface areas of the tops and bottoms. Outlined below are some particular solids and how to find their total surface area.

■ **Cylinder**

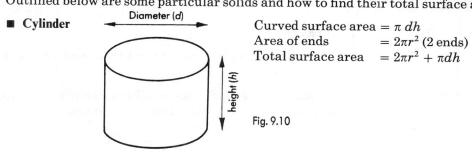

Curved surface area = πdh
Area of ends = $2\pi r^2$ (2 ends)
Total surface area = $2\pi r^2 + \pi dh$

Fig. 9.10

■ **Sphere**

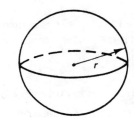

Fig. 9.11

Surface area $= 4\pi r^2$

■ **Cone**

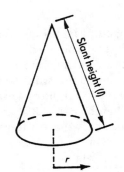

Curved surface area $= \pi\,rl$
Area of end $\quad = \pi r^2$
Total surface area $\quad = \pi r^2 + \pi rl$

Fig. 9.12

EXERCISE 2

The earth has a diameter of 12 762 km. Two thirds of the earth is covered by water. What will be the total surface area of all the water in the seas and lakes in the world?

5 > PYTHAGORAS

You should be familiar with the theory of Pythagoras, which is illustrated in Fig. 9.13.

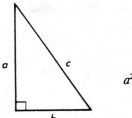

Fig. 9.13

$$a^2 + b^2 = c^2$$

WORKED EXAMPLE 2

The regular octagon in Fig. 9.14, of side 13 cm, was being cut out of a square piece of card. What is the smallest sized piece of card that this could be?

Fig. 9.14

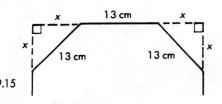

Fig. 9.15

Consider one end of the card, the corners cut off form a right angled triangle with the hypotenuse 13 cm and the smaller sides the same length of x, as in Fig. 9.15.

Hence $x^2 + x^2 = 13^2$ $\quad 2x^2 = 169$ $\quad x^2 = 84.5$ $\quad x = 9.2$ cm.

So the length of the square will be $13 + (2 \times 9.2) = 31.4$ cm.

EXERCISE 3

Draw a right angled triangle and then construct a semi-circle on each side, as in Fig. 9.16.

i) See if the area of the two smaller semi-circles add up to the area of the large one.
ii) Do you think this will always be the case?

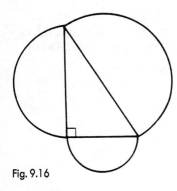

Fig. 9.16

6 ▷ TRIGONOMETRY

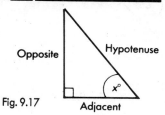

Fig. 9.17

You must be familiar with the simple trig' ratios found in right angled triangles, illustrated in Fig. 9.17.

$$\tan x = \frac{\text{opposite}}{\text{adjacent}} \qquad \sin x = \frac{\text{opposite}}{\text{hypotenuse}} \qquad \cos x = \frac{\text{adjacent}}{\text{hypotenuse}}$$

Note, we use the abbreviated form of the trigonometrical ratios of:

tan . . . for tangent
sin . . . for sine
cos . . . for cosine
and trig . . . for trigonometry

> No one gets a grade A without being able to do trigonometry, so do try to take it all in and learn as much off by heart as you can.

You must be able to recognise when trig is needed and be able to quickly recognise which of the trig ratios to use, tan, sin or cos. You will need to use trig if you wish to find:

angles from information about lengths
or lengths from information about angles and length.

You need to be familiar with the above trig ratios to enable you to go straight to the correct trig ratio. Try the following way of spotting which is needed from the involved sides:

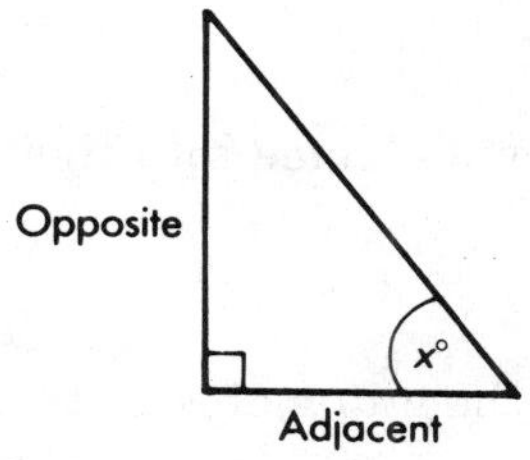

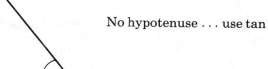

Fig. 9.18

No hypotenuse . . . use tan

Angle 'cosy' between two sides . . . use cos

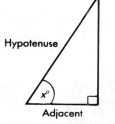

Fig. 9.19

Side next to angles (adjacent) not involved . . . use sin

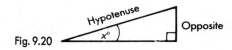

Fig. 9.20

Use any way of being able to recognise which to use, but do find one that *you* can remember. (Try 'Tommy On A Ship Of His Caught All Herring'.)

The way you set out your trig questions can lose you marks, so do be careful, set out correctly, use correct trig statements, and unless told otherwise 'round off to one more significant figure than the given information'.

WORKED EXAMPLE 3

In Fig. 9.21, calculate x.

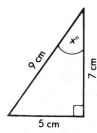

$\text{Cos } x = \dfrac{7}{9} = 0.777$. (Use INV cos or $\cos^{-1}$ on your calculator.)

$x = 39°$.

Fig. 9.21

WORKED EXAMPLE 4

In Fig. 9.22, find x.

$\dfrac{x}{5} = \tan 70 \rightarrow x = 5 \tan 70$

$x = 13.7$ cm.

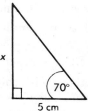

Fig. 9.22

**WORKED
EXAMPLE 5**

In Fig. 9.23, find x.

$\dfrac{4}{x} = \sin 65 \rightarrow \dfrac{4}{\sin 65} = x$

$x = 4.41$ cm.

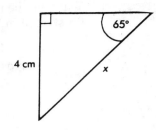

Fig. 9.23

Note the kind of information that you need to write down as your solution, it's not much but it's vital to be correct. At this high level, you will lose marks for not writing down your trig statements as above . . . be warned!

EXERCISE 4

A regular pentagon is drawn inside a circle of radius 8 cm. Find the length of one straight edge of the pentagon.

SPECIAL TRIG FACTS

You may have discovered the following facts in your coursework; if not then try yourself to show that they are true:

$$\tan x = \frac{\sin x}{\cos x} \text{ and } (\sin x)^2 + (\cos x)^2 = 1.$$

At this stage, these facts do not have a lot of use, but they do 'come into their own' at A level—look out for them.

**7   TRIGONO-
METRICAL
GRAPHS**

You need to be able to recognise the special features about the *graph* of each trig function, so that you can sketch them when necessary.

THE SINE CURVE

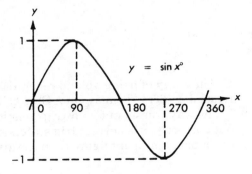

Fig. 9.24

In Fig. 9.24, see how the sine of angles between 0 and 180 are positive, and the sine of angles between 180 and 360 are negative.

**WORKED
EXAMPLE 6**

Solve the equation $\sin x = 0.5$ $(0 < x < 180)$.
Using $\sin^{-1} x$ on the calculator gives $x = 30°$, but look at the graph and you will see that there are two angles with a sine of 0.5. One is 30° (check with the calculator). Now, from the symmetry of the graph you can see that the other angle will be $(180 - 30)$ which is 150°.

Hence $x = 30°$ and $x = 150°$.

Check then from the graph that:

for $0 < x \leqslant 180$ $\sin (180 - x) = \sin x$.
for $180 < x \leqslant 360$ $\sin (180 + x) = -\sin x$.

Play about with these two facts on your calculator and show to yourself that they are true. They are difficult facts to learn, but if you learn the shape of the sine curve and its main points then you can always work them out again for yourself.

Sketch the graph of $y = \sin 3x$ $\qquad 0 < x < 180$
A table of values can be built as in Fig. 9.25.

x	0	30	60	90	120	150	180
$3x$	0	90	180	270	360	450	540
$y = \sin 3x$	0	1	0	−1	0	1	0

Fig. 9.25

Sketched smoothly this gives Fig. 9.26.

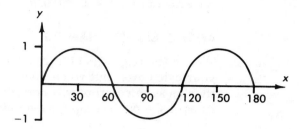

Fig. 9.26

EXERCISE 5

Sketch the graph of $y = 3 \sin x$.

Similar facts and statements can be made about cos and tan. Follow through them now.

THE COSINE CURVE

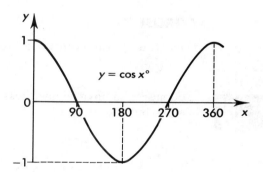

Fig. 9.27

In Fig. 9.27, see how the cosine of angles between 0 and 90, or 270 and 360 are positive, and of angles between 90 and 270 are negative.
From the symmetry of the graph: $\cos(180 - x) = -\cos x$
$$\cos(180 + x) = -\cos x$$
$$\cos(360 - x) = \cos x$$

NB. The sine curve and the cosine curve are exactly the same shape, where the graph of cos x is just the same as sin x moved down (i.e. to left) 90°.

THE TANGENT CURVES

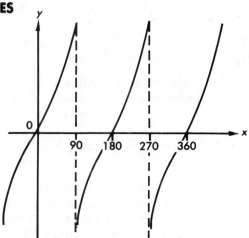

Fig. 9.28

Notice that Fig. 9.28 is a series of parallel curves with what we call 'asymptotes' at $x = 90$ and 270. (But more of that at A level.) It is quite different from the sin and cos curves, yet it still has symmetry to enable us to see that

$$\tan (180 - x) = -\tan x$$
$$\tan (180 + x) = \tan x.$$

EXERCISE 6

Sketch the graphs of $y = \cos 2x$ and $y = \tan x$ to estimate a solution to $\cos 2x = \tan x$. $0 < x < 180$.

ANGLES BIGGER THAN 90°

To find the trig ratio of angles bigger than 90° just press the correct buttons on your calculator, but when given a ratio and you are asked for possible angles, then most calculators will not tell you. You need either to remember the above rules or sketch the graph to remind you.

Solve the equation $\cos x = 0.8.$ $(0 < x < 360)$.
On the calculator $\cos^{-1} 0.8 = 36.9°$.
Also, $\cos (360 - x) = \cos x$, hence where $x = 36.9°$; another solution is $(360 - 36.9)$, which is $323.1°$. So $x = 36.9°$ and $323.1°$.
(You can always easily check the solutions by the use of cos on the calculator.)

EXERCISE 7

Solve the equation $\tan x = 2$ $(0 < x < 360)$.

You may also have come across the *sine rule* as a piece of coursework; it is a very simple, but useful, fact.

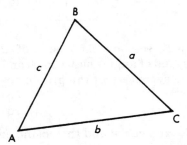

Fig. 9.29

For *any* triangle (label as in Fig. 9.29), then:

Learn the sine rule.

$$\frac{a}{\sin A} = \frac{b}{\sin B} = \frac{c}{\sin C} = 2R$$

(where R is the radius of the circumscribed circle, that is the circle that will touch each vertex of the triangle ABC).
Sometimes it is more useful to look at the rule the other way round, that is:

$$\frac{\sin A}{c} = \frac{\sin B}{b} = \frac{\sin C}{c} = \frac{1}{2R}$$

You use the *sine rule* when
    i) you have *not* got a right angle
    ii) you have actual information about one side and its opposite angle
    iii) you have actual information about either one more side or angle.

| WORKED EXAMPLE 9 | In Fig. 9.30, find x.
Use the sine rule and start with what it is you are looking for. |

So $\dfrac{x}{\sin C} = \dfrac{a}{\sin A} \rightarrow \dfrac{x}{\sin 41} = \dfrac{8}{\sin 63}$

$\rightarrow x = \dfrac{8 \times \sin 41}{\sin 63} = 5.9$ cm.

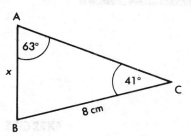

Fig. 9.30

| WORKED EXAMPLE 10 | In Fig. 9.31, find angle x. |

Apply the sine rule to give $\dfrac{\sin x}{15} = \dfrac{\sin 31}{8}$

$\rightarrow \sin x = \dfrac{15 \sin 31}{8} = 0.9657$

giving $x = 74.9°$ or $(180 - 74.9)$
$\qquad x = 74.9°$ or $105.1°$

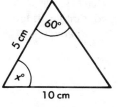

Fig. 9.31

Note: there are sometimes two possible solutions from the sine rule.

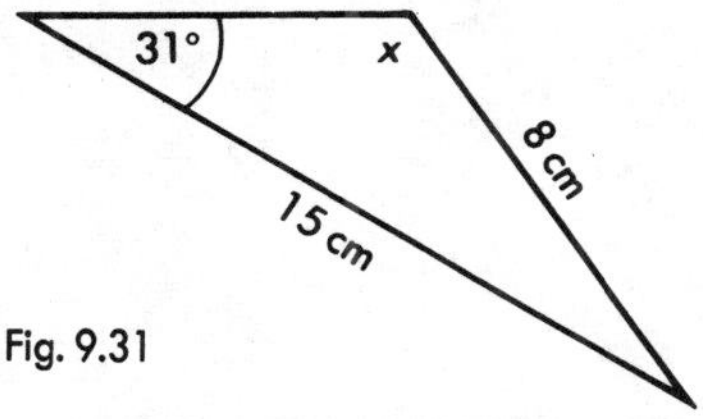

| WORKED EXAMPLE 11 | In Fig. 9.32 find $x°$. |

We cannot go straight to x here but to the other unknown angle, let's call it y, then apply

the sine rule: $\dfrac{\sin y}{5} = \dfrac{\sin 60}{10}$

$\rightarrow \sin y = \dfrac{5 \sin 60}{10} = 0.4330$

Fig. 9.32

$\rightarrow \qquad y = 25.7$ or $(180 - 25.7) = 154.3$

Since one angle is already given as $60°$, then another angle cannot be 154.3, since $60 + 154.3 > 180$.
Hence $y = 25.7$ and so $x = 180 - (60 + 25.7)$
$\qquad\qquad x = 94.3°$.

EXERCISE 8

In Fig. 9.33, find the length of the side marked x.

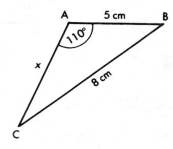

Fig. 9.33

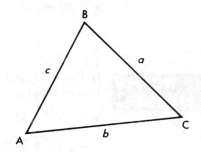

Fig. 9.34

AREA OF TRIANGLES BY SINE RULE

The *area* of any triangle can be found by one of the formulae:
$\qquad$ Area $= \frac{1}{2}ab \sin C$
or Area $= \frac{1}{2}bc \sin A$
or Area $= \frac{1}{2}ac \sin B$.
You can use the sine rule for area of triangle when you know two sides and the angle in between them (the *included* angle).

WORKED EXAMPLE 12

In Fig. 9.35, find the area of triangle ABC.
Use the sine rule as: Area $= \frac{1}{2} \times 4 \times 5 \times \sin 120 = 8.7 \text{ cm}^2$.

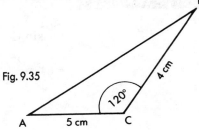

Fig. 9.35

EXERCISE 9

Find the area of the triangle ABC in Fig. 9.36.

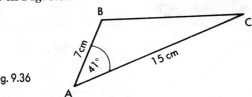

Fig. 9.36

9 > THE COSINE RULE

Don't use this on a right angled triangle, its too heavy!

This rule appears in two different forms and we use each one depending on whether we are calculating a side or an angle.

1 TO FIND A SIDE

If, as in the 'sine area rule', we are given two sides and the included angle, then we can use the *cosine rule* as:

$$a = \sqrt{b^2 + c^2 - 2bc \cos A}$$

$$\text{or } b = \sqrt{a^2 + c^2 - 2ac \cos B}$$

$$\text{or } c = \sqrt{a^2 + b^2 - 2ab \cos C}$$

Fig. 9.37

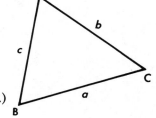

(Look at the pattern of what is given and how you use it.)

WORKED EXAMPLE 13

In Fig. 9.38, find x.
Use the cosine rule as:

$$x = \sqrt{(6^2 + 7^2 - 2 \times 6 \times 7 \times \cos 65)}$$

$$= \sqrt{(49.5)}$$

$$x = 7.0 \text{ cm}.$$

Fig. 9.38

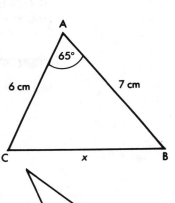

WORKED EXAMPLE 14

In Fig. 9.39, find x.
Use the cosine rule as

$$x = \sqrt{(3^2 + 5^2 - 2 \times 3 \times 5 \times \cos 115)}$$

$$= \sqrt{(46.678548)}$$

$$x = 6.8 \text{ cm}.$$

Fig. 9.39

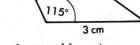

(Note the cos 115 was negative, but should have caused no problems.)

EXERCISE 10

In Fig. 9.40, find x.

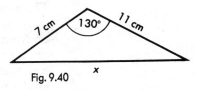

Fig. 9.40

2 TO FIND AN ANGLE

When you know **all** the three sides of a triangle you can use this form of the cosine rule to find any angle:

> Using the cosine rule to find an angle.

$$\cos A = \frac{b^2 + c^2 - a^2}{2bc}$$

or $\cos B = \dfrac{a^2 + c^2 - b^2}{2ac}$

or $\cos C = \dfrac{a^2 + b^2 - c^2}{2ab}$

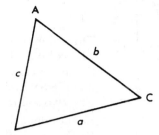

Fig. 9.41

(Look at the pattern of each one and learn the pattern.)

WORKED EXAMPLE 15

In Fig. 9.42, find the size of angle A.

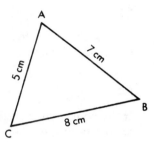

Fig. 9.42

WORKED EXAMPLE 16

Use the Cosine Rule to give $\cos A = \dfrac{5^2 + 7^2 - 8^2}{2 \times 5 \times 7} = 0.1429$

giving $A = 81.8° = 82°$

In Fig. 9.43, find the size of angle B.

Use the Cosine Rule to give $\cos B = \dfrac{9^2 + 8^2 - 15^2}{2 \times 9 \times 8} = -0.5556$

giving $B = 123.7° = 124°$.

(Note that if the cosine works out to be negative, the angle will be obtuse.)

EXERCISE 11

In the triangle ABC in Fig. 9.44 calculate the size of the
  i) smallest angle
  ii) largest angle.

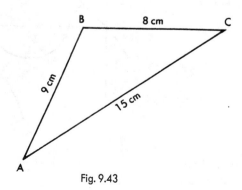

Fig. 9.43

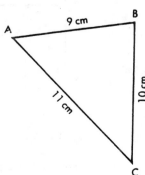

Fig. 9.44

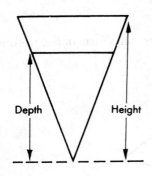

Fig. 9.45

SOLUTIONS TO EXERCISES

S1

The volume of ice cream is given by $\frac{4}{3}\pi r^3 = \frac{4}{3}\pi \times (2.5)^3 = 65.4$ cm^3.
The volume of the cone is given by $\frac{1}{3}\pi r^2 h = \frac{1}{3}\pi \times (2.5)^2 \times 12 = 78.5$ cm^3.
So the ratio of volume between the melted ice cream and the cone is given by 65.4 : 78.5 which is 0.8331 : 1.
The two volumes are similar shapes (see Fig. 9.45) with volume ratio of 0.8331 : 1, hence a length ratio of $\sqrt[3]{0.8331} : 1$ which is 0.941 : 1.
So the depth of ice cream will be $12 \times 0.941 = 11.3$ cm.

S2

Surface area of earth given by $4\pi r^2 = 4 \times \pi \times (6381)^2$.
So two thirds will be given by $\frac{2}{3} \times 4 \times \pi \times (6381)^2 = 3.4 \times 10^8$ km^2.

S3

i) Yes, they should do: ii) Yes, it will always be the case.

S4

If the pentagon is divided into triangles, then the angle of each triangle at the centre, O, of the circle will be $360 \div 5 = 72°$ (see Fig. 9.46). The right angled triangle as shown in the diagram can be formed where $x = 72 \div 2 = 36°$ and its base length, y, is half the side, d, of the pentagon.
Hence $y = 8 \sin 36°$
and so $d = 2 \times 8 \times \sin 36 = 9.4$ cm.

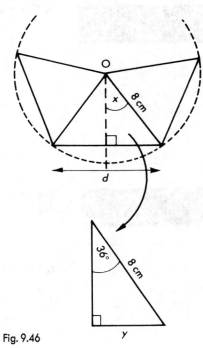

Fig. 9.46

S5

See Fig. 9.47.

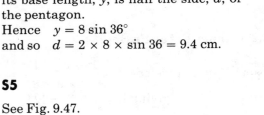

Fig. 9.47

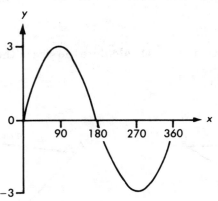

Fig. 9.48

S6

See Fig. 9.48. The intersection will be the solution of approximately $x = 29°$.

S7

Tan $x = 2$ $x = 63.4$ and $180 + 63.4 = 243.4$

(In any question like this you can always test your answers by finding their tangents on the calculator and checking that indeed they are equal to what you started with.)

S8

Since the information given (see Fig. 9.49) is an angle and its opposite side, no right angle or another side, then first find angle C. Here I use the sine rule as:

$$\frac{\sin C}{5} = \frac{\sin 110}{8} \rightarrow \sin C = \frac{5 \sin 110}{8} = 0.5873$$

$$\rightarrow C = 36°.$$

Then angle B $= 180 - (110 + 36) = 34°$.

Use sine rule again to give $\dfrac{x}{\sin B} = \dfrac{8}{\sin 110}$

$$\rightarrow x = \frac{8 \sin 34}{\sin 110} = 4.8 \text{ cm}$$

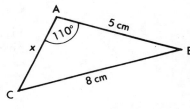

Fig. 9.49

S9

Area $= \frac{1}{2} \times 7 \times 15 \times \sin 41 = 34.4 \text{ cm}^2$.

S10

Use cosine rule to give $x = \sqrt{(11^2 + 7^2 - 2 \times 11 \times 7 \times \cos 130)}$

$$= \sqrt{(121 + 49 + 99)} = \sqrt{269}$$

$$x = 16.4 \text{ cm}.$$

(The most common mistake is to forget to square root, but if you are in the correct habit of checking that your answers are sensible then you will spot that error.)

S11

The smallest angle is always opposite the smallest length and similarly, the largest angle is opposite the largest length. Hence smallest angle is opposite the smallest side of 9, hence C. This is found by the cosine rule as:

$$\cos C = \frac{a^2 + b^2 - c^2}{2ab} \rightarrow \cos C = \frac{10^2 + 11^2 - 9^2}{2 \times 10 \times 11} = 0.6364$$

$$\rightarrow C = 50.5°.$$

The largest angle is opposite 11, the largest side, hence B. This also is found by the cosine rule to give B $= 70.5°$.

EXAMINATION TYPE QUESTIONS

> Always round off your answers to a suitable degree of accuracy. If in doubt, round off to one more significant figure than the numbers given in the problem.

Q1

Find the value of x such that $90 < x < 180$ and $\sin x° = 0.4567$.   (NEAB)

Q2

Fig 9.50 shows a metal plate with four quadrants of a circle cut away at the corners. Calculate:

a)   the radius of the circle of which the quadrants are a part,
b)   the total area cut away.   (NISEAC)

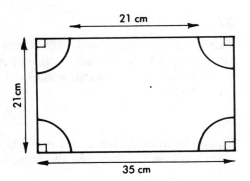

Fig. 9.50

Q3

Figure 9.51 shows that airport A is 400 km from airport B on a bearing of 120°. An aircraft leaves A at 2155 hours to fly to B. Its speed over the ground is 320 km/h.

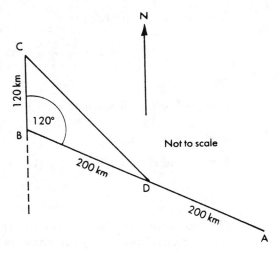

Fig. 9.51

a) Calculate the time at which the aircraft is expected to arrive at B.
b) When the aircraft is at D, halfway between A and B, it is diverted to airport C because of fog at airport B. Airport C is 120 km due North of B.
  i) Calculate the distance from D to C.
  ii) Calculate the bearing of C from D.
  iii) The point on the aircraft's path nearest to B is X. Calculate the distance of X from B.   (MEG)

Q4

(In this question, give all distances to the nearest 0.01 km and all angles to the nearest one-tenth of a degree.)

Figure 9.52 represents three villages A, B and C on a hillside. A, C and N are the same height above sea level and N is vertically below B. Angle CAB is 90° and angle BAN is 2.5°. The villages are linked by three straight roads AB, AC and CB, where AB = 8 km and AC = 12 km.

Calculate a) the height of B above N,   b) the horizontal distance AN,
c) the horizontal distance CN,   d) the angle of elevation of B from C.   (ULEAC)

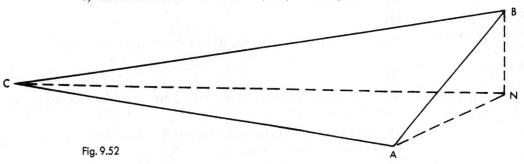

Fig. 9.52

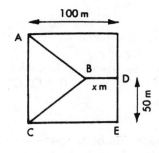

Fig. 9.53

Q5

A field 100 metres square is divided into two trapeziums and a triangle, as shown in Fig. 9.53. BD is x metres long.

a) What is the perpendicular distance from B to AC in terms of x?
b) What is the area of triangle ABC in terms of x?
c) What is the area of trapezium CBDE in terms of x?
d) Each of the three parts of the field has the same area. What is the length of BD? (WJEC)

Q6

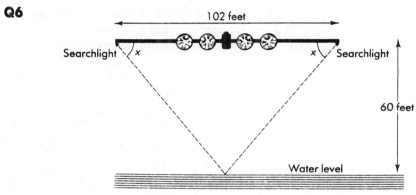

Fig. 9.54

In 1943 the Royal Air Force had to fly an aeroplane at exactly 60 feet above the water level.

To do this two searchlights were fitted, one at the end of each wing, so that they were 102 feet apart.

The rays shone down onto the water below. When the rays coincided on the surface of the water the pilot knew that he was flying at 60 feet above the water level.

Calculate the angle (marked x in the diagram), at which the searchlights had to be fitted to the aeroplane's wings. (NEAB)

Q7

Fig. 9.55

To estimate the volume of timber in the trunk of the conifer in Fig. 9.55, a pupil considered the trunk to be a cone and measured the circumference of the base to be 68 cm. To find the height she walked back 30 m from the base of the tree and took a sighting of the top of the tree. From her eye level (1.2 m above the ground) the angle of the elevation of the top of the tree was 26°.

a) Calculate the height of the tree.
b) Calculate the volume of timber (in m³) in the trunk of the tree. (NEAB)

Q8

A flat metal component is to be made in the shape shown in Fig. 9.56. The curves AB and DC are both arcs of circles with centre O. The radius of the arc AB is r, the radius of the arc DC is R. The angle AOB = 60°.

a) i) Write down a formula for the area of sector ODC in terms of R.
   ii) Show that the area of the shaded region ABCD is $\frac{1}{6}\pi(R^2 - r^2)$.

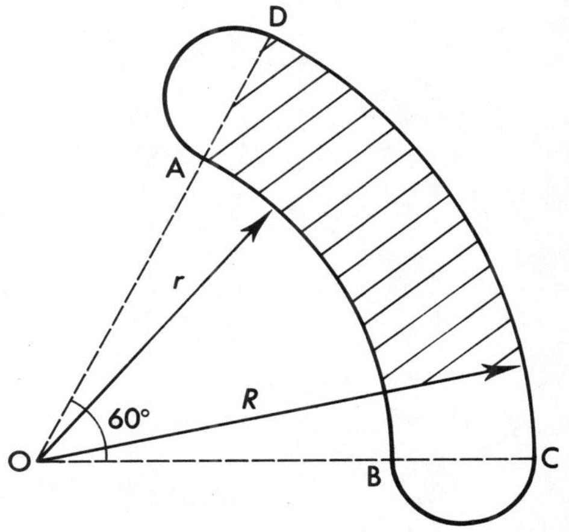

Fig. 9.56

The unshaded ends of the shape are both semi-circles.

b) i) Write down the length of the diameter BC in terms of R and r.
    ii) Find the total area of the two semicircles in terms of R and r.

c) Find the area, in mm², to the nearest mm², of metal sheet required to make
    the component when OD = 39 mm and OA = 27 mm. (ULEAC)

Q9

The box for a chocolate mint is a square-based pyramid with its point vertically
above the middle of the base, as in Fig. 9.57. The sides of the base of the box are
6 cm long and the box is 6 cm tall.

a) i) Calculate the diagonal distance across the base.
    ii) Calculate the length of a sloping edge.
b) Sketch a net for the box, indicating the lengths of the sides. (WJEC)

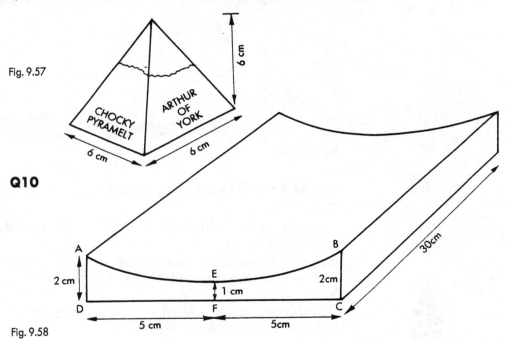

Fig. 9.57

Q10

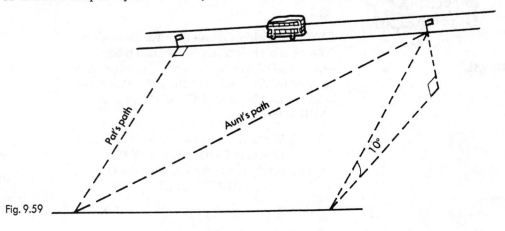

Fig. 9.58

Figure 9.58 shows a shallow glass dish of uniform cross-section. The dimensions of
the cross-section ABCD are as shown in the diagram.

a) The curve AEB is the arc of a circle. Find the radius of the circle.
b) Given that the length of the dish is 30 cm and that the mass of 1 cm³ of glass is
    2.45 g, find the mass of the dish. (WJEC)

Q11

A hillside slopes up at a steady 10° to the horizontal, as shown in Fig. 9.59.

Fig. 9.59

A horizontal road runs along the ridge at the top of the hill. Pat and her aunt want to walk up the hill to catch a bus which runs along the road. Pat takes the path which goes straight up the hill and meets the road at right angles; but her aunt prefers a gentler path which climbs at only 5° to the horizontal. Pat's path is 100 metres long. Calculate:

a) the height of the hill
b) the length of her aunt's path
c) the angle between their paths
d) how far apart they are when they reach the road.   (OCSEB)

Q12

a) Figure 9.60(a) shows a circle touching the sides of a square and a square drawn inside the circle with its vertices touching the circle at the mid-points of the sides of the outside square. Given that the radius of the circle is 1 cm find the perimeters of the two squares.
b)   i) Figure 9.60(b) is like Fig. 9.60(a), but regular octagons are drawn instead of squares. Find the perimeter of the two octagons.
     ii) What can you deduce from your results about the numerical value of π?
                                                                      (WJEC)

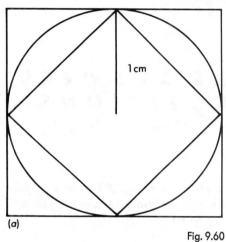
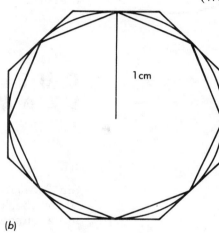

(a)   (b)

Fig. 9.60

Q13

In Fig. 9.61, AB is an arc of a circle, whose centre is at O. The radius is r, and the angle AOB is $x°$. Show that the length of the arc AB is given by the formula:

$$\text{arc length} = \frac{\pi}{180} xr.$$

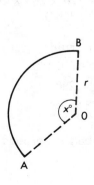

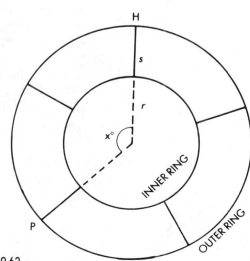

Fig. 9.61   Fig. 9.62

b) A housing estate has two circular roads with the same centre (the inner ring and the outer ring), with several radial roads joining them, as shown in Fig. 9.62. The inner ring has radius r metres, and the radial roads have length s metres, so that the outer ring has radius $(r + s)$ metres. My house H and the post office P are both on the outer ring, at the ends of radial roads. The angle between the radial roads leading to H and P is $x°$. Use the result in a) to write down formulas for the distance from H to P.

  i) if I go by the two radial roads and the inner ring,

  ii) if I go by the outer ring.

c) If $x = 120$, which of the distances is greater? By how much? (The answer may involve r or s, or both.)

d) Write down an equation if the two distances i) and ii) in b) are equal. Solve it to find x to the nearest whole number of degrees. What is surprising about the answer? (OCSEB)

Q14

Figure 9.63 shows a cone with circular base of radius 5 cm. The slant height of the cone is 20 cm. AB is a diameter of the base and V is the vertex of the cone. P is a point on VB such that VP:PB = 1:3. Find the shortest distance from A to P along the surface of the cone. (WJEC)

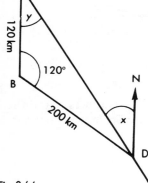

Fig. 9.63

OUTLINE ANSWERS TO EXAM QUESTIONS

A1

$\text{Sin}^{-1} 0.4567 = 27.2$, since $90 < x < 180$, then $x = 180 - 27.2 = 152.8°$.
(If you check this answer by finding sin 152.8, you will not get exactly 0.4567 since it is a rounded off answer.)

A2

a) Radius is $(35 - 21) \div 2 = 7$ cm.

b) Total area is a complete circle of radius 7 cm, which is 153.9 cm².

A3

a) Time = distance ÷ speed, hence the time of the journey is 400 km divided by 320 km/h to give 1.25 hours, that is 1 hour 15 minutes. So from 2155, add on 1 hour 15 minutes to get to 2310, which is 'ten past eleven'.

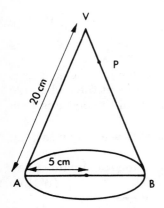

Fig. 9.64

b) i) Since we have two sides and an included angle, we use the cosine rule to give
$$CD = \sqrt{(120^2 + 200^2 - 2 \times 120 \times 200 \times \cos 120)} = 280 \text{ km}.$$

 ii) Bearing $= 360° - x°$ (see Fig. 9.64).

$x° = y°$ (alternate angles).

Hence find y and use the sine rule.

$$\frac{\sin y}{200} = \frac{\sin 120}{280} \rightarrow \sin y = \frac{200 \sin 120}{280}$$

$$\rightarrow y = 38.2°.$$

So the bearing of C from D is 322°.

 iii) The nearest distance will be the perpendicular from B to CD as shown in Fig. 9.65.

$$\text{Hence } \frac{BX}{120} = \sin 38.2$$

$$BX = 120 \sin 38.2 = 74.2 \text{ km}.$$

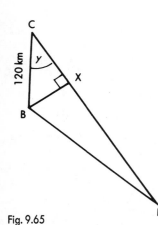

Fig. 9.65

A4

a) $BN = 8 \sin 2.5° = 0.35$ km.
b) $AN = 8 \cos 2.5 = 7.99$ km.
c)   By Pythagoras $CN^2 = AC^2 + AN^2 = 12^2 + 7.99^2$,
       hence $CN = 14.42$ km.

b) $\text{Tan (BCN)} = \dfrac{BN}{CN} = \dfrac{0.35}{14.42} = 0.0242$,

so the angle of elevation is 1.4°.

A5

a) $100 - x$
b) $\frac{1}{2} \times 100 \times (100 - x) = 50(100 - x) = 5000 - 50x$

c) $\dfrac{50}{2}(x + 100) = 25x + 2500$

d)   If area of trapezium = area of triangle then:
$$25x + 2500 = 5000 - 50x$$
$$\to 25x + 50x = 5000 - 2500$$
$$\to 75x = 2500$$
$$x = \dfrac{2500}{75} = 33\tfrac{1}{3} \text{ metres.}$$

A6

All that is needed is to consider one side of the diagram, a right angled triangle
and $\tan x = \dfrac{60}{51} \Rightarrow x = 49.6°$.

A7

i) You should have sketched a shape like that in Fig. 9.66. (You could
perhaps make the horizontal distances more accurate by calculating the
radius of the tree to be $68 \div 2\pi = 10.8$ cm $= 0.108$ m. Marks would not be
lost whichever way you did it.)
Hence $x = 30 \tan 26 = 14.6$ m (14.7 if the more accurate result were used) so
height of tree $= 14.6 + 1.2 = 15.8$ m (or 15.9 m).

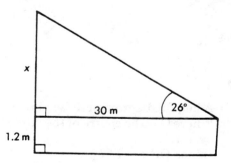

Fig. 9.66

ii) Use the formula for the volume of a cone,
$$V = \tfrac{1}{3}\pi r^2 h = \tfrac{1}{3} \times \pi \times (0.108)^2 \times 15.8 = 0.193 \text{ m}^3 \text{ (or } 0.194 \text{ m}^3).$$
This is one of those GCSE questions that allows you to estimate in your own way,
and hence gives you the choice of actual method and accuracy at the end. There
is, of course, no 'correct' answer to this question, only acceptable ones.

A8

a)   i) $\dfrac{60}{360} \times \pi \times R^2 = \dfrac{1}{6}\pi R^2 =$ area of sector ODC.

ii) Area of sector OAB $= \frac{1}{6}\pi r^2$.

So, area of ABCD $= \frac{1}{6}\pi R^2 - \frac{1}{6}\pi r^2 = \frac{1}{6}\pi(R^2 - r^2)$.

b)   i) $R - r$

     ii) $\pi\left(\dfrac{R - r}{2}\right)^2$ or $\dfrac{\pi}{4}(R - r)^2$.

c)   Total area of the shape is given by $\dfrac{1}{6}\pi(R^2 - r^2) + \dfrac{\pi}{4}(R - r)^2$.

When $R = 39$ mm and $r = 27$ mm then toal area $=$

$\dfrac{1}{6} \times \pi \times 792 + \dfrac{\pi}{4} \times 144 = 528$ mm^2.

A9

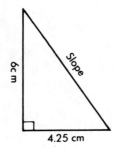

Fig. 9.67

a)   i)   Use Pythagoras' theorem to give diagonal $= \sqrt{(6^2 + 6^2)} = 8.5$ cm.

     ii)   Form a diagram as shown in Fig. 9.67, showing the right angled triangle formed with the perpendicular from the vertex to the centre of the base and the sloping edge. Using Pythagoras again to give,

         slope $= \sqrt{(6^2 + 4.25^2)}$ (4.25 being half of the diagonal)
                $= 7.3$ cm.

b)   A net is shown in Fig. 9.68, although this is not the only possible net for the pyramid.

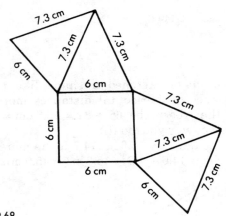

Fig. 9.68

A10

a)   i)   A helpful diagram here (see Fig. 9.69) will help see us through the problem. Where O is the centre of the circle having the arc AEB, angle OEB is found by: tan E = 5
Hence OEB = 78.7
and OBE   = 78.7 (since OEB is isosceles).
Hence BOE = 180 − 2 × 78.7 = 22.6°.

So radius OB is found by; $\dfrac{5}{r} = \sin 22.6$

$\rightarrow r = \dfrac{5}{\sin 22.6} = 13$ cm.

(It is helpful, and most accurate, to keep the angles found as accurately as you can in your calculator, and only write down the rounded off value as we did here.)

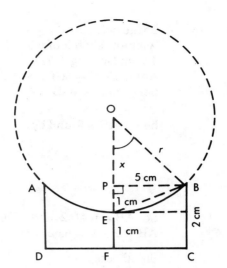

Fig. 9.69

b) The area of the cross section of the dish EBCF is made up of a rectangle 5 cm², plus a triangle 2.5 cm² and minus the segment EB of the circle.
Area of segment EB = Area of sector OEB − Area of triangle OEB.

Area of sector OEB = $\dfrac{22.6}{360} \times \pi \times 13^2 = 33.36$

Area of triangle OEB = $\frac{1}{2} \times 13 \times 5 = 32.5$
Hence area of segment EB = $33.36 − 32.5 = 0.86$ cm².
Hence area of cross section EFCB = $(5 + 2.5 − 0.86)$ cm² $= 6.64$ cm².
Hence area of cross section ADFCBE = $2 \times 6.64 = 13.28$ cm².
Hence volume of dish = $13.28 \times 30 = 398.4$ cm³.
Hence mass of dish = 398.4×2.45 g $= 976$ g.

A11

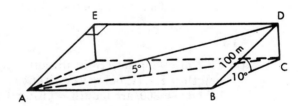

Fig. 9.70

Draw a diagram and fully label it as shown in Fig. 9.70 to help you see the triangles involved.

a) Height DC given by DC $= 100 \sin 10° = 17.4$ m.

b) Length AD given by $\dfrac{DC}{AD} = \sin 5°$,

  hence AD $= \dfrac{DC}{\sin 5°} = \dfrac{17.4}{\sin 5°} = 199$ m.

c) Angle EAD found by $\cos A = \dfrac{AE}{AD} = \dfrac{100}{199} = 0.5019$,

  hence angle $= 60°$.

d) Length ED given by AD sin A $= 199 \sin 60 = 172$ m.

A12

a) Perimeter of large square $= 4 \times 2$ cm $= 8$ cm. The length of the side of the smaller square is found by Pythagoras see Fig. 9.71: if x is half the length, then $x^2 + x^2 = 1^2 \to 2x^2 = 1 \to x = \sqrt{(0.5)} = 0.71$ cm. (Keep the accurate value in the calculator.) So the perimeter of the small square $= 4 \times 2 \times 0.71 = 5.66$ cm.

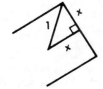

Fig. 9.71

b)   i) Large octagon:

A simple sketch of part of the octagon, where O is the centre of the circle is drawn (see Fig. 9.72).

Angle BOC $= 360 \div 8 = 45°$,

hence angle AOB $= 45 \div 2 = 22.5°$,

hence AB is found by $\dfrac{AB}{1} = \tan 22.5$

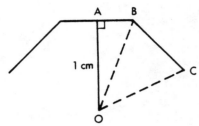

Fig. 9.72

So AB $= 0.4142$ and then the total perimeter of the large octagon $=$ AB $\times 2 \times 8 = 6.627$ cm.

Small octagon:

A similar sketch (see Fig. 9.73), but this time OB $= 1$ cm, angle AOB is still $22.5°$, hence   AB $= 1 \times \sin 22.5 = 0.3827$. Hence the total perimeter of the small octagon $=$ AB $\times 2 \times 8 = 6.123$ cm.

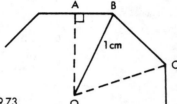

Fig. 9.73

ii) Since the value of the circumference of the circle lies between the perimeters of the octagons, then $6.123 <$ circumference < 6.627. The circumference of the circle is given by πD, so where D $= 2$ cm, circumference $= 2\pi$.

So in this situation we have:

$$6.123 < 2\pi < 6.627$$
$$\rightarrow 3.062 < \pi < 3.314.$$

A13

a)   The arc length AB is directly proportional to the angle x, hence arc length $=$ Kx. (K being a constant.)

When $x = 360$, arc length $=$ circumference $= 2\pi r$,

hence $2\pi r =$ K.360

$$\rightarrow \frac{2\pi r}{360} = K = \frac{\pi r}{180}$$

so arc length $= \dfrac{\pi r}{180} \times x = \dfrac{\pi}{180} xr.$

b)   i) $s + \dfrac{\pi}{180} xr + s = 2s + \dfrac{\pi}{180} xr.$

ii) $\dfrac{\pi}{180} x(r + s).$

c)   When $x = 120$ then   i) $= 2s + \dfrac{\pi \times 120 \times r}{180} = 2s + \tfrac{2}{3}\pi r$

ii) $= \tfrac{2}{3}\pi(r + s).$

Assume i) to be the largest value, then the difference is given by i)–ii)

$$= 2s + \tfrac{2}{3}\pi r - \tfrac{2}{3}\pi r - \tfrac{2}{3}\pi s = 2s - \tfrac{2}{3}\pi s$$

$$= 2s\left(1 - \frac{\pi}{3}\right) = -0.09s.$$

Since this value is negative, then i) must be the shortest route. So the greatest distance is given by the outer ring road by the length $0.09s$.

d)   The two distances are equal when $2s + \dfrac{\pi x r}{180} = \dfrac{\pi x r}{180} + \dfrac{\pi x s}{180} \rightarrow 2s = \dfrac{\pi x s}{180}$

$\rightarrow 360s = \pi x s$

$\rightarrow \ 360 = \pi x$

$\rightarrow \qquad x = \dfrac{360}{\pi} = 115°.$

What is surprising is that this answer is totally independent of the lengths of r and s.

A14

Sketch a net of the cone to give a sector as in Fig. 9.74, with the dotted line AP being the shortest distance.
We need to find angle AVP, call it x.
Arc distance AB is half the circumference of the base of the cone, i.e. $\pi \times 5 = 5\pi$.
But from the circle with radius 20 cm,

arc length $AB = \dfrac{x}{360} \times \pi \times 2 \times 20 = \dfrac{40\pi x}{360}$

hence $\dfrac{40\pi}{360} x = 5\pi \rightarrow x = \dfrac{5\pi \times 360}{40\pi} = 45.$

Since $VP : PB = 1 : 3$, then $VP = \frac{1}{4} \times 20 = 5$ cm.
Hence we can use the cosine rule to give

$AP = \sqrt{(20^2 + 5^2 - 20 \times 5 \times \cos 45)} = \sqrt{(354.3)}$
$AP = 18.8$ cm.

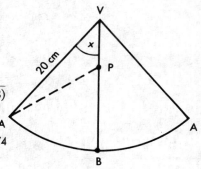

Fig. 9.74

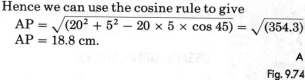

GRADE CHECKLIST

For a grade B you should:

Be able to: Calculate areas and volumes
Use trigonometry in right angled triangles
Use Pythagoras' Theorem

For a grade A you should also:

Be able to: Calculate angles and distances in solids
Calculate arc lengths
Calculate sector areas
Calculate the surface area of cylinders
Calculate the volumes of cones and spheres
Find the sine, cosine or tangent of angles of any size
Sketch the graphs of trigonometrical functions

For a grade A* you should also:

Understand: The sine rule
The cosine rule

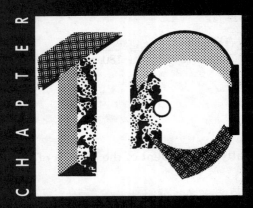

TRANSFORMATION GEOMETRY

MATRICES

VECTORS

SOME TRANSFORMATIONS

TRANSFORMATION MATRICES

INVERSE TRANSFORMATIONS

GETTING STARTED

It will be assumed in this chapter that you are familiar with the ideas of reflection, rotation, enlargement and translation, as the emphasis at this level will be matrix transformations as well as vector work. At the higher level questions are often set on transformation geometry.

USEFUL DEFINITIONS

Colinear	In the same straight line.
Enlargement	A change in size to a mathematically similar shape (could be smaller).
Invariant	Does not alter under a transformation.
Invariant line	The line of points that will not alter under a transformation.
Invariant point	The point that will not alter under a transformation.
Matrix	A collection of numbers in some specific order.
Reflection	A mirror-image through a particular line.
Rotation	A turn around some particular point.
Shear	A 'pushing' over of a shape; involves a scale factor and an invariant line.
Stretch	A 'pull' on a shape; involves a scale factor and an invariant line.
Transformation	A change of position of a given shape.
Translation	A slide with no turning.
Vector	A movement of a specific magnitude and direction.

ESSENTIAL PRINCIPLES

A *matrix* is a set of numbers put in rows and columns in a particular way.

For example $\begin{pmatrix} 8 & 6 & 5 \\ 7 & 5 & 3 \end{pmatrix}$ is a matrix representing the medals won in an Olympic competition by two teams A and B.

■ Team A has won 8 gold, 6 silver and 5 bronze, while
■ Team B has won 7 gold, 5 silver and 3 bronze.

So you see, the order and position of the numbers is important; each number represents a particular piece of data.

The size (order) of a matrix

We often represent a matrix by capital letters, and we describe the *size* of a matrix, known as its *order*, by saying how many rows and how many columns the matrix has (rows then columns). For example

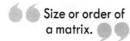
Size or order of a matrix.

i) $T = \begin{pmatrix} 3 & 0 & 1 \\ 2 & 4 & 5 \end{pmatrix}$ or
■ is a (2 by 3) matrix
■ has an order of (2 by 3)

ii) $P = \begin{pmatrix} 3 & 1 & 2 & 0 \\ 0 & 1 & 5 & 1 \\ 1 & 2 & 4 & 6 \end{pmatrix}$ or
■ is a (3 by 4) matrix
■ has an order of (3 by 4)

MATRIX ADDITION AND SUBTRACTION

It only makes any sense to add or subtract matrices of the SAME ORDER. We *add* two matrices by adding the numbers in corresponding positions,

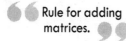
Rule for adding matrices.

e.g. $\begin{pmatrix} a & b \\ c & d \end{pmatrix} + \begin{pmatrix} e & f \\ g & h \end{pmatrix} = \begin{pmatrix} a+e & b+f \\ c+g & d+h \end{pmatrix}$

We *subtract* two matrices by subtracting the numbers in corresponding positions,

Rule for subtracting matrices.

e.g. $\begin{pmatrix} a & b & c \\ d & e & f \end{pmatrix} - \begin{pmatrix} g & h & i \\ j & k & l \end{pmatrix} = \begin{pmatrix} a-g & b-h & c-i \\ d-j & e-k & f-l \end{pmatrix}$

WORKED EXAMPLE 1

$P = \begin{pmatrix} 3 & 4 & 1 \\ 2 & 0 & 7 \end{pmatrix}$ $Q = \begin{pmatrix} -1 & 2 & 5 \\ 6 & 3 & 0 \end{pmatrix}$

Calculate   i) $P + Q$ ii) $P - Q$

i) $P + Q = \begin{pmatrix} 3 & 4 & 1 \\ 2 & 0 & 7 \end{pmatrix} + \begin{pmatrix} -1 & 2 & 5 \\ 6 & 3 & 0 \end{pmatrix} = \begin{pmatrix} 2 & 6 & 6 \\ 8 & 3 & 7 \end{pmatrix}$

ii) $P - Q = \begin{pmatrix} 3 & 4 & 1 \\ 2 & 0 & 7 \end{pmatrix} - \begin{pmatrix} -1 & 2 & 5 \\ 6 & 3 & 0 \end{pmatrix} = \begin{pmatrix} 4 & 2 & -4 \\ -4 & -3 & 7 \end{pmatrix}$

MULTIPLES OF MATRICES (SCALARS)

The matrix $2P$ is $P + P$ which you can easily show to be each number in P multiplied by 2.

In general, if P is the matrix $\begin{pmatrix} a & b & c \\ d & e & f \end{pmatrix}$

then $nP = \begin{pmatrix} na & nb & nc \\ nd & ne & nf \end{pmatrix}$

Definition of a scalar.

where n is a number. (Also called a *scalar*.)

WORKED EXAMPLE 2

Using P and Q as above, calculate $3P - 2Q$

$$3P = 3\begin{pmatrix} 3 & 4 & 1 \\ 2 & 0 & 7 \end{pmatrix} = \begin{pmatrix} 9 & 12 & 3 \\ 6 & 0 & 21 \end{pmatrix}$$

$$2Q = 2\begin{pmatrix} -1 & 2 & 5 \\ 6 & 3 & 0 \end{pmatrix} = \begin{pmatrix} -2 & 4 & 10 \\ 12 & 6 & 0 \end{pmatrix}$$

$$3P - 2Q = \begin{pmatrix} 11 & 8 & -7 \\ -6 & -6 & 21 \end{pmatrix}$$

EXERCISE 1

a) Given that $B = \begin{pmatrix} 3 & 1 \\ 4 & 2 \\ 0 & 3 \end{pmatrix}$, find a matrix P such that

    i) $2P = B$ ii) $\frac{1}{2}P = B$

b) $P = \begin{pmatrix} 2 & x \\ 3 & 4 \end{pmatrix}$ $Q = \begin{pmatrix} 5 & 2 \\ y & 1 \end{pmatrix}$

     Find the values of x and y if $2P + Q = \begin{pmatrix} 9 & 8 \\ 10 & 9 \end{pmatrix}$.

MATRIX MULTIPLICATION

> Multiplying matrices.

Matrix *multiplication* was invented in the 19th Century as a useful way of combining two suitable matrices.

For example, a company sells pens in four sizes: very small, small, medium, large, and receives orders as (100, 500, 400, 80) which tells us exactly how many of each are needed, as the order of the numbers is important. The costs can be as given:

very small   ...   45p

small   ...   55p

medium   ...   65p

large   ...   85p

This price list (in order) can be given as $\begin{pmatrix} 45 \\ 55 \\ 65 \\ 85 \end{pmatrix}$.

We can then price up an order as:

$$(100 \quad 500 \quad 400 \quad 80)\begin{pmatrix} 45 \\ 55 \\ 65 \\ 85 \end{pmatrix} = (100 \times 45 + 500 \times 55 + 400 \times 65 + 80 \times 85)$$

$$= 60\,750p.$$

$$= £607.50.$$

It is this way of combining numbers that is called *matrix multiplication*, a row combined with a column, to produce *one* number.

The principle of combining rows with columns in this way is easily extended to using *more than one row*.

> Combining more than one *row* with a column.

$$\text{e.g.} \begin{pmatrix} 2 & 4 & 3 \\ 1 & 5 & 7 \end{pmatrix}\begin{pmatrix} 6 \\ 8 \\ 9 \end{pmatrix} = \begin{pmatrix} 2 \times 6 + 4 \times 8 + 3 \times 9 \\ 1 \times 6 + 5 \times 8 + 7 \times 9 \end{pmatrix} = \begin{pmatrix} 71 \\ 109 \end{pmatrix}.$$

So two rows combined with one column will produce *two* numbers in a single column.

Combining more than one *column* with a row.

This principle can also be used to combine one row with *more than one column*.

e.g. $(5 \ 4 \ 2) \begin{pmatrix} 0 & 7 \\ 3 & 6 \\ 1 & 8 \end{pmatrix} + (5 \times 0 + 4 \times 3 + 2 \times 1, \ 5 \times 7 + 4 \times 6 + 2 \times 8) = (14 \ 75)$

Hence your row combined with two columns will produce *two* numbers in a single row.

Combining more than one row with more than one column.

This now brings us to the point of trying to combine *more than one row* with *more than one column*.

This can be done so long as one thing is true, namely that the number of elements (numbers) in each row *must* be the same as the number of elements (numbers) in each column,

e.g. $\begin{pmatrix} 2 & 1 & 5 & 2 \\ 6 & 1 & 4 & 1 \end{pmatrix} \begin{pmatrix} 3 & 1 & 3 \\ 0 & 0 & 2 \\ 1 & 1 & 0 \\ 2 & 1 & 1 \end{pmatrix}$

this has *four* numbers in EACH ROW

this has *four* numbers in EACH COLUMN

> Generally, a (P by Q) matrix can be multiplied to a (Q by R) matrix to produce a (P by R) matrix.

An important rule.

This condition is necessary since when multiplying matrices you combine:

- each ROW in the left hand matrix to
- each COLUMN in the right hand matrix.

It follows that there must be a match between the number of elements in the rows and columns to be combined.

Example: $\begin{pmatrix} 2 & 1 & 4 \\ 3 & 0 & 2 \end{pmatrix} \begin{pmatrix} 1 & 2 & 0 & 1 \\ 0 & 3 & 1 & 3 \\ 1 & 1 & 2 & 0 \end{pmatrix} = \begin{pmatrix} 6 & 11 & 9 & 5 \\ 5 & 8 & 4 & 3 \end{pmatrix}$

(2 by 3) (3 by 4) $\Rightarrow$ (2 by 4)

EXERCISE 2

Where $M = \begin{pmatrix} 1 & 2 \\ 3 & 1 \end{pmatrix}$ $N = \begin{pmatrix} -1 & 2 \\ 0 & 1 \end{pmatrix}$ $P = \begin{pmatrix} 0 & 2 \\ 3 & -1 \end{pmatrix}$

calculate a) MN b) N + P c) M(N + P) d) M^2

IDENTITY MATRIX (MULTIPLICATIVE)

The identity matrix.

A (multiplicative) *identity matrix* is one which, when multiplied to another matrix, leaves it unaltered. They will all be square matrices having the leading diagonal as 'ones', with all other digits being zero.

e.g. $\begin{pmatrix} 1 & 0 \\ 0 & 1 \end{pmatrix}$ $\begin{pmatrix} 1 & 0 & 0 \\ 0 & 1 & 0 \\ 0 & 0 & 1 \end{pmatrix}$, $\begin{pmatrix} 1 & 0 & 0 & 0 \\ 0 & 1 & 0 & 0 \\ 0 & 0 & 1 & 0 \\ 0 & 0 & 0 & 1 \end{pmatrix}$ etc.

Examples:

$$\begin{pmatrix} 1 & 0 \\ 0 & 1 \end{pmatrix}\begin{pmatrix} 1 & 5 \\ 2 & -3 \end{pmatrix} = \begin{pmatrix} 1 & 5 \\ 2 & -3 \end{pmatrix}$$

$$\begin{pmatrix} 1 & 0 \\ 0 & 1 \end{pmatrix}\begin{pmatrix} 5 & -1 & 2 \\ 2 & 3 & -4 \end{pmatrix} = \begin{pmatrix} 5 & -1 & 2 \\ 2 & 3 & -4 \end{pmatrix}$$

$$\begin{pmatrix} 1 & 0 & 0 \\ 0 & 1 & 0 \\ 0 & 0 & 1 \end{pmatrix}\begin{pmatrix} 2 & 7 & 1 & 3 \\ 4 & 5 & 0 & 2 \\ -1 & 2 & 1 & 5 \end{pmatrix} = \begin{pmatrix} 2 & 7 & 1 & 3 \\ 4 & 5 & 0 & 2 \\ -1 & 2 & 1 & 5 \end{pmatrix}.$$

> *Multiplying an identity matrix to other matrices.*

The one identity you will use far more than any other is the 2×2 identity matrix $\begin{pmatrix} 1 & 0 \\ 0 & 1 \end{pmatrix}$.

INVERSE MATRICES (MULTIPLICATIVE)

The (multiplicative) *inverse* of a matrix is the matrix which, when multiplied to it, gives the *identity* matrix.

> *The inverse of a matrix.*

e.g. The inverse of $\begin{pmatrix} 3 & 7 \\ 2 & 5 \end{pmatrix}$ is $\begin{pmatrix} 5 & -7 \\ -2 & 3 \end{pmatrix}$ since $\begin{pmatrix} 3 & 7 \\ 2 & 5 \end{pmatrix}\begin{pmatrix} 5 & -7 \\ -2 & 3 \end{pmatrix} = \begin{pmatrix} 1 & 0 \\ 0 & 1 \end{pmatrix}$.

INVERSE OF 2 x 2 MATRICES WITH MULTIPLICATION

Where $A = \begin{pmatrix} a & b \\ c & d \end{pmatrix}$, then the multiplicative *inverse* is called A^{-1}

where $A^{-1} = \dfrac{1}{ad - bc}\begin{pmatrix} d & -b \\ -c & a \end{pmatrix}$.

> *Note the use of the determinant here.*

Here $(ad - bc)$ is called the *determinant*.
Example:

The inverse of $\begin{pmatrix} 5 & 3 \\ 1 & 2 \end{pmatrix}$ is given by $\dfrac{1}{7}\begin{pmatrix} 2 & -3 \\ -1 & 5 \end{pmatrix}$.

Hence $\dfrac{1}{7}\begin{pmatrix} 2 & -3 \\ -1 & 5 \end{pmatrix}\begin{pmatrix} 5 & 3 \\ 1 & 2 \end{pmatrix} = \begin{pmatrix} 1 & 0 \\ 0 & 1 \end{pmatrix}$ ... which is the identity matrix

$$\boxed{A \cdot A^{-1} = I}$$

where A = a matrix
A^{-1} = its (multiplicative) inverse
I = the identity matrix.

Note that any 2×2 matrix having a determinant equal to 0 cannot have an inverse; we call it 'singular'.

> *A singular matrix has no inverse.*

E.g. $\begin{pmatrix} 3 & 2 \\ 6 & 4 \end{pmatrix}$ is *singular*, it has no inverse.

EXERCISE 3

Find the multiplicative inverse matrices of the following matrices. (Some may be singular.)

a) $\begin{pmatrix} 3 & 4 \\ 1 & 2 \end{pmatrix}$ b) $\begin{pmatrix} 4 & 3 \\ 3 & 2 \end{pmatrix}$ c) $\begin{pmatrix} 6 & 3 \\ 4 & 2 \end{pmatrix}$ d) $\begin{pmatrix} 2 & -1 \\ 3 & -2 \end{pmatrix}$

What is a vector?

A *vector* has magnitude (size) and direction, and can be represented by a straight line.

Some examples of vectors are:

velocity   ....e.g. 16 km/h   due west
acceleration ....e.g. 10 km/s² north west
displacement ....e.g. 8 km   due south.

Each of these could be represented by a suitable straight line drawn on a grid.

The mathematics of all these types of vectors is the same, but it is easiest to study the type of vector involving displacement, hence that is why most of our vector work is based on displacement.

REPRESENTATION OF A VECTOR

If we use a grid then the line representing a vector can be described by using the *displacements* parallel to the x and y axes.

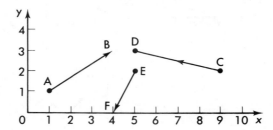

Fig. 10.1

> In a printed book the bold **a** would be used — you will write a underlined.

The vector can be named in three different ways.

⇒ by using the end letters   e.g. $\overrightarrow{AB}, \overrightarrow{CD}, \overrightarrow{EF}$
⇒ by giving it a letter printed bold or underlined   e.g. $\underline{a}$ or **a**, $\underline{c}$ or **c**, $\underline{f}$ or **f**
⇒ by using the horizontal and vertical displacement written as column matrices.

e.g. $\begin{pmatrix} 3 \\ 2 \end{pmatrix}, \begin{pmatrix} -4 \\ 1 \end{pmatrix}, \begin{pmatrix} -1 \\ -2 \end{pmatrix}$

Note 1. that when using the column matrix form for a vector:
- the *top number* is the displacement parallel to the x axis

$$\begin{pmatrix} +\text{ve when displacing from left to right} \\ -\text{ve when displacing from right to left} \end{pmatrix}$$

- the *bottom number* is the displacement parallel to the y axis

$$\begin{pmatrix} +\text{ve when moving up} \\ -\text{ve when moving down} \end{pmatrix}$$

2. Each vector must use an arrowhead to show its direction.

Equal and parallel vectors

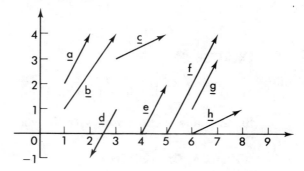

Fig. 10.2

■ From the diagram $\underline{a} = \begin{pmatrix} 1 \\ 2 \end{pmatrix}$ and $\underline{e} = \begin{pmatrix} 1 \\ 2 \end{pmatrix}$ so we can say that $\underline{a} = \underline{e}$.

■ The lines representing a and e are parallel and equal in length.
■ Also from the diagram

$$f = \begin{pmatrix} 2 \\ 4 \end{pmatrix} \text{ and } g = \begin{pmatrix} 1 \\ 2 \end{pmatrix} \text{ so } f = 2g$$

■ The lines representing f and g are of different lengths but are parallel to each other.
■ Also from the diagram

$$a = \begin{pmatrix} 1 \\ 2 \end{pmatrix} \text{ and } d = \begin{pmatrix} -1 \\ -2 \end{pmatrix} \text{ so } a = -d$$

i.e. a and d are parallel and the same size, but they are in opposite directions.

■ And finally from the diagram $a = \begin{pmatrix} 1 \\ 2 \end{pmatrix}$ and $c = \begin{pmatrix} 2 \\ 1 \end{pmatrix}$.

Although a and c are the same length, they are not parallel and so $a \neq c$.

Two important points. ⇒ Parallel vectors are multiples of each other.
⇒ Equal vectors are parallel and of the same size (order).

EXERCISE 4

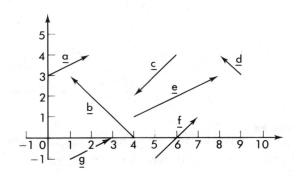

Fig. 10.3

a)   Write down each vector in the diagram in the form $\begin{pmatrix} x \\ y \end{pmatrix}$.

b)   Find the relationships between as many pairs of vectors as possible, giving them in the form $p = Kq$.

THE MAGNITUDE OF A VECTOR

The *magnitude* of a vector that is represented by a line is the length of that line.

For example, where $a = \begin{pmatrix} 5 \\ 3 \end{pmatrix}$ then the magnitude of the vector, written as |a| will be found by Pythagoras

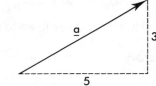

i.e. $|a| = \sqrt{(5^2 + 3^2)}$
$= \sqrt{(25 + 9)} = \sqrt{34}$.
$|a| = 5.83 \ (3 \text{ sf}).$

Fig. 10.4

EXERCISE 5

a) $\overrightarrow{AB} = \begin{pmatrix} 5 \\ -1 \end{pmatrix}$, calculate $|\overrightarrow{AB}|$.

b)   A shape is translated with the vector $\begin{pmatrix} -4 \\ 3 \end{pmatrix}$. How far has it actually moved?

ADDITION OF VECTORS

Did you know that aeroplanes often don't fly in the direction they are pointing? Or have you noticed that if you try to swim or row across a river, you do not always go in the direction in which you are pointing?

This is because forces are acting together and this gives a RESULTANT force acting in a completely different direction and of a different magnitude.

We can see examples of this if we look at column vectors and their displacement.

For example, when $\underline{a} = \begin{pmatrix} 3 \\ 2 \end{pmatrix}$ and $\underline{b} = \begin{pmatrix} 2 \\ -1 \end{pmatrix}$ then $\underline{a} + \underline{b}$ can be defined as a move, first with $\underline{a}$ then with $\underline{b}$. What single vector would have the same effect.

Let's draw a diagram (Fig. 10.5)

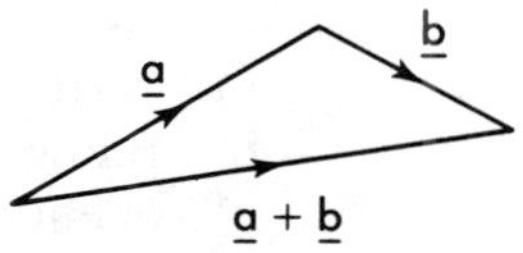

Fig. 10.5

$$\underline{a} + \underline{b} = \begin{pmatrix} 5 \\ 1 \end{pmatrix}, \text{ notice } \begin{pmatrix} 3 \\ 2 \end{pmatrix} + \begin{pmatrix} 2 \\ -1 \end{pmatrix} = \begin{pmatrix} 5 \\ 1 \end{pmatrix}.$$

This follows the same rules as matrix addition.

SUBTRACTION OF VECTORS

Remember that if $\overrightarrow{AB} = \underline{a}$

then $\overrightarrow{BA} = -\underline{a}$

So we see that $-\underline{a}$ is the vector $\underline{a}$ in the opposite direction.

So if $\quad \underline{a} = \begin{pmatrix} 4 \\ 2 \end{pmatrix}$ then $-\underline{a} = -\begin{pmatrix} 4 \\ 2 \end{pmatrix} = \begin{pmatrix} -4 \\ -2 \end{pmatrix}$

and if $\quad \underline{b} = \begin{pmatrix} 3 \\ -2 \end{pmatrix}$ then $-\underline{b} = \begin{pmatrix} -3 \\ 2 \end{pmatrix}$.

It will help us to see $\underline{x} - \underline{y}$ as $\underline{x} + (-\underline{y})$.

For example, when $\underline{a} = \begin{pmatrix} 4 \\ 2 \end{pmatrix}$ and $\underline{b} = \begin{pmatrix} 3 \\ -4 \end{pmatrix}$

then $\underline{a} - \underline{b} = \begin{pmatrix} 4 \\ 2 \end{pmatrix} + -\begin{pmatrix} 3 \\ -1 \end{pmatrix} = \begin{pmatrix} 4 \\ 2 \end{pmatrix} + \begin{pmatrix} -3 \\ 1 \end{pmatrix}$

$$= \begin{pmatrix} 4 \\ 2 \end{pmatrix} - \begin{pmatrix} 3 \\ -1 \end{pmatrix} = \begin{pmatrix} 1 \\ 3 \end{pmatrix}.$$

EXERCISE 6

Where $\underline{a} = \begin{pmatrix} 4 \\ 3 \end{pmatrix}$ $\quad \underline{b} = \begin{pmatrix} -2 \\ 4 \end{pmatrix}$ $\quad \underline{c} = \begin{pmatrix} -1 \\ -2 \end{pmatrix}$.

Draw diagrams to represent the following vectors and check that the calculated values agree with the diagram.
a) $\underline{a} + \underline{b}$　　b) $\underline{a} - \underline{c}$　　c) $\underline{c} + \underline{b}$　　d) $(\underline{a} + \underline{b}) - \underline{c}$

VECTORS AND GEOMETRY

As you have seen already in this chapter, every vector can be represented by a straight line of some length and direction. We can put them together to form triangles and other plane figures. For example, in Fig. 10.6 we have $\overrightarrow{AB} + \overrightarrow{BC} = \overrightarrow{AC}$.

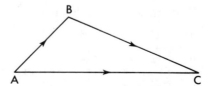

Fig. 10.6

Many vector problems come in the form of plane diagrams through the following worked examples.

WORKED EXAMPLE 3

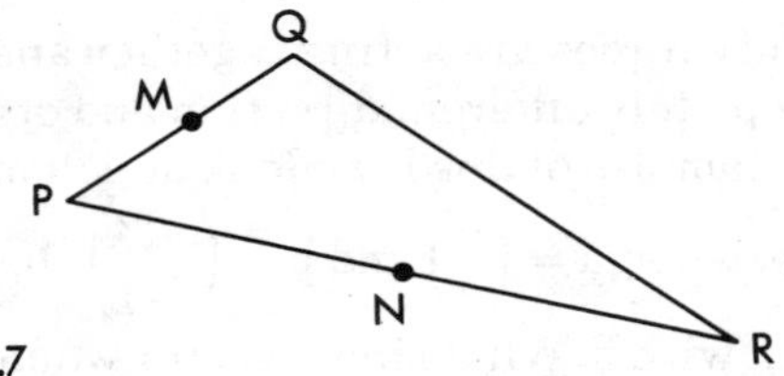

Q
M
P
N
R

Fig. 10.7

$\vec{PQ} = \underline{p}$ $\vec{PR} = \underline{r}$
M and N are the mid-points of
PQ and PR respectively.

a)   Write in terms of $\underline{p}$ and $\underline{r}$ i) $\vec{QR}$ ii) $\vec{PM}$ iii) $\vec{PN}$ iv) $\vec{MN}$
b)   Show that MN is parallel to QR.
c)   What can be said about the lengths of MN and QR?

Solution
a)   i) $\vec{QR} = \vec{QP} + \vec{PR} = -\underline{p} + \underline{r} = \underline{r} - \underline{p}$
      ii) $\vec{PM} = \tfrac{1}{2}\vec{PQ} = \tfrac{1}{2}\underline{p}$
      iii) $\vec{PN} = \tfrac{1}{2}\vec{PR} = \tfrac{1}{2}\underline{r}$
      iv) $\vec{MN} = \vec{MP} + \vec{PN} = -\tfrac{1}{2}\underline{p} + \tfrac{1}{2}\underline{r} = \tfrac{1}{2}\underline{r} - \tfrac{1}{2}\underline{p} = \tfrac{1}{2}(\underline{r} - \underline{p})$
b) $\vec{MN} = \tfrac{1}{2}(\underline{r} - \underline{p}), \vec{QR} = \underline{r} - \underline{p}$
      hence $\vec{MN} = \tfrac{1}{2}\vec{QR}$

      hence MN and QR are parallel.
c)   Since $\vec{MN} = \tfrac{1}{2}\vec{QR}$, the length of QR is twice that of MN.

WORKED EXAMPLE 4

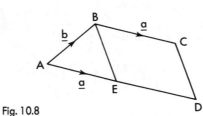

Fig. 10.8

$\vec{AB} = \underline{b}$ $\vec{AE} = \vec{BC} = \underline{a}$ $\vec{CD} = \underline{a} - \underline{b}$

a)   Find $\vec{BE}$ and $\vec{AD}$ in terms of $\underline{a}$ and $\underline{b}$.
b)   What type of quadrilateral is BCDE?
c)   What can be said about points A, E and D?

Solution
a) $\vec{BE} = \vec{BA} + \vec{AE} = -\underline{b} + \underline{a} = \underline{a} - \underline{b}$.
      $\vec{AD} = \vec{AB} + \vec{BC} + \vec{CD} = \underline{b} + \underline{a} + (\underline{a} - \underline{b}) = \underline{b} + \underline{a} + \underline{a} - \underline{b} = 2\underline{a}$.
b)   Since $\vec{AD} = 2\underline{a}$, then $\vec{ED} = \underline{a} = \vec{BC}$, and $\vec{BE} = \vec{CD}$
      hence BC is parallel to ED, and BE is parallel to CD,
      hence BCDE is a parallelogram.
c)   Since $\vec{AD} = 2\underline{a}$, then AD is parallel to AE and AE = ED, hence A, E and D are
      collinear (on the same straight line) and E is the midpoint of AD.

EXERCISE 7

P, Q, R and S are the mid-points of OA, AB, BC and OC respectively.

$\vec{OA} = \underline{a}, \vec{OB} = \underline{b}$ and $\vec{OC} = \underline{c}$.

State in terms of $\underline{a}$, $\underline{b}$ and $\underline{c}$

a) $\vec{OP}$ b) $\vec{AB}$ c) $\vec{AQ}$
d) $\vec{PQ}$ e) $\vec{SR}$
f)   Show that PQ is parallel to SR.
g)   Show that PS is parallel to QR.
h)   What type of quadrilateral is PQRS?

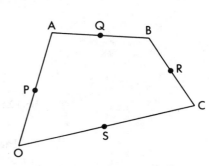

Fig. 10.9

HARDER VECTOR PROBLEMS AS APPLIED TO GEOMETRY

**WORKED
EXAMPLE 5**

OACB is a parallelogram (Fig. 10.10).
E and F are mid-points of the
sides AC and CB respectively.
Find the ratios $\dfrac{AD}{DF}$ and $\dfrac{OD}{DE}$.

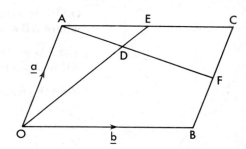

Fig. 10.10

Solution

We have given our diagram (Fig. 10.10) the two basic vectors a and b, which will
define the parallelogram OACB.

We can now write the other lines on the diagram in terms of a and b.

i.e. $\overrightarrow{AC} = b$, $\overrightarrow{AE} = \frac{1}{2}b$

hence $\overrightarrow{OE} = \overrightarrow{OA} + \overrightarrow{AE} = a + \frac{1}{2}b$

and as $\overrightarrow{BC} = a$, $\overrightarrow{CB} = -a$, $\overrightarrow{CF} = -\frac{1}{2}a$

hence $\overrightarrow{AF} = \overrightarrow{AC} + \overrightarrow{CF} = b + (-\frac{1}{2}a) = b - \frac{1}{2}a$.

So far then $\overrightarrow{OA} = a$, $\overrightarrow{BC} = a$, $\overrightarrow{OB} = b$, $\overrightarrow{AC} = b$, $\overrightarrow{OE} = a + \frac{1}{2}b$, $\overrightarrow{AF} = b - \frac{1}{2}a$.

Now, $\overrightarrow{OD}$ is in the same direction as $\overrightarrow{OE}$

hence $\overrightarrow{OD} = h\overrightarrow{OE}$

hence $\overrightarrow{OD} = h(a + \frac{1}{2}b)$.

Similarly $\overrightarrow{AD} = k\overrightarrow{AF}$

$\overrightarrow{AD} = k(b - \frac{1}{2}a)$.

We need to link $\overrightarrow{OD}$ and $\overrightarrow{AD}$ in some way.

Look at the diagram and we see $\overrightarrow{OD} = \overrightarrow{OA} + \overrightarrow{AD}$

$$\overrightarrow{OD} = a + k(b - \tfrac{1}{2}a)$$

but $\overrightarrow{OD}$ also equals $h(a + \frac{1}{2}b)$

hence $h(a + \frac{1}{2}b) = a + k(b - \frac{1}{2}a)$

$$ha + \frac{h}{2}b = a + kb - \frac{k}{2}a$$

$$ha - a + \frac{k}{2}a = kb - \frac{h}{2}b$$

$$\left(h - 1 + \frac{k}{2}\right)a = \left(k - \frac{h}{2}\right)b$$

but since a and b are NOT parallel this can only happen when

$h - 1 + \dfrac{k}{2} = k - \dfrac{h}{2} = 0$.

This gives us two simultaneous equations $h - 1 + \dfrac{k}{2} = 0$

$$k - \tfrac{1}{2}h = 0$$

The simultaneous equations are solved to give the solution

$$h = \frac{4}{5} \text{ and } k = \frac{2}{5}$$

hence $\overrightarrow{OD} = \dfrac{4}{5}\overrightarrow{OE}$ and $\overrightarrow{AD} = \dfrac{2}{5}\overrightarrow{AF}$

hence D divides OE into the ratio 4:1; $\dfrac{OD}{DE} = \dfrac{4}{1}$

D divides AF into the ratio 2:3; $\dfrac{AD}{DF} = \dfrac{2}{3}$.

EXERCISE 8

OABC is a trapezium (Fig. 10.11)
where AB and OC are parallel

and $\overrightarrow{AB} = 2\overrightarrow{OC}$.
AC intersects with OB at D.

Find the ratios $\dfrac{OD}{DB}$ and $\dfrac{AD}{DC}$

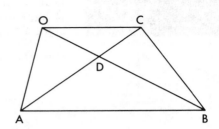

Fig. 10.11

**A stretch has a
scale factor and an
invariant line.**

THE STRETCH

A *stretch* is often called one-way stretch, as it is usually in one direction only
(usually in the direction of one of the axes). A stretch is like a pull on a shape from
one particular line, usually an axis.

A stretch has a *scale factor,* n, which will move every point on the shape a
distance of (n times its current distance from a given line). This line is called the
invariant line, because points on it will not move.

Examples

i)

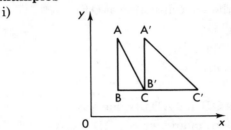

Fig. 10.12

Triangle ABC (Fig. 10.12) has
been stretched parallel to the *x*
axis with a scale factor 2, with
the *y* axis being the invariant
line.

ii)

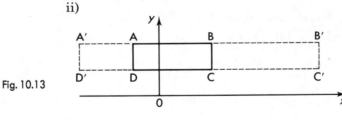

Fig. 10.13

The rectangle ABCD (Fig. 10.13)
has been stretched parallel to
the *x* axis with a scale factor
3, with the *y* axis being the invariant line.

iii)

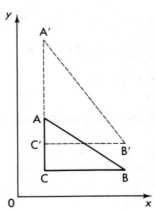

Fig. 10.14

The triangle ABC (Fig. 10.14)
has been stretched parallel to
the *y* axis with a scale factor
of 2, with the *x* axis being the
invariant line.

EXERCISE 9

a) Draw the triangle with vertices A(1, 1), B(3, 2), C(2, 2).
b) Draw the image of ABC after a stretch parallel to the *x* axis, scale factor 3,
with the *y* axis invariant.

THE SHEAR

> **A shear has a scale factor and an invariant line.**

A *shear* can be thought of as 'pushing a shape over'.

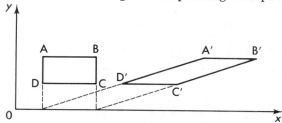

Fig. 10.15

- A shear will have an *invariant line* where points do not move.
- A shear will have a *scale factor*, say n.

Each point on the shape will be moved parallel to the invariant line a distance equal to:

- n × the distance from the invariant line.

The example above is a shear, scale factor 3, with the *x* axis invariant.

Examples

a)

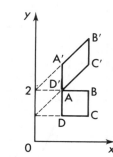

Fig. 10.16

The square ABCD (Fig. 10.16) has been sheared with a scale factor of 1, and with the *y* axis invariant.

⇒ Note: each point moves up a distance of (1 × its distance from the *y* axis).

b)

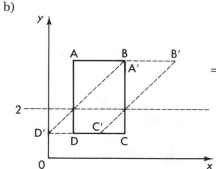

Fig. 10.17

The rectangle ABCD (Fig. 10.17) has been sheared with a scale factor of 2 and with the line $y = 2$ invariant, to give the image $A^1B^1C^1D^1$.

⇒ Note: each point moves 'clockwise' a distance of (2 × its distance from the line $y = 2$).

EXERCISE 10

a) Draw the triangle with vertices F(1, 1), G(3, 1), H(1, 2).
b) Draw the image of FGH after a shear with scale factor 2, *y* axis invariant.

4 ▷ TRANS-FORMATION MATRICES

WORKED EXAMPLE 6

> **Exam questions are often phrased this way, do be familiar with it.**

A *transformation matrix* is usually a (2 by 2) matrix. If it is multiplied to a matrix containing the position vectors of any shape, then the resulting product will determine the transformed shape.

A transformation T is defined as

$$T: \begin{pmatrix} x \\ y \end{pmatrix} \rightarrow \begin{pmatrix} 1 & 0 \\ 0 & -1 \end{pmatrix} \begin{pmatrix} x \\ y \end{pmatrix}$$

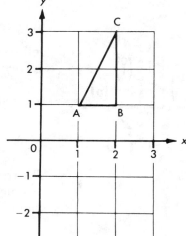

Fig. 10.18

Use this to transform the triangle in Fig. 10.18, then fully describe the transformation T. By putting the position vectors of the triangle ABC into a matrix we can evaluate

$$\begin{matrix} & \text{A B C} & & \text{A' B' C'} \end{matrix}$$
$$\begin{pmatrix} 1 & 0 \\ 0 & -1 \end{pmatrix} \begin{pmatrix} 1 & 2 & 2 \\ 1 & 1 & 3 \end{pmatrix} = \begin{pmatrix} 1 & 2 & 2 \\ -1 & -1 & -3 \end{pmatrix}$$

Then plotting the transformed shape onto a diagram (see Fig. 10.19) gives us,

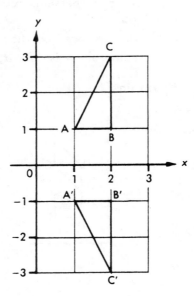

Fig. 10.19

which illustrates that T is a reflection in the x axis.

EXERCISE 11

By use of the triangle ABC in Worked Example 6 above, fully describe transformations represented by the matrices

i) $\begin{pmatrix} 0 & 1 \\ 1 & 0 \end{pmatrix}$ ii) $\begin{pmatrix} 0 & -1 \\ 1 & 0 \end{pmatrix}$ iii) $\begin{pmatrix} 2 & 0 \\ 0 & 2 \end{pmatrix}$

BASE VECTORS

Base vectors, often called *unit vectors*, can be used to define very quickly a matrix transformation, or even to help evaluate that transformation. For example, where T:

$$T: \begin{pmatrix} x \\ y \end{pmatrix} \rightarrow \begin{pmatrix} 0 & -1 \\ -1 & 0 \end{pmatrix} \begin{pmatrix} x \\ y \end{pmatrix}$$

then consider how the unit matrix, $\begin{pmatrix} 1 & 0 \\ 0 & 1 \end{pmatrix}$ transforms to $\begin{pmatrix} 0 & -1 \\ -1 & 0 \end{pmatrix}$ where the columns of the matrices are position vectors.

Then it can be seen in Fig. 10.20 what happens to them.

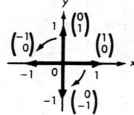

see that $\begin{pmatrix} 1 \\ 0 \end{pmatrix} \rightarrow \begin{pmatrix} 0 \\ -1 \end{pmatrix}$

$$\begin{pmatrix} 0 \\ 1 \end{pmatrix} \rightarrow \begin{pmatrix} -1 \\ 0 \end{pmatrix}$$

Fig. 10.20

The transformation can now be seen as 'reflection in the line $y = -x$'. Try this technique out on the matrices in Exercise 11 to see how much simpler it is to define the matrix in this way.

WORKED EXAMPLE 7

Find the transformation matrix that describes a rotation of 90° clockwise around the origin (see Fig. 10.21).
Consider the base vectors, then

$$\begin{pmatrix} 1 \\ 0 \end{pmatrix} \rightarrow \begin{pmatrix} 0 \\ -1 \end{pmatrix} \text{ and } \begin{pmatrix} 0 \\ 1 \end{pmatrix} \rightarrow \begin{pmatrix} 1 \\ 0 \end{pmatrix} \text{ (see Fig. 10.21)}$$

hence $\begin{pmatrix} 1 & 0 \\ 0 & 1 \end{pmatrix} \rightarrow \begin{pmatrix} 0 & 1 \\ -1 & 0 \end{pmatrix}$

so rotation of 90° clockwise around the origin is defined as

$$T: \begin{pmatrix} x \\ y \end{pmatrix} \rightarrow \begin{pmatrix} 0 & 1 \\ -1 & 0 \end{pmatrix} \begin{pmatrix} x \\ y \end{pmatrix}$$

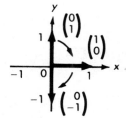

Fig. 10.21

EXERCISE 12

Use the same technique as above with the base vectors to find the transformation matrices of

a) reflection in the y axis
b) rotation of 90° clockwise about (0, 0)
c) rotation of 180° about (0, 0)
d) rotation of 90° anti-clockwise about (0, 0)
e) reflection in the line $y = x$
f) reflection in the line $y = -x$
g) enlargement of 2, centre (0, 0)
h) enlargement of 3, centre (0, 0)
i) one way stretch parallel to the x axis, scale factor 2, with y axis invariant
j) one way stretch parallel to the y axis, scale factor 2, with x axis invariant
k) a shear with scale factor 1, x axis invariant
l) a shear with scale factor 2, y axis invariant.

COMBINATIONS OF TRANSFORMATIONS

Two or more matrices can quite easily be *combined* by finding the product of their transformation matrices.

WORKED EXAMPLE 8

A transformation is defined as 'reflect in the Y axis, then rotate through 90° anti-clockwise (around the origin)'. What single transformation will this represent? Find the transformation matrix for each transformation.

Reflect in Y axis (see Fig. 10.22):

$$\begin{pmatrix} 1 \\ 0 \end{pmatrix} \rightarrow \begin{pmatrix} -1 \\ 0 \end{pmatrix} \text{ and } \begin{pmatrix} 0 \\ 1 \end{pmatrix} \rightarrow \begin{pmatrix} 0 \\ 1 \end{pmatrix}$$

hence $\begin{pmatrix} 1 & 0 \\ 0 & 1 \end{pmatrix} \rightarrow \begin{pmatrix} -1 & 0 \\ 0 & 1 \end{pmatrix}$

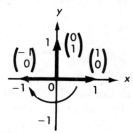

Fig. 10.22

Rotate anticlockwise 90° (see Fig. 10.23)

$$\begin{pmatrix} 1 \\ 0 \end{pmatrix} \rightarrow \begin{pmatrix} 0 \\ 1 \end{pmatrix} \text{ and } \begin{pmatrix} 0 \\ 1 \end{pmatrix} \rightarrow \begin{pmatrix} -1 \\ 0 \end{pmatrix}$$

hence $\begin{pmatrix} 1 & 0 \\ 0 & 1 \end{pmatrix} \rightarrow \begin{pmatrix} 0 & -1 \\ 1 & 0 \end{pmatrix}$

Hence the *combined* transformation will be:

$$\begin{pmatrix} x \\ y \end{pmatrix} \rightarrow \begin{pmatrix} 0 & -1 \\ 1 & 0 \end{pmatrix} \begin{pmatrix} -1 & 0 \\ 0 & 1 \end{pmatrix} \begin{pmatrix} x \\ y \end{pmatrix}$$

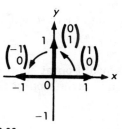

Fig. 10.23

(note how the first transformation performed needs to be on the right),

i.e. $\begin{pmatrix} x \\ y \end{pmatrix} \rightarrow \begin{pmatrix} 0 & -1 \\ -1 & 0 \end{pmatrix} \begin{pmatrix} x \\ y \end{pmatrix}$

which is $\begin{pmatrix} 1 \\ 0 \end{pmatrix} \rightarrow \begin{pmatrix} 0 \\ -1 \end{pmatrix}$ and $\begin{pmatrix} 0 \\ 1 \end{pmatrix} \rightarrow \begin{pmatrix} -1 \\ 0 \end{pmatrix}$

seen as Fig. 10.24. Hence a reflection in the line $y = -x$.

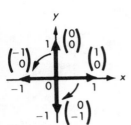

Fig. 10.24

> Remember, give the answer as a single transformation. It's wrong if you state two transformations.

EXERCISE 13

Find the combination of the transformations:

i) rotate 90° clockwise around the origin then reflect in the x axis.
ii) reflect in the x axis and then rotate 90° clockwise around the origin.

5 > INVERSE TRANS-FORMATIONS

The *inverse* of a transformation is that transformation which moves a shape back to where it started. For example:
the inverse of 'rotation of 90° clockwise around the origin' is . . .
        a 'rotation of 90° anticlockwise around the origin.'
Or, the inverse of 'an enlargement of scale factor 3, centre of enlargement (0, 0)', is 'an enlargement of scale factor $\frac{1}{3}$, centre of enlargement (0, 0)'. *Self inverses* are those that are the inverses of themselves; all reflections are self inverses. For example, the inverse of

   'reflection in the x-axis' is 'reflection in the x-axis'.

The matrix representing the inverse of a transformation T, will be the inverse matrix of the matrix representing T.

WORKED EXAMPLE 9

Find the matrix defining the inverse of the transformation T, where $T: \begin{pmatrix} x \\ y \end{pmatrix} \rightarrow \begin{pmatrix} 2 & 3 \\ 1 & 2 \end{pmatrix} \begin{pmatrix} x \\ y \end{pmatrix}$, and hence find the point P that has the image under T of (3, 1).

Inverse matrix of $\begin{pmatrix} 2 & 3 \\ 1 & 2 \end{pmatrix}$ is given by $\dfrac{1}{ad - bc} \begin{pmatrix} d & -b \\ -c & a \end{pmatrix}$

where $a = 2, b = 3, c = 1$ and $d = 2$.

Hence inverse matrix is $\dfrac{1}{(4 - 3)} \begin{pmatrix} 2 & -3 \\ -1 & 2 \end{pmatrix} = \begin{pmatrix} 2 & -3 \\ -1 & 2 \end{pmatrix}$

So the point P will be $\begin{pmatrix} 2 & -3 \\ -1 & 2 \end{pmatrix} \begin{pmatrix} 3 \\ 1 \end{pmatrix} = \begin{pmatrix} 3 \\ -1 \end{pmatrix}$

INVARIANCE

Most transformations have a point or a line of points that do not alter under the transformation. These are called 'invariant points' or the 'invariant line'. For example: in the transformation 'rotation of 90° clockwise about (0, 0)' the point (0, 0) is the invariant point (see Fig. 10.25).
NB. The centre of rotation will always be the point of invariance of a rotation.
As in any reflection, the line of reflection is the invariant line.
   Most transformations have some invariant points, i.e. points that will not change under the transformation.

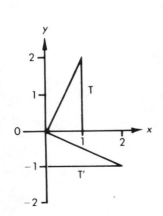

Fig. 10.25

⇒ Reflections   . . . have the mirror line as invariant.
⇒ Rotations   . . . have the centre of rotation as an invariant point.
⇒ Enlargements . . . have the centre of enlargement as an invariant point.
⇒ Stretches   . . . have any given line as invariant.
⇒ Shears   . . . have any given line as invariant.
⇒ Translations . . . have no invariant points.

EXERCISE 14

Write down the invariant point(s) of the transformations represented by:

i) $\begin{pmatrix} 0 & -1 \\ -1 & 0 \end{pmatrix}$ ii) $\begin{pmatrix} 2 & 0 \\ 0 & 1 \end{pmatrix}$

AREA FACTORS OF TRANSFORMATIONS

Some transformations, like rotations and reflections, do not change the area of the shape when it is transformed.

Yet others like enlargements and stretches *do* change the area of the shape. The increase of the area is given by the *area factor*, which is equal to the value of the determinant of the transformation matrix.

For example.

The transformation represented by the matrix $\begin{pmatrix} 2 & 3 \\ 0 & 2 \end{pmatrix}$ will have an area factor of 4, because the determinant is $(2 \times 2 - 3 \times 0) = 4$.

> **Finding the area factor.**

EXERCISE 15

a) What is the area factor of the matrix $\begin{pmatrix} 4 & 2 \\ 2 & 1 \end{pmatrix}$?

b) Explain the geometrical significance of your answer to a).

S O L U T I O N S   T O   E X E R C I S E S

S1

a) i) $2P = B \Rightarrow P = \frac{1}{2}B = \frac{1}{2}\begin{pmatrix} 3 & 1 \\ 4 & 2 \\ 0 & 3 \end{pmatrix} = \begin{pmatrix} 1\frac{1}{2} & \frac{1}{2} \\ 2 & 1 \\ 0 & 1\frac{1}{2} \end{pmatrix}$

ii) $\frac{1}{2}P = B \Rightarrow P = 2B = 2\begin{pmatrix} 3 & 1 \\ 4 & 2 \\ 0 & 3 \end{pmatrix} = \begin{pmatrix} 6 & 2 \\ 8 & 4 \\ 0 & 6 \end{pmatrix}$

b) $2P + Q = \begin{pmatrix} 4 & 2x \\ 6 & 8 \end{pmatrix} + \begin{pmatrix} 5 & 2 \\ y & 1 \end{pmatrix}$

$\Rightarrow 2x = 2 \Rightarrow x = 1; y = 6.$

S2

a) $MN = \begin{pmatrix} 1 & 2 \\ 3 & 1 \end{pmatrix}\begin{pmatrix} -1 & 2 \\ 0 & 1 \end{pmatrix} = \begin{pmatrix} -1+0 & 2+2 \\ -3+0 & 6+1 \end{pmatrix} = \begin{pmatrix} -1 & 4 \\ -3 & 7 \end{pmatrix}$

b) $N + P = \begin{pmatrix} -1 & 2 \\ 0 & 1 \end{pmatrix} + \begin{pmatrix} 0 & 2 \\ 3 & -1 \end{pmatrix} = \begin{pmatrix} -1 & 4 \\ 3 & 0 \end{pmatrix}$

c) $M(N + P) = \begin{pmatrix} 1 & 2 \\ 3 & 1 \end{pmatrix}\begin{pmatrix} -1 & 4 \\ 3 & 0 \end{pmatrix} = \begin{pmatrix} 5 & 4 \\ 0 & 12 \end{pmatrix}$

d) $M^2 = \begin{pmatrix} 1 & 2 \\ 3 & 1 \end{pmatrix}\begin{pmatrix} 1 & 2 \\ 3 & 1 \end{pmatrix} = \begin{pmatrix} 7 & 4 \\ 6 & 7 \end{pmatrix}$

S3

a) $\dfrac{1}{6-4}\begin{pmatrix} 2 & -4 \\ -1 & 3 \end{pmatrix} = \dfrac{1}{2}\begin{pmatrix} 2 & -4 \\ -1 & 3 \end{pmatrix} = \begin{pmatrix} 1 & -2 \\ -\frac{1}{2} & 1\frac{1}{2} \end{pmatrix}$

b) $\dfrac{1}{8-9}\begin{pmatrix} 2 & -3 \\ -3 & 4 \end{pmatrix} = -1\begin{pmatrix} 2 & -3 \\ -3 & 4 \end{pmatrix} = \begin{pmatrix} -2 & 3 \\ 3 & -4 \end{pmatrix}$

c) singular since determinant is zero.

d) $\dfrac{1}{-4+3}\begin{pmatrix} -2 & 1 \\ -3 & 2 \end{pmatrix} = -1\begin{pmatrix} -2 & 1 \\ -3 & 2 \end{pmatrix} = \begin{pmatrix} 2 & -1 \\ 3 & -2 \end{pmatrix}$

S4

a) $\underline{a} = \begin{pmatrix} 2 \\ 1 \end{pmatrix}$ $\underline{b} = \begin{pmatrix} -3 \\ 3 \end{pmatrix}$ $\underline{c} = \begin{pmatrix} -2 \\ -2 \end{pmatrix}$ $\underline{d} = \begin{pmatrix} -1 \\ 1 \end{pmatrix}$ $\underline{e} = \begin{pmatrix} 4 \\ 2 \end{pmatrix}$ $\underline{f} = \begin{pmatrix} 2 \\ 2 \end{pmatrix}$ $\underline{g} = \begin{pmatrix} 2 \\ 1 \end{pmatrix}$

b) $\underline{e} = 2\underline{a}, \quad \underline{a} = \underline{g}, \quad \underline{d} = 2\underline{g}; \quad \underline{b} = 3\underline{d}, \quad \underline{c} = -\underline{f}$

S5

a) $|\vec{AB}| = \sqrt{(5^2 + (-1)^2)} = \sqrt{(25+1)} = \sqrt{26} = 5.1$

b) It has moved the length of the vector $\begin{pmatrix} -4 \\ 3 \end{pmatrix}$

$= \sqrt{(-4^2 + 3^2)} = \sqrt{(16+9)} = \sqrt{25} = 5.$

S6

a) $\underline{a} + \underline{b} = \begin{pmatrix} 2 \\ 7 \end{pmatrix}$ b) $\underline{a} - \underline{c} = \begin{pmatrix} 5 \\ 5 \end{pmatrix}$ c) $\underline{c} + \underline{b} = \begin{pmatrix} -3 \\ 2 \end{pmatrix}$

d) $(\underline{a} + \underline{b}) - \underline{c} = \begin{pmatrix} 3 \\ 9 \end{pmatrix}$

S7

a) $\vec{OP} = \frac{1}{2}\underline{a}$ b) $\vec{AB} = \underline{b} - \underline{a}$ c) $\vec{AQ} = \frac{1}{2}(\underline{b} - \underline{a})$

d) $\vec{PQ} = \vec{PA} + \vec{AQ} = \frac{1}{2}\underline{a} + \frac{1}{2}(\underline{b} - \underline{a}) = \frac{1}{2}\underline{b}$

e) $\vec{SR} = \vec{SC} + \vec{CR} = \frac{1}{2}\underline{c} + \frac{1}{2}(\underline{b} - \underline{c}) = \frac{1}{2}\underline{b}$

f) $\vec{PQ} = \frac{1}{2}\underline{b}$ and $\vec{SR} = \frac{1}{2}\underline{b}$ hence $\vec{PQ} = \vec{SR}$, parallel and equal.

g) $\vec{PS} = \frac{1}{2}\underline{c} - \frac{1}{2}\underline{a} = \frac{1}{2}(\underline{c} - \underline{a})$

$\vec{QR} = \vec{QB} + \vec{BR} = \frac{1}{2}(\underline{b} - \underline{a}) + \frac{1}{2}(\underline{c} - \underline{b}) = \frac{1}{2}\underline{b} - \frac{1}{2}\underline{a} + \frac{1}{2}\underline{c} - \frac{1}{2}\underline{b} = \frac{1}{2}(\underline{c} - \underline{a})$

hence $\vec{PS} = \vec{QR}$, parallel and equal.

h) the quadrilateral PQRS is a parallelogram.

S8

We need to define a minimum number of vectors.

Let $\vec{OC} = \underline{c}$ then $\vec{AB} = 2\underline{c}$ and $\vec{OA} = \underline{a}$.

It then follows that

$\vec{OB} = \underline{a} + 2\underline{c}$

and $\vec{AC} = -\underline{a} + \underline{c} = \underline{c} - \underline{a}$

To define D

$\vec{OD} = h\vec{OB}$ $\vec{AD} = k\vec{AC}$

$= h(\underline{a} + 2\underline{c})$ $= k(\underline{c} - \underline{a})$

Express $\vec{OD}$ in two different ways:

$\vec{OD} = h(\underline{a} + 2\underline{c})$ and $\vec{OD} = \vec{OA} + \vec{AD}$

$= \underline{a} + k(\underline{c} - \underline{a})$

hence h($\underline{a}$ + 2$\underline{c}$) = $\underline{a}$ + k($\underline{c}$ − $\underline{a}$)

h$\underline{a}$ + 2h$\underline{c}$ = $\underline{a}$ + k$\underline{c}$ − k$\underline{a}$

h$\underline{a}$ − $\underline{a}$ + k$\underline{a}$ = k$\underline{c}$ − 2h$\underline{c}$

(h − 1 + k)$\underline{a}$ = (k − 2h)$\underline{c}$

Since $\underline{a}$ and $\underline{c}$ are NOT parallel

then (h − 1 + k) = (k − 2h) = 0

This forms two simultaneous equations which solve to give

h = $\frac{1}{3}$ and k = $\frac{2}{3}$

hence $\overrightarrow{OD}$ = $\frac{1}{3}\overrightarrow{OB}$ and $\overrightarrow{AD}$ = $\frac{2}{3}\overrightarrow{AC}$

hence D divides OB into the ratio 1:2, $\dfrac{OD}{DB} = \dfrac{1}{2}$

D divides AC into the ratio 2:1, $\dfrac{AD}{DC} = \dfrac{2}{1}$

S9

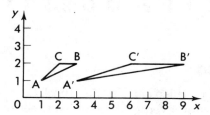

Fig. 10.26

S10

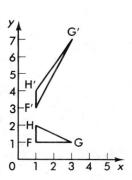

Fig. 10.27

S11

i) reflection in the line $y = x$
ii) rotation of 90° anticlockwise around the origin
iii) enlargement, scale factor 2, centre of enlargement the origin.

S12

a) $\begin{pmatrix} -1 & 0 \\ 0 & 1 \end{pmatrix}$ b) $\begin{pmatrix} 0 & 1 \\ -1 & 0 \end{pmatrix}$ c) $\begin{pmatrix} -1 & 0 \\ 0 & -1 \end{pmatrix}$ d) $\begin{pmatrix} 0 & -1 \\ 1 & 0 \end{pmatrix}$

e) $\begin{pmatrix} 0 & 1 \\ 1 & 0 \end{pmatrix}$ f) $\begin{pmatrix} 0 & -1 \\ -1 & 0 \end{pmatrix}$ g) $\begin{pmatrix} 2 & 0 \\ 0 & 2 \end{pmatrix}$ h) $\begin{pmatrix} 3 & 0 \\ 0 & 3 \end{pmatrix}$

i) $\begin{pmatrix} 2 & 0 \\ 0 & 1 \end{pmatrix}$ j) $\begin{pmatrix} 1 & 0 \\ 0 & 2 \end{pmatrix}$ k) $\begin{pmatrix} 1 & 1 \\ 0 & 1 \end{pmatrix}$ l) $\begin{pmatrix} 1 & 2 \\ 0 & 1 \end{pmatrix}$

S13

i) combine the two transformations with base vectors or otherwise to give a 'reflection in the line $y = x$'.
ii) reflection in the line $y = -x$.

(Note that when you combine transformations in different orders, you usually get a different result.)

S14

i) the matrix can be seen to represent a reflection in the line $y = -x$, which is the invariant line.

ii) try out the transformation to see that it 'stretches' out from the y axis, which is the invariant line.

S15

a) the determinant of the matrix is $4 - 4 = 0$; scale factor is 0.

b) the transformation $\begin{pmatrix} 4 & 2 \\ 2 & 1 \end{pmatrix}$ will reduce any shape to a flat line.

EXAMINATION TYPE QUESTIONS

Q1

In a video game in Fig. 10.28, the screen is 100 units by 100 units. The player has to enter a vector to give the direction the ball will travel. The ball starts at O(0, 0).

John enters the vector $\begin{pmatrix} 1 \\ 2 \end{pmatrix}$ and the ball moves, making an angle $a°$ with OR.

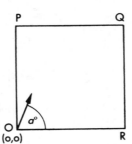

Fig. 10.28

a) What is the value of a?

b) The position of the ball as it moves to the top of the screen, PQ, can be written as $K\begin{pmatrix} 1 \\ 2 \end{pmatrix}$. What is the value of K when the ball reaches PQ?

c) What are the co-ordinates of the point where the ball hits PQ?

d) When the ball hits PQ it rebounds so that the 'new' path is at 90° to the 'old' path. Which vector describes the ball's direction after it rebounds from PQ?

e) What are the co-ordinates of the point where the ball hits QR?　　(WJEC)

Q2

On the isometric grid in Fig. 10.29, $\overrightarrow{OA}$ and $\overrightarrow{OB}$ represent $\underline{a}$ and $\underline{b}$ respectively.

> Remember, underlined letters or bold letters (as in diagram) indicate vectors.

Fig. 10.29

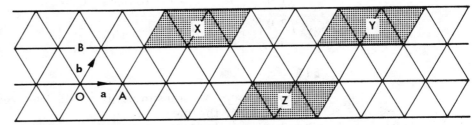

Express, in terms of $\underline{a}$ and $\underline{b}$, the translation which maps

a) shape X onto shape Y.

b) shape X onto shape Z.　　(NEAB)

Q3

Transformation A is 'reflect in the line y = x,' followed by the translation $\begin{pmatrix} -1 \\ 1 \end{pmatrix}$.

Transformation B is 'reflect in the line x + y = 0.'

a) On graph paper, using a scale of 2 cm to 1 unit on each axis,
   i) draw the triangle, T, with corners at (0, 0), (2, 0) and (2, 1),
   ii) draw the image of T under A. Label it T'.
b) Draw the image of T' under B. Label it T''.
c) T may be mapped directly onto T'' by the transformation C:

   'half-turn about point W, followed by a translation $\begin{pmatrix} p \\ q \end{pmatrix}$'.

   Find the co-ordinates of W and the vector $\begin{pmatrix} p \\ q \end{pmatrix}$.
            (ULEAC)

Q4

OPQR is a parallelogram. The vectors x and y are such that
$$\overrightarrow{OP} = \underline{x} + \underline{y} \text{ and } \overrightarrow{OR} = \underline{x} - \underline{y}.$$

a) Express, as simply as possible, in terms of x and/or y
   i) $\overrightarrow{OQ}$; ii) $\overrightarrow{RP}$
b) What special type of parallelogram is OPQR
   i) when $|\underline{x} + \underline{y}| = |\underline{x} - \underline{y}|$?
   ii) when $|\underline{x}| = |\underline{y}|$?
            (MEG)

Q5

> Remember base vectors, but do explain what you've done.

A transformation, T, consists of a 90° anti-clockwise rotation about the origin (0, 0) followed by a translation of $\begin{pmatrix} 6 \\ 4 \end{pmatrix}$.

a) Work out and write down the matrix which represents a 90° anti-clockwise rotation about the origin (0, 0).
b) AB is a line segment with co-ordinates A(1, 2) and B(2, 4). Find the image of this line segment AB under the transformation T. Draw both AB and its image on a suitable pair of axes.
c) There is one point (called the invariant point) which remains in its original position under the transformation T. Find the co-ordinates of this point.
d) The transformation T is equivalent to a single rotation. State the centre and the angle of the rotation.
            (NEAB)

Q6

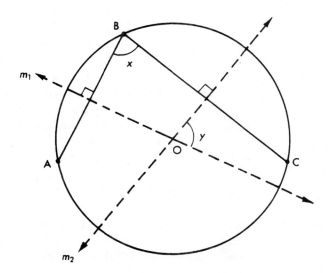

Fig. 10.30

In Fig. 10.30, A, B and C are three points on the circumference of a circle with centre O. The diameters at right-angles to AB and BC are m_1 and m_2 respectively. M_1 and M_2 are the transformations 'reflect in m_1' and 'reflect in m_2' respectively.

a) Identity $M_1(A)$, the image of A under the transformation M_1.
b) Identify   i) $M_2(B)$;   ii) $M_2M_1(A)$.
c) Explain why, in the figure, the angles marked x and y are equal.
d) Describe fully the single transformation equivalent to M_2M_1 and hence express angle AOC in terms of y.
e) Comment on the relationship between the angles AOC and ABC.   (MEG)

Q7

The matrix M is defined as $M = \begin{pmatrix} -1 & 3 \\ -1 & 1 \end{pmatrix}$

a) Calculate M^2.
    The triangle T has vertices A(1, 1), B(4, 1) and C(1, 2).
b) Find the co-ordinates of the vertices of T_1, the image of T under the transformation whose matrix is M^2.
c) Using graph paper and taking a scale of 1 cm to 1 unit on each axis, draw and label the triangles T and T_1.
d) Describe fully, in words, the *single* transformation which maps T onto T_1.
                                                                        (ULEAC)

Q8

Look at Fig. 10.31.

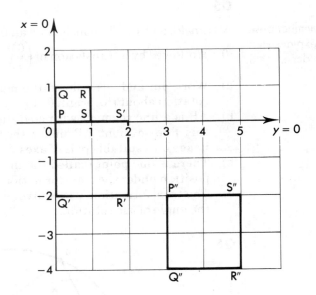

Fig. 10.31

a) Describe *two* successive transformations which will map the unit square PQRS onto the square PQ′R′S′.
b) Hence, or otherwise, give the transformation matrix which will map the square PQRS onto the square PQ′R′S.
c) A transformation T which maps the unit square PQRS onto the square

P″Q″R″S″ is given by $\begin{pmatrix} x \\ y \end{pmatrix} \rightarrow \begin{pmatrix} ax + b \\ cy + d \end{pmatrix}$.

    By using the result obtained in part b), or otherwise, find the values of a, b, c and d.
d) What transformation matrix will map the square PQ′R′S′ onto the square PQRS?
                                                                        (NEAB)

Q9

In Fig. 10.32, OABC is a plane quadrilateral with $\vec{OA} = 4\underline{a}$, $\vec{OB} = 2\underline{a} + 2\underline{c}$, $\vec{OC} = 3\underline{c}$.

> Again, remember you can underline a letter or (as in the diagram) show the letter as bold to indicate a vector.

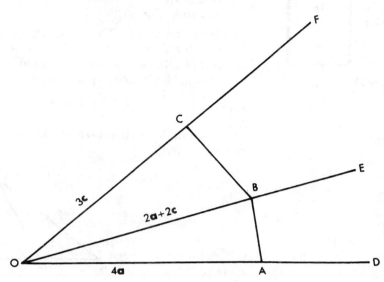

Fig. 10.32

a) Express the vectors $\vec{CO}$, $\vec{CB}$ and $\vec{AB}$ in terms of $\underline{a}$ or $\underline{c}$ or $\underline{a}$ and $\underline{c}$.

The lines OA, OB and OC are produced to D, E and F respectively, where OC = CF and OB : BE = OA : AD = 2 : 1.

b) Find $\vec{FC}$, $\vec{FE}$ and $\vec{DE}$ in terms of $\underline{a}$ or $\underline{c}$ or $\underline{a}$ and $\underline{c}$.

c) Write down two geometrical facts about the points D, E and F. (ULEAC)

Q10

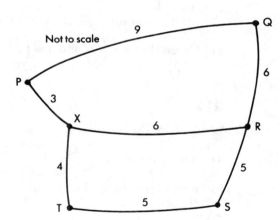

Fig. 10.33

The map in Fig. 10.33 shows the main roads between five villages, P, Q, R, S and T, X is merely a road junction. The numbers on the map are distances in kilometres.

A wholesaler wishes to site his warehouse so that he can best serve the small shops in each village. The wholesaler takes the goods to the shops visiting a different village each day.

a) Complete the matrix **D** in Fig. 10.34 which shows the least road distance between any pair of villages.

$$
\mathbf{D} = \begin{array}{c} \\ P \\ Q \\ R \\ S \\ T \end{array}
\begin{array}{c} \begin{array}{ccccc} P & Q & R & S & T \end{array} \\
\left[\begin{array}{ccccc}
0 & 9 & 9 & 12 & 7 \\
9 & 0 & 6 & 11 & 16 \\
 & & & & \\
 & & & & \\
 & & & & \\
\end{array} \right] \end{array}
$$

Fig. 10.34

$$N = \begin{array}{c} P \\ Q \\ R \\ S \\ T \end{array} \left[\begin{array}{c} 12 \\ 16 \\ 7 \\ 6 \\ 20 \end{array} \right]$$

Fig. 10.35

b) The running costs for the wholesaler depend on both the bulk of goods to be transported and the distance to be travelled. He therefore considers the product of distance and population (assuming that bulk of goods is proportional to the population). The matrix, **N**, of populations (in hundreds) is shown in Fig. 10.35.

Form the matrix **DN** and, on the basis of your result, advise the wholesaler in which village he should place his warehouse.

c) A suitable site becomes available at X. Investigate whether the wholesaler should be advised to take this site. (MEG)

Q11

In the triangle OAB shown in Fig. 10.36, T is the mid-point of AB, and M is the mid-point of AT.

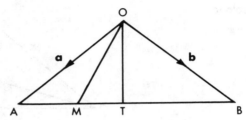

Fig. 10.36

a) Given that $\vec{OA} = \underline{a}$ and $\vec{OB} = \underline{b}$, express as simply as possible in terms of $\underline{a}$ and/or $\underline{b}$:

i) $\vec{AM}$; ii) $\vec{OM}$.

b) Given that $\underline{a} = \begin{pmatrix} 5 \\ 3 \end{pmatrix}$ and $\vec{AB} = \begin{pmatrix} -2 \\ 1 \end{pmatrix}$ find:

i) the co-ordinates of B

ii) $|\vec{AB}|$

iii) the co-ordinates of a point R such that $\vec{OR} = \vec{BA}$.

c) Given that $\underline{s} = \begin{pmatrix} 1 \\ 1 \end{pmatrix}$ and $\underline{u} = \begin{pmatrix} 8 \\ 2 \end{pmatrix}$ and that $k\underline{a} + l\underline{s} = \underline{u}$ then find the values of k and l.

Q12

Write down the inverse of

a) a translation of $\begin{pmatrix} 2 \\ -1 \end{pmatrix}$,

b) a reflection in the line $y = x$,.

Q13

A mapping is defined by $\begin{pmatrix} X \\ Y \end{pmatrix} = R \begin{pmatrix} x \\ y \end{pmatrix}$

where R is the matrix $\begin{pmatrix} 0 & -1 \\ 1 & 0 \end{pmatrix}$

a) Find the image of the point (2, 1) under this mapping.

b) Describe the mapping in terms of a rotation.

c) What is the effect of mapping the R^4?

Q14

a) A translation, T, maps the point (5, 7) to the point $(-2, 6)$.

Express this translation in the form $\begin{pmatrix} x' \\ y' \end{pmatrix} = \begin{pmatrix} x \\ y \end{pmatrix} + \begin{pmatrix} a \\ b \end{pmatrix}$, stating the values of a and b.

b) State the inverse of the translation T.
c) Give the coordinates of the point that would be translated to $(4, -1)$, under the translation T.

Q15

A transformation, T, consists of a reflection in the line $y = x$ followed by a clockwise rotation of 90°, centre the origin. Write down matrices for

a) the reflection,
b) the rotation,
c) the transformation T.

OUTLINE ANSWERS TO EXAM QUESTIONS

A1

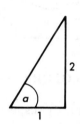

Fig. 10.37

a) $a = \tan^{-1} \dfrac{2}{1}$, giving $a = 63.4°$. See Fig. 10.37.

b) At the top of the screen, the y ordinate will be 100, hence K will be 50 as $2 \times 50 = 100$.

c) $50\begin{pmatrix} 1 \\ 2 \end{pmatrix} = \begin{pmatrix} 50 \\ 100 \end{pmatrix}$, hence co-ordinate is (50, 100).

d) As in Fig. 10.38, the vector perpendicular to $\begin{pmatrix} 1 \\ 2 \end{pmatrix}$ will be $\begin{pmatrix} 2 \\ -1 \end{pmatrix}$.

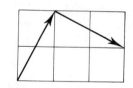

Fig. 10.38

e) The ball needs to go 50 units to the right, hence the ball will move $25\begin{pmatrix} 2 \\ -1 \end{pmatrix} = \begin{pmatrix} 50 \\ -25 \end{pmatrix}$.

25 units down from the top is 75 on the y axis, and QR is $x = 100$, so the co-ordinate where QR is hit is (100, 75).

A2

a) Count how many moves equivalent to a **each** point takes, and this is 4, hence the translation is given by 4a.
b) $3\underline{a} - 2\underline{b}$. Notice how to move down the grid you need to use $-\underline{b}$.

A3

a), b), c). Your solution should be as in Fig. 10.39.

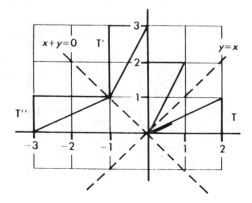

Fig. 10.39

d) There are many different possible answers here, some of which are:

half turn about $(0, 0)$ followed by $\begin{pmatrix} -1 \\ 1 \end{pmatrix}$

or half turn about $(2, 1)$ followed by $\begin{pmatrix} -5 \\ -1 \end{pmatrix}$

or half turn about $(-\frac{1}{2}, \frac{1}{2})$ followed by $\begin{pmatrix} 0 \\ 0 \end{pmatrix}$!!

Could your solution be one of these above?

A4

a) Find your parallelogram from the vectors $\underline{x}$ and $\underline{y}$, as in Fig. 10.40:

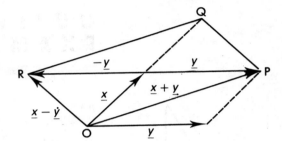

Fig. 10.40

Then it can clearly be seen that
i) $\overrightarrow{OQ} = \underline{x} + \underline{y} + (\underline{x} - \underline{y}) = 2\underline{x}$.
ii) $\overrightarrow{RP} = (\underline{x} + \underline{y}) - (\underline{x} - \underline{y}) = 2\underline{y}$.

b) When $|\underline{x} + \underline{y}| = |\underline{x} - \underline{y}|$ then the sides of the parallelogram OPQR are equal, hence it is a rhombus.

c) When $|\underline{x}| = |\underline{y}|$, then the diagonals RP and OQ, given by $2\underline{x}$ and $2\underline{y}$ respectively, will be the same length, hence it will be a rectangle.

A5

a) Consider base vectors as in Fig. 10.41:

$$\begin{pmatrix} 1 \\ 0 \end{pmatrix} \to \begin{pmatrix} 0 \\ 1 \end{pmatrix} \text{ and } \begin{pmatrix} 0 \\ 1 \end{pmatrix} \to \begin{pmatrix} -1 \\ 0 \end{pmatrix}$$

hence $\begin{pmatrix} 1 & 0 \\ 0 & 1 \end{pmatrix} \to \begin{pmatrix} 0 & -1 \\ 1 & 0 \end{pmatrix}$

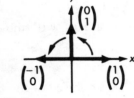

Fig. 10.41

so the transformation matrix will be $\begin{pmatrix} 0 & -1 \\ 1 & 0 \end{pmatrix}$.

b) You should have a diagram as in Fig. 10.42.
The dotted AB being the first rotation of 90° anticlockwise.

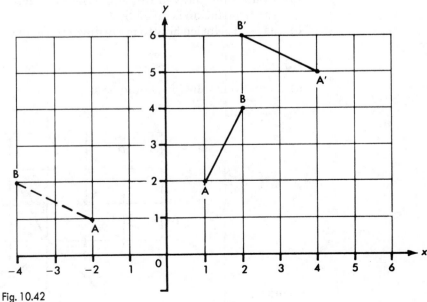

Fig. 10.42

c)   If we define the transformation as T: $\begin{pmatrix} x \\ y \end{pmatrix} \rightarrow \begin{pmatrix} 0 & -1 \\ 1 & 0 \end{pmatrix}\begin{pmatrix} x \\ y \end{pmatrix} + \begin{pmatrix} 6 \\ 4 \end{pmatrix}$

then we obtain $\begin{pmatrix} x \\ y \end{pmatrix} \rightarrow \begin{pmatrix} -y \\ x \end{pmatrix} + \begin{pmatrix} 6 \\ 4 \end{pmatrix}$

So for the invariant point $x = -y + 6 \rightarrow x + y = 6$
and $y = x + 4 \rightarrow -x + y = 4$
Solving these two simultaneous equations we get: $y = 5$ and $x = 1$, hence the invariant point is $(1, 5)$.

d)   The centre of rotation is the invariant point $(1, 5)$. Since the lines AB and A'B' are perpendicular, we just need to look at how the line AB will rotate around $(1, 5)$ to give A'B', and we see it is an anti-clockwise rotation of 90°.

A6

a) $M_1(A)$ will be point B.
b)   i) $M_2(B)$ will be point C;   ii) $M_2M_1(A)$ will be point C.
c)   Sketch the shape as in Fig. 10.43 and label the midpoints of AB and BC, P and Q respectively. Then since angles BPO and BQO are 90° each, $x + QOP = 180°$ and $y + QOP = 180°$. Hence $x = y$.
d)   The combination of two reflections always gives a rotation with centre of rotation the point of intersection of both lines of reflection, with the angle of rotation double the size of the angle both lines of reflection make.

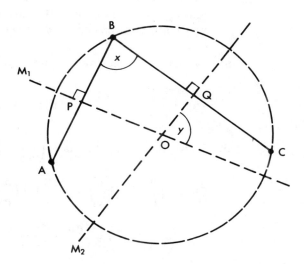

Fig. 10.43

So here the transformation is a rotation, centre of rotation O, through an angle of $2y$. Hence $AOC = 2y$.
e)   AOC is double the size of ABC.

A7

a) $M^2 = \begin{pmatrix} -1 & 3 \\ -1 & 1 \end{pmatrix}\begin{pmatrix} -1 & 3 \\ -1 & 1 \end{pmatrix} = \begin{pmatrix} -2 & 0 \\ 0 & -2 \end{pmatrix}$

b) $\begin{pmatrix} -2 & 0 \\ 0 & -2 \end{pmatrix}\begin{pmatrix} 1 & 4 & 1 \\ 1 & 1 & 2 \end{pmatrix} = \begin{pmatrix} -2 & -8 & -2 \\ -2 & -2 & -4 \end{pmatrix}$

Hence the images of A, B and C respectively are $(-2, -2), (-8, -2)$ and $(-2, -4)$.
c)   See Fig. 10.44.

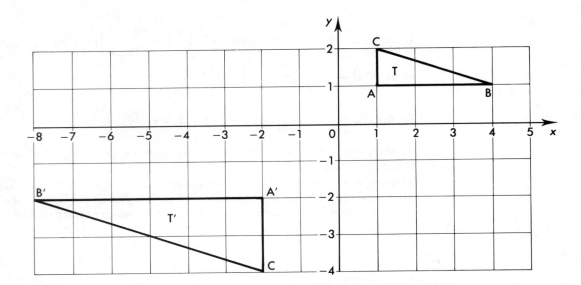

Fig. 10.44

d) An enlargement, scale factor −2, centre of enlargement the origin.

A8

a) Reflection in the x-axis followed by enlargement of scale factor 2, centre of enlargement the origin. (Or the other way round.) (There are more obtuse ways, but none so simple as the above.)

b) Look at base vectors, and see that $\begin{pmatrix} 1 \\ 0 \end{pmatrix} \rightarrow \begin{pmatrix} 2 \\ 0 \end{pmatrix}$ and $\begin{pmatrix} 0 \\ 1 \end{pmatrix} \rightarrow \begin{pmatrix} 0 \\ -2 \end{pmatrix}$.

Hence $\begin{pmatrix} 1 & 0 \\ 0 & 1 \end{pmatrix} \rightarrow \begin{pmatrix} 2 & 0 \\ 0 & -2 \end{pmatrix}$ the matrix.

c) T can also be written as T: $\begin{pmatrix} x \\ y \end{pmatrix} \rightarrow \begin{pmatrix} 2 & 0 \\ 0 & -2 \end{pmatrix}\begin{pmatrix} x \\ y \end{pmatrix} + \begin{pmatrix} 3 \\ -2 \end{pmatrix}$.

Hence $\begin{pmatrix} 2 & 0 \\ 0 & -2 \end{pmatrix}\begin{pmatrix} x \\ y \end{pmatrix} + \begin{pmatrix} 3 \\ -2 \end{pmatrix} = \begin{pmatrix} ax + b \\ cx + d \end{pmatrix}$

$\rightarrow \begin{pmatrix} 2x + 3 \\ -2y - 2 \end{pmatrix} = \begin{pmatrix} ax + b \\ cx + d \end{pmatrix} \rightarrow \begin{matrix} a = 2 \text{ and } b = 3 \\ c = -2 \text{ and } d = -2 \end{matrix}$

d) The answer is the inverse matrix of $\begin{pmatrix} 2 & 0 \\ 0 & -2 \end{pmatrix} = \dfrac{1}{-4}\begin{pmatrix} -2 & 0 \\ 0 & 2 \end{pmatrix} = \begin{pmatrix} \frac{1}{2} & 0 \\ 0 & -\frac{1}{2} \end{pmatrix}$.

A9

a) $\overrightarrow{CO} = -3\underline{c}, \overrightarrow{CB} = -3\underline{c} + (2\underline{a} + 2\underline{c}) = 2\underline{a} - \underline{c}$

$\overrightarrow{AB} = -4\underline{a} + 2\underline{a} + 2\underline{c} = 2\underline{c} - 2\underline{a}$

b) $\overrightarrow{FC} = -3\underline{c}, \overrightarrow{BE} = \frac{1}{2}(2\underline{a} + 2\underline{c}) = \underline{a} + \underline{c}$

$\overrightarrow{FE} = -6\underline{c} + (3\underline{a} + 3\underline{c}) = 3\underline{a} - 3\underline{c}$

$\overrightarrow{DE} = -6\underline{a} + (3\underline{a} + 3\underline{c}) = 3\underline{c} - 3\underline{a}$

c) $\overrightarrow{FE} = 3\underline{a} - 3\underline{c}$ and $\overrightarrow{DE} = -3\underline{a} + 3\underline{c} = -(3\underline{a} - 3\underline{c})$

Hence $\overrightarrow{FE} = -\overrightarrow{DE}$ or rather $\overrightarrow{FE} = \overrightarrow{ED}$.
Hence we see that F, E and D are co-linear (all in the same straight line) and that E is exactly halfway between F and D.

A10

a) See Fig. 10.45

$$D = \begin{array}{c c} & \begin{array}{c c c c c} P & Q & R & S & T \end{array} \\ \begin{array}{c} P \\ Q \\ R \\ S \\ T \end{array} & \left[\begin{array}{c c c c c} 0 & 9 & 9 & 12 & 7 \\ 9 & 0 & 6 & 11 & 16 \\ 9 & 6 & 0 & 5 & 10 \\ 12 & 11 & 5 & 0 & 5 \\ 7 & 16 & 10 & 5 & 0 \end{array} \right] \end{array}$$

Fig. 10.45

b) See Fig. 10.46

$$\left[\begin{array}{c c c c c} 0 & 9 & 9 & 12 & 7 \\ 9 & 0 & 6 & 11 & 16 \\ 9 & 6 & 0 & 5 & 10 \\ 12 & 11 & 5 & 0 & 5 \\ 7 & 16 & 10 & 5 & 0 \end{array} \right] \left[\begin{array}{c} 12 \\ 16 \\ 7 \\ 6 \\ 20 \end{array} \right] = \left[\begin{array}{c} 419 \\ 536 \\ 434 \\ 455 \\ 440 \end{array} \right]$$

Fig. 10.46

The product matrix gives the running costs for the warehouse at P, Q, R, S and T respectively. Hence P is the cheapest at 419.

If a site is available at X, then the distances to each P, Q, R, S and T is given by (3, 12, 6, 9, 4), hence running costs are proportional to the product of this matrix and **N** (see Fig. 10.47), which is less than the previous lowest. So, yes, the wholesaler should be advised to take this site.

$$\begin{pmatrix} 3 & 12 & 6 & 9 & 4 \end{pmatrix} \begin{pmatrix} 12 \\ 16 \\ 7 \\ 6 \\ 20 \end{pmatrix} = 404$$

Fig. 10.47

A11

a) i) $\vec{AM} = \tfrac{1}{4}\vec{AB}$, and $\vec{AB} = \underline{b} - \underline{a}$, hence $\vec{AM} = \tfrac{1}{4}(\underline{b} - \underline{a})$.

ii) $\vec{OM} = \underline{a} + \vec{AM} = \underline{a} + \tfrac{1}{4}(\underline{b} - \underline{a}) = \tfrac{3}{4}\underline{a} + \tfrac{1}{4}\underline{b} = \tfrac{1}{4}(3\underline{a} + \underline{b})$.

b) i) Position vector of B given by $\begin{pmatrix} 5 \\ 3 \end{pmatrix} + \begin{pmatrix} -2 \\ 1 \end{pmatrix} = \begin{pmatrix} 3 \\ 4 \end{pmatrix}$,

hence co-ordinate of B is (3, 4).

ii) Modulus of $\vec{AB} = \sqrt{(2^2 + 1^2)} = \sqrt{5} = 2.24$.

iii) $\vec{AB} = \begin{pmatrix} -2 \\ 1 \end{pmatrix}$ then $\vec{BA} = \begin{pmatrix} 2 \\ -1 \end{pmatrix}$, hence $\vec{OR} = \begin{pmatrix} 2 \\ -1 \end{pmatrix}$, so co-ordinate of R will be $(2, -1)$.

c) $k\begin{pmatrix} 5 \\ 3 \end{pmatrix} + l\begin{pmatrix} 1 \\ 1 \end{pmatrix} = \begin{pmatrix} 8 \\ 2 \end{pmatrix} \rightarrow \begin{array}{l} 5k + l = 8 \\ 3k + l = 2 \end{array}$

Solve simultaneously to give $k = 3$, $l = -7$.

A12

a) translation of $\begin{pmatrix} -2 \\ 1 \end{pmatrix}$.

b) a reflection in the line $y = x$.

A13

a) $\begin{pmatrix} 0 & -1 \\ 1 & 0 \end{pmatrix} \begin{pmatrix} 2 \\ 1 \end{pmatrix} = \begin{pmatrix} -1 \\ 2 \end{pmatrix}$, image is $(-1, 2)$.

b) 90° anticlockwise about the origin.

c) R^4 means the operation R four times in succession hence leaving the shape where it started, i.e. R^4 is the identity.

A14

a) $\begin{pmatrix} x' \\ y' \end{pmatrix} = \begin{pmatrix} x \\ y \end{pmatrix} + \begin{pmatrix} -7 \\ -1 \end{pmatrix}$

b) $T^{-1}: \begin{pmatrix} x' \\ y' \end{pmatrix} = \begin{pmatrix} x \\ y \end{pmatrix} + \begin{pmatrix} 7 \\ 1 \end{pmatrix}$

c) $\begin{pmatrix} 4 \\ -1 \end{pmatrix} + \begin{pmatrix} 7 \\ 1 \end{pmatrix} = \begin{pmatrix} 11 \\ 0 \end{pmatrix}$ answer (11, 0)

A15

a) $\begin{pmatrix} 0 & 1 \\ 1 & 0 \end{pmatrix}$ b) $\begin{pmatrix} 0 & 1 \\ -1 & 0 \end{pmatrix}$

c) $\begin{pmatrix} 0 & 1 \\ -1 & 0 \end{pmatrix} \begin{pmatrix} 0 & 1 \\ 1 & 0 \end{pmatrix} = \begin{pmatrix} 1 & 0 \\ 0 & -1 \end{pmatrix}.$

GRADE CHECKLIST

For a Grade B you should:

Understand: Vector notation and its uses.

For a Grade A you should also:

Understand: The laws of addition and subtraction of vectors.

For a Grade A* you should also:

Understand: How transformations are related by combinations and inverses.
Be able to: Use matrices to define transformations.

A STUDENT'S ANSWER WITH EXAMINER'S COMMENTS

Question

The vertices of a rectangle OABC are O(0, 0), A(5, 0), B(5, 2) and C(0, 2).

a) Taking 1 cm to represent 1 unit on each axis and marking each axis from -6 to 6 draw and label the rectangle OABC. (2)

b) The rectangle OABC is mapped onto rectangle $OA_1B_1C_1$ by the transformation represented by the matrix **P** where

$$\mathbf{P} = \begin{pmatrix} 0 & 1 \\ 1 & 0 \end{pmatrix}.$$

Draw and label rectangle $OA_1B_1C_1$ on your diagram, and describe the transformation fully in geometrical terms. (3)

c) The original rectangle OABC is mapped onto another rectangle $OA_2B_2C_2$ by reflection in the x-axis. Draw and label the rectangle $OA_2B_2C_2$ on your diagram. Write down the matrix **Q** which represents this transformation. (3)

d) The rectangle $OA_1B_1C_1$ can be mapped onto the rectangle $OA_2B_2C_2$ by a single transformation represented by matrix **R**. Describe this transformation fully in geometrical terms and state the relationship between the matrices **P**, **Q**, **R**. (3)

e) Find the smallest positive integer n for which $\mathbf{R}^n = \mathbf{I}$, where **I** is the identity matrix. (2)

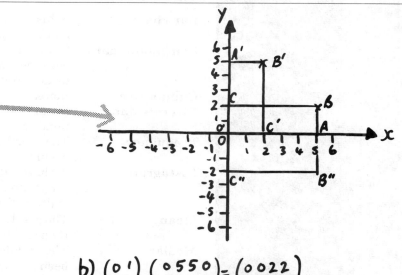

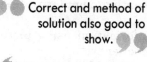

> Good, clear diagram and well labelled, though you might have used the notation of the question.

> Correct and method of solution also good to show.

> The rotation would have been clearer as 90° anticlockwise (but it is still correct).

> It would help if you could show how you got to this answer.

b) $\begin{pmatrix} 0 & 1 \\ 1 & 0 \end{pmatrix} \begin{pmatrix} 0 & 5 & 5 & 0 \\ 0 & 0 & 2 & 2 \end{pmatrix} = \begin{pmatrix} 0 & 0 & 2 & 2 \\ 0 & 5 & 5 & 0 \end{pmatrix}$

reflection in the line $y=x$

c) $\begin{matrix} 1 & 1 \\ 0 & 0 \end{matrix}$, $\begin{matrix} 0 & 0 \\ 1 & 1 \end{matrix}$ so $\begin{pmatrix} 1 & 0 \\ 0 & 1 \end{pmatrix} \rightarrow \begin{pmatrix} 1 & 0 \\ 0 & -1 \end{pmatrix}$

d) rotation of 90° around (0,0).
   P multiplied to Q represents R.

e) $n = 4$

> A good clear answer would get almost full marks, except for missing out on the last part.

PROBABILITY AND STATISTICS

AVERAGE

ILLUSTRATING DATA

DISCRETE OR
CONTINUOUS DATA

CUMULATIVE FREQUENCY

DISPERSION: STANDARD
DEVIATION

PROBABILITY AND
EXPECTATION

CRITICAL PATH ANALYSIS

GETTING STARTED

At the Higher level of GCSE mathematics, probability and statistics is an important topic area. You must be able to read and construct charts and graphs in order to find out information. You may well be asked to draw conclusions from the statistics that you are faced with.

USEFUL DEFINITIONS

Bar chart	A histogram with equal intervals, but may include a space between bars.
Continuous data	Data that can take on every possible value between two numbers and when measured is usually rounded off.
Cumulative	Increasing by successive additions.
Discrete data	Data that can be identified by a single number.
Frequency	The number of times some defined event occurs.
Histogram	A chart with rectangular bars whose area is proportional to the frequency. Often the width of the bars will be different.
Mean	The result of adding together n items of data, then dividing by n.
Median	The middle item of data once the data have been put into order.
Mode	The item of data which occurs most frequently.
Ogive	The line representing cumulative frequency on a graph.
Pictogram	A display of information using pictures to represent the frequency.
Pie chart	A circular picture divided in the ratio of the frequencies it is illustrating.

ESSENTIAL PRINCIPLES

1 ▷ AVERAGE

You need to know how to calculate the mode, median and mean from a *frequency distribution*. Now from a given list of data this is usually no problem. It is when we have *grouped* frequency and need to estimate our averages that the fun begins!

GROUPED FREQUENCY

Score	Frequency
0–20	8
21–40	15
41–60	36
61–80	27
81–100	14

Fig. 11.1

Suppose we are told the information in Fig. 11.1 about a maths exam, and the scores that the 5th year had obtained.

We can tell straight away that the *modal group* is 41–60. We have no way of estimating the modal individual score, without drawing a bar chart.

Estimating the median

This can be done in a number of ways. One is by using a cumulative graph and this will be fully explained in the later part of this chapter dealing with cumulative frequency. The other way is to do a 'linear interpolation', estimating where the median item of data is within its group. Here, we assume that items are spread evenly among any group (or class interval).

For the example given, the median item is the $(100 + 1)/2 = 50\frac{1}{2}$th item of data. We need to find a score corresponding to that item. Just evaluate the cumulative frequency here as 8, 23, 59 . . . until you get beyond the median ($50\frac{1}{2}$). Now we say that the median is

$$\frac{(50\frac{1}{2} - 23)}{(59 - 23)} \times (60 - 41) + 41 = 55.51 \text{ or } 56.$$

What we have done is to work out what *fraction of the way along the group* (41–60) the median is:

hence $\dfrac{50\frac{1}{2} - 23}{59 - 23}$ works out this fraction of (60–41),

Which is then added onto the *lowest value* of that group.

NB. Be careful with *continuous data,* since the lowest value of the group is often found *halfway between* the bottom value of that group and the top of the previous group.

Estimating the mean

This can be done by assuming that each person scored the middle mark of the group they are in, then calculating the total estimated scores and hence the mean. The table of values to do this will be as in Fig. 11.2.

> 66 Notice how the midway is found by adding each 'end score' and dividing by 2. Check it. 99

Score	Midway (m)	Frequency (f)	m × f
0–20	10	8	80
21–40	30.5	15	457.5
41–60	50.5	36	1818
61–80	70.5	27	1903.5
81–100	90.5	14	1267
Totals		100	5526

Fig. 11.2

So the estimated mean is $5526 \div 100$, which is 55.26 or 55.

2 ▷ ILLUSTRATING DATA

You need to be familiar with bar charts and pictograms, but it is unlikely that you will have questions involving these at this high level of GCSE mathematics.

PIE CHARTS

You could well be asked to interpret information from, or construct, a *pie chart*. You should be familiar with this, but do follow through the two worked examples.

WORKED EXAMPLE 1

The 'average family' split their net income in the way indicated in the pie chart in Fig. 11.3. Malcolm had an average family who one month spent £56 on clothes. Calculate i) How much they spent on leisure that month; ii) How much their net income was that month.

i) $£\dfrac{56}{24} \times 136 = £317.33$

(Notice we do it by simple proportions.)

ii) $£\dfrac{56}{24} \times 360 = £840.$

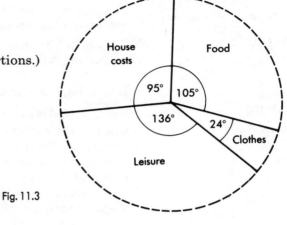

Fig. 11.3

WORKED EXAMPLE 2

A simple survey was done of the supporters of 'Sheffield Wednesday' and it was found to show the following age distribution of people present at one particular match:

Under 16   ... 5770
Over 60   ... 9800
The rest   ... 16 450

Present this information on a Pie Chart. Build up a table to evaluate the angles of the chart, as in Fig. 11.4.

Age	Frequency	Angle
Under 16	5770	$\dfrac{5770}{32020} \times 360 = 65°$
Over 60	9800	$\dfrac{9800}{32020} \times 360 = 110°$
The rest	16450	$\dfrac{16450}{32020} \times 360 = 185°$
Totals	32020	360°

Fig. 11.4

This now needs drawing, starting with the smallest angles first, as in Fig. 11.5.

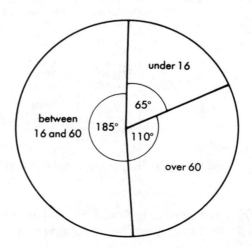

Fig. 11.5

Data is either *discrete* or *continuous*, it cannot be both!

Discrete Data: This is data that can only take on a limited number of different values.

for example:
⇒ the number of children in a family
⇒ the number of cars in a car park
⇒ the price of sweets.

All these examples can only take on a limited number of values, and these are usually integers (whole numbers).

Continuous Data: This is data that can take on an infinite number of different values.

for example:
⇒ your height
⇒ your age
⇒ the weight of a banana
⇒ the amount of petrol in a tank.

All these examples can take on any value and need not be integers; for example height could be 75 cm or 75.1 cm or 75.11 cm or 75.111 cm and so on.
Continuous data are often 'rounded' off to a particular number of decimal places for practical purposes, but nevertheless there are still an infinite number of actual possible numbers.

HISTOGRAMS

A **histogram** is quite similar to a bar graph. The three main differences being that in a histogram:

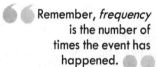

> Remember, *frequency* is the number of times the event has happened.

- there are no gaps between the bars
- the horizontal axis will have a continuous scale
- the areas of the bars represent the frequency of the distribution; hence the frequency scale will always start at 0.

Equal-width Histograms

We first look at histograms in which the width of each bar is the same for all the bars in the histogram.

Here is an example of a *grouped frequency table* showing the time that 165 different people had to wait to catch a train one morning. On each occasion, instead of being recorded separately, the data was placed in a *group* showing the time to the nearest minute.

Time (nearest minute)	0	1	2	3	4	5	6	7	8	9	10
Frequency	15	27	35	30	21	15	9	6	4	2	1

Fig. 11.6 presents a visual picture of this data in the form of a histogram. It is important to draw a *boundary* for each bar in the histogram. This boundary tells us the value of the observation which separates one group in the frequency distribution from another group.

Note that the boundary of each bar in Fig. 11.6 is half-way between the times. This is due to the fact that 1 minute will be in the group $0.5 \leqslant$ time < 1.5 minutes, and so on (since we take the time to the nearest minute).
(Note also that in this case we start the first group at -0.5 minutes to allow the bar for 0 minutes to be of an equal width to the others.)
When we use equal-width histograms we can write *frequency* on the vertical axis. As we shall see, we have to use a different term when we consider unequal-width histograms below.

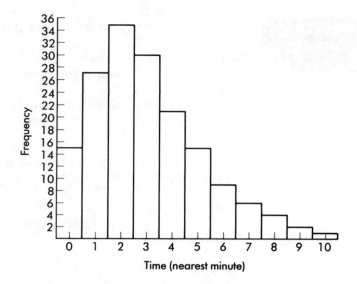

Fig. 11.6

Unequal-width histograms

Sometimes the data will be such that we define our *groups* to be of different sizes. In the previous example each group was one minute in size. In this next example we have a frequency table in which the sizes of the groups vary between 1 minute and 2 minutes.

Time (nearest minute)	0–1	2	3	4	5	6–7	8–9	10
Frequency	42	35	30	21	15	15	6	1

> The vertical axis on a histogram of equal widths is labelled *frequency*, while the vertical axis on a histogram of unequal widths is labelled *frequency density*.

The histogram representing this frequency table is drawn in Fig. 11.7.

Remember that in a histogram it is the *area* of each bar that represents the frequency. So if we *double* the *width* of the bar, we *halve* the *height* of the bar. Instead of 'frequency' on the vertical axis we now have 'frequency density'. This is because we need to multiply each vertical height by the group width in order to find the 'frequency'.

Hence a bar of half a unit width will have a *frequency* of its height multiplied by one half; and a bar of three units width will have a *frequency* of the height multiplied by three.

Notice how the group 6–7 minutes in Fig. 11.7 is shown on the histogram as $5.5 \leqslant$ time < 7.5, a width of 2 units. Hence the *frequency* is found by 2×7.5 (the frequency density) to give 15, which is shown in our group frequency table. The same principles apply to the 0–1 and 8–9 minute groups.

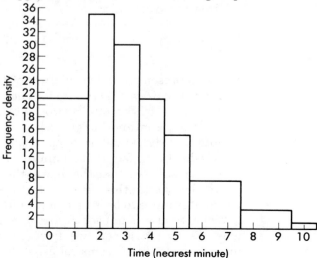

Fig. 11.7

WORKED EXAMPLE 3

The heights of a group of boys were measured to the nearest centimetre. The results were classified in groups, as shown.

Height (nearest cm)	162	163	164	165	166	167	168	169	170	171
Frequency	41	72	87	89	77	60	44	34	21	8

Make a histogram to illustrate the data. Use the groups of 162–163, 164, 165, 166–167, 168–170, 171.

Working

Draw up a new grouped frequency table.

Height (nearest cm)	162–163	164	165	166–167	168–170	171
Frequency	113	87	89	137	99	8

The unit common to all the groups is 1 cm (or some multiple of 1 cm). We will therefore use 1 cm as our unit.

Each of the 'class intervals' shown in the top row of our table will therefore be treated in the following way in our histogram.

162–163 will be 2 units wide
164 and 165 will each be 1 unit wide
166–167 will be 2 units wide
168–170 will be 3 units wide
171 will be 1 unit wide

The heights on the 'frequency density' axis will be as shown in this table.

Groups	Unit width	Frequency	Height on frequency density
161.5–163.5	2 units	113	$113 \div 2 = 56.5$
163.5–164.5	1 unit	87	87
164.5–165.5	1 unit	89	89
165.5–167.5	2 units	137	$137 \div 2 = 68.5$
167.5–170.5	3 units	99	$99 \div 3 = 33$
170.5–171.5	1 unit	8	8

So the unequal-width histogram for this table will be constructed as shown in Fig. 11.8

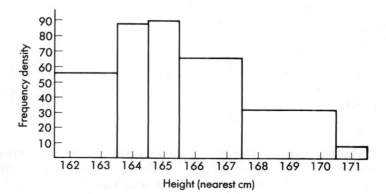

Fig. 11.8

EXERCISE 1

a)   Draw a histogram for the following grouped frequency distribution.

Age (nearest year)	12–15	16–17	18–19	20–21	22–25
Frequency	54	40	24	15	6

b)   Write down the grouped frequency table from which this histogram has been drawn.

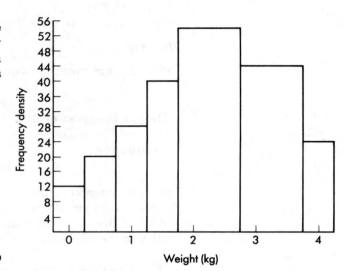

Fig. 11.9

---

4 CUMULATIVE FREQUENCY

It is on your syllabus and there is a very good chance that you will find a question on *cumulative frequency*. It is usually used to create an 'ogive', which is the graph you get if you graph the cumulative frequency. From this ogive you can estimate the median as well as quartiles and percentiles.

It is often called a running total, since that indeed is how the cumulative frequency is calculated. Follow through the example below to see how we draw the graph and how we find information from it.

On September 5th 1988, all the pupils in Pope Pius X School were measured in height to the nearest centimetre; Fig. 11.10 illustrates the distribution.

Heights (cm)	Frequency (f)	Cumulative frequency (cf)
115–120	6	6
121–130	30	36
131–140	85	121
141–150	160	281
151–160	180	461
161–170	41	502
171–175	2	504

Fig. 11.10

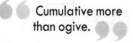 Cumulative more than ogive.

The cumulative frequency has been graphed against the height to give the ogive. Notice its distinctive shape and that the cumulative frequency (c.f.) is on the vertical axis, as it should always be.

We can estimate information such as 'How many pupils were over 165 cm.' We look at the c.f. for 165 cm by reading up, then along to 490, then we know that 504–490 = 14, representing 14 pupils over 165 cm.

Do draw the graphs carefully and accurately as you may need to read information from them.

ESTIMATING THE MEDIAN

From the c.f., find the middle item of data, where n is the total of the c.f., then the median is found by reading along, from $(n + 1)/2$ on the c.f., to the ogive and down.

When we have large numbers, as in our example of 504, then it is often just as good to use the $n/2$ on the c.f. Here, the estimated median can be found by reading along from 252 on the c.f. to the ogive and down, to give the estimated median as 148.5 cm.

QUARTILES

Quartiles are found by dividing the c.f. into quarters and finding the 'quarter' marks. There are three divisions of the c.f. if we quarter it. The first one, the *lower* quartile is found by reading along from $\frac{1}{4}(n + 1)$ on the c.f. The second one is the *median*, and the third is the *upper* quartile found by reading along from $\frac{3}{4}(n + 1)$. Again, for large n you would round off to the nearest suitable integer to read on the c.f.

So for our example already given, we will have quartiles as in Fig. 11.11.

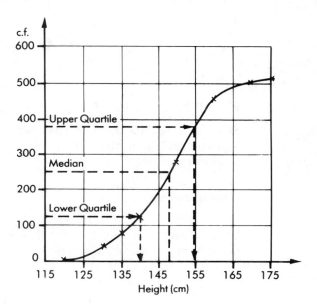

Fig. 11.11

$\frac{1}{4}(504) \rightarrow$ 126 on c.f. to give lower quartile of 140.5 cm.
$\frac{3}{4}(504) \rightarrow$ 378 on c.f. to give upper quartile of 154.5 cm.

THE INTERQUARTILE RANGE

This is the difference between the upper quartile and the lower quartile, and is expressed simply as this difference. Hence for our example above, the interquartile range is 154.5–140.5 = 14 cm.

This range is useful to see how well the frequency is dispersed, as is the 'semi-interquartile range' which is simply half of the interquartile range!

EXERCISE 2

Find the semi-interquartile range, and estimate the median for the distribution of the weights of boxes of chocolates that were supposed to be 200 g, shown in Fig. 11.12.

Weight (g)	–196	–197	–198	–199	–200	–201	–202	–203	–204
Frequency	6	23	35	50	65	44	36	32	9

Fig. 11.12

STANDARD DEVIATION

As well as having an idea of the 'average' of the data it is useful to know how the data is distributed around the average. Do most observations occur near to the 'average' or well away from the 'average'? The interquartile range and the **standard deviation** are called 'measures of dispersion' as they tell us something about how the data is dispersed (distributed) around the 'average'.

We will illustrate the calculation of the standard deviation by comparing the homework marks of a group of ten students in Maths and Science. The table below shows the marks, with A, B, C, etc., being used as a code to represent the ten different students.

INDIVIDUAL	MATHS MARK	SCIENCE MARK
A	3	2
B	9	3
C	3	4
D	6	6
E	5	3
F	10	10
G	7	5
H	4	1
I	8	8
J	5	6

We will start with the Maths marks.

First, we calculate the **mean average** in the normal way, by adding all the marks together and then dividing by the number of marks. For our maths homework marks this gives

$$\text{mean average} = \frac{60}{10} = 6$$

We now add a column to our table, showing the **deviation** (difference) of each mark from this mean value. Our table looks like this.

INDIVIDUAL	MATHS MARK	DEVIATION
A	3	-3
B	9	$+3$
C	3	-3
D	6	0
E	5	-1
F	10	$+4$
G	7	$+1$
H	4	-2
I	8	$+2$
J	5	-1
TOTALS	60	0

Notice that the total of the deviations from the mean is zero, which is what we should expect for any distribution, because the mean is calculated as the arithmetical centre of the distribution of values.

A value that is zero for any distribution is useless for making comparisons between distributions so, to produce a value that differs from distribution to distribution, we now *square* the deviations.

This has the effect of making all the quantities positive. Our table now looks like this.

INDIVIDUAL	MATHS MARK	DEVIATION	SQUARED DEVIATION
A	3	−3	9
B	9	3	9
C	3	−3	9
D	6	0	0
E	5	−1	1
F	10	4	16
G	7	1	1
H	4	−2	4
I	8	2	4
J	5	−1	1
TOTALS	60	0	54

So our 10 marks have a total squared deviation of 54 from the mean average. We now calculate the mean average of these squared deviations. This value is called the **variance** of a distribution. For our maths mark we have

$$\text{variance} = \frac{54}{10} = 5.4$$

Finally, we calculate the **standard deviation**. This is defined as the **square root of the variance**. So, for our maths marks, standard deviation $= \sqrt{5.4} = 2.3$ (to 1 d.p.). Here is a summary of the calculation in the example.

The standard deviation

The standard deviation is a **measure of dispersion**, that is to say, a measure of how widely the values in a distribution are spread. We calculate it by

1. Finding the mean average of the distribution (i.e., arithmetic mean)
2. Finding the deviation (d), of each value from the mean average.
3. Squaring the deviations (d^2) from the mean.
4. Finding the total of the squared deviations. (Σd^2)
5. Dividing this total by the number of values in the distribution to find the variance $\left(\dfrac{\Sigma d^2}{n}\right)$.
6. Square rooting the variance to find the standard deviation $\sqrt{\left[\dfrac{\Sigma d^2}{n}\right]}$.

It should be obvious that a distribution in which the values are widely spread will produce a high value for the standard deviation and a distribution in which the values are closely grouped will produce a low value for the standard deviation. The standard deviation is a useful way to compare the spread of values in two or more distributions.

These are the required calculations to find the standard deviation of our Science marks.

INDIVIDUAL	SCIENCE MARK	DEVIATION	SQUARED DEVIATION
A	2	−2.8	7.84
B	3	−1.8	3.24
C	4	−0.8	0.64
D	6	1.2	1.44
E	3	−1.8	3.24
F	10	5.2	27.04
G	5	0.2	0.04
H	1	−3.8	14.44
I	8	3.2	10.24
J	6	1.2	1.44
TOTALS	48	0	69.60

$$\text{mean average} = \frac{48}{10} = 4.8 \qquad\qquad \text{variance} = \frac{69.6}{10} = 6.96$$

$$\text{standard deviation} = \sqrt{6.96} = 2.6 \text{ (to 1 d.p.)}$$

So, for our mark distributions, we have

MATHS   mean = 6   standard deviation = 2.3
SCIENCE   mean = 4.8   standard deviation = 2.6

From these calculations we can compare the mark distributions and conclude that the Maths marks tended to be higher and more tightly grouped than the Science marks.

WORKED EXAMPLE 4

Calculate the arithmetic mean and standard deviation of the following distribution of heights of 8 plants (in cm).

    4,   6,   7,   9,   10,   13,   14,   17

Working

PLANT	HEIGHT (cm)	DEVIATION, d(cm)	SQUARED DEVIATION, d^2(cm^2)
A	4	−6	36
B	6	−4	16
C	7	−3	9
D	9	−1	1
E	10	0	0
F	13	3	9
G	14	4	16
H	17	7	49
TOTALS	80	0	$\Sigma d^2 = 136$

$$\text{Mean average} = \frac{80}{8} = 10 \text{ cm} \qquad\qquad \text{Variance} = \frac{136}{8} = 17 \text{ cm}^2$$

$$\text{Standard deviation} = \sqrt{17} = 4.12 \text{ cm.}$$

So the arithmetic mean of the plant heights is 10 cm and the standard deviation is 4.12 cm (to 2 d.p.)

EXERCISE 3

Calculate the arithmetic mean and the standard deviation of the marks of 6 pupils.

11, 14, 18, 22, 27, 28

6 > PROBABILITY AND EXPECTATION

You need to be able to work out fractions with probability, you'll score few marks if you can't.

COMBINED EVENTS

Combined events are where two or more events are being combined in some way. When this happens we need to be aware of whether the events are dependent, independent, happening at the same time, or maybe one can happen without the other. We need to consider two main situations 'AND' and 'OR'.

AND

AND is the type where two or more events happen at the same time. You need to multiply together each probability.

WORKED EXAMPLE 5

Find the probability of tossing a coin 10 times and getting a head each time.
    The chance of tossing a head is $\frac{1}{2}$ each time, hence for ten heads in a row, calculate $\frac{1}{2} \times \frac{1}{2} \times \frac{1}{2} \ldots$ (ten times) which is $(\frac{1}{2})^{10} = 9.8 \times 10^{-4}$.

EXERCISE 4

Calculate the probability of dealing four cards face up on the table and each one being an Ace.

OR

OR is the type when either one event *or* the other *or* both occur. In this case we must add together the probabilities. This only makes sense, however, in a situation where all the possible combinations have been considered.

WORKED EXAMPLE 6

Find the probability of cutting a pack of cards and finding a king or a queen.

    The probability of a king is $\frac{1}{13}$, of a queen is $\frac{1}{13}$ and they cannot both happen at the same time, hence the probability of cutting one or the other is $\frac{1}{13} + \frac{1}{13} = \frac{2}{13}$.

AND and OR

This is how many of your examination problems are going to come, in situations where you need a combination of AND and OR.

WORKED EXAMPLE 7

The probability of Paul getting to school on time is 0.95. The probability of Michael being late for school is 0.1. What is the probability on any one day that either Paul or Michael (or both) are late for school?
    The events that we can have are:

A : Paul late AND Michael not late.
B : Paul not late AND Michael late.
C : Paul late AND Michael late.

As the probability of Paul not being late is 0.95, the probability that he is late is $(1 - 0.95) = 0.05$.
As the probability of Michael being late is 0.1, the probability that he is not late is $(1 - 0.1) = 0.9$.

Hence the P(A) = 0.05 × 0.9 = 0.045
        P(B) = 0.95 × 0.1 = 0.095
        P(C) = 0.05 × 0.1 = 0.005.

As we can have A OR B OR C, then add the probabilities to give

P(A) + P(B) + P(C) = 0.145.

Note: The last worked example illustrated the way in which AND and OR can be combined, but for that example there is a quicker way of getting to the final answer. That is to first find the probability of neither being late, i.e. Paul is on time AND Michael is on time. This is $0.95 \times 0.9 = 0.855$.

The probability that one or the other is late = 1—the probability of both not being late = $1 - 0.855 = 0.145$.

As you see, this way is much quicker—if you spot it.

TREE DIAGRAMS

Tree diagrams are useful to illustrate some situations, but are often misused, and in fact used quite unnecessarily in many questions! If you can see what parts you need to get through a probability question then only use a tree diagram if you are specifically told to:

WORKED EXAMPLE 8

When Brian goes to Wales for his holiday he reckons that the chances of a hold up on the motorway are:

on the M1 a probability of 0.4, and
on the M50 a probability of 0.05.

What are the chances of his being held up on the motorways on his holiday to Wales? Here we can illustrate the chances on a tree diagram, as in Fig. 11.13.

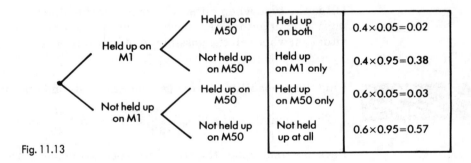

Fig. 11.13

NB. In this situation we were not asked for any one or two probabilities, but for all of them. Hence the tree diagram was useful to do this. Note also that all the final probabilities add up to 1.

WORKED EXAMPLE 9

In a group of 12 men and 9 women, two of them only are known to be Welsh. What is the probability that they are both of the same sex?
This problem, as far as we can tell, then is about choosing, at random, two people both of them being of the same sex.
Here we either choose:

$$\text{man} \quad \text{then man} \quad \dots \frac{12}{21} \times \frac{11}{20} = \frac{132}{420}$$

$$\text{or woman then woman} \quad \dots \frac{9}{21} \times \frac{8}{20} = \frac{72}{420}$$

(Note how the second fraction is changed by the first one.)

Hence both the same sex has a chance of $\dfrac{132 + 72}{420} = \dfrac{204}{420}$.

EXERCISE 5

In a bag of sweets there are 10 chocolates, 5 jellies and 6 mints. Find the probability of taking out any two sweets and both of them being different.

EXPECTATION

One of the main uses of probability is that of predicting some *expected* results. The expected number of times that event A will happen is found by multiplying the probability of A by the number of times the event has the opportunity of happening.

WORKED EXAMPLE 10

The A.A. reckon that any car taken at random has a probability of 0.004 of breaking down. They estimate that on August Bank Holiday there are 300 000 cars using the motorway networks. If they tried to have one patrol car for every 25 breakdowns, then how many patrol cars should they use on August Bank Holiday?

The expected number of breakdowns is $0.004 \times 300\,000$ which is 1200. So the number of patrol cars will be $1200 \div 25 = 48$.

7 ⟩ CRITICAL PATH ANALYSIS

This is the analysis of complex problems, to decide on which tasks to do when, and in what order, so as to complete the task in the shortest possible time. Sometimes you may have a set number of workers to do the task. Other times you may have as many workers as necessary!

The 'critical path' is the set of jobs that *have* to be done in a particular order so as to minimise the time taken to complete the whole job.

WORKED EXAMPLE 11

From the tasks given below to paint and decorate a room, plan a critical path for 2 people to finish the job in the shortest time.

Task	Time	Previous Tasks
A. Strip paint off woodwork	3 h	
B. Strip wallpaper	2 h	
C. Rub down walls	1 h	B
D. Paint door	1 h	A, C
E. Paint window	3 h	A, C
F. Paint skirting board	2 h	A, C
G. Paint ceiling	3 h	
H. Wallpaper walls	6 h	C, F, G

A critical path diagram that splits these jobs into two lines is shown in Fig. 11.14.

Fig. 11.14

The shortest time to do this task is 11 hours.

There are a number of different ways of illustrating these critical paths. Follow through the following worked examples.

WORKED EXAMPLE 12

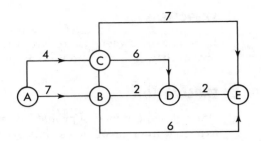

Fig. 11.15

The network illustrates a manufacturing process.
The tasks are marked as Ⓐ, Ⓑ etc and their preceding (previous) tasks are indicated by arrows, i.e. Ⓐ is the first task and Ⓒ and Ⓑ must both be completed before Ⓓ. Ⓔ is the end.

a) How many different ways can the tasks be done
b) Which is the critical path from Ⓐ to Ⓔ

a) The different routes of the network taking in all tasks are:

ACBDE, ABCDE, ACDBE

So there are three possible different ways.

b) By looking at what MUST precede what, leads us to the critical path of Ⓐ—Ⓑ—Ⓔ, which is 13 hours.

WORKED EXAMPLE 13

From the tasks given to cook breakfast, plan a critical path to cook the breakfast. (Assume you can keep cooked food warm). You have a helper.

Task	Time	Preceding Activity
A. Lay the table	5 min	
B. Fry bacon	15 min	
C. cook beans	5 min	
D. defrost bread	5 min	
E. fry bread	4 min	D
F. Boil kettle	5 min	
G. Brew the tea	5 min	F
H. Fry egg	4 min	
I. Eat the meal	8 min	ABCDEFGH

You can cook the bacon, beans, bread at the same time! Try to get the tea brewed just before eating the meal.

Solution

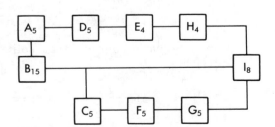

Fig. 11.16

The critical path is A—D—E—H—I which is 26 minutes.

EXERCISE 6

Use a critical path diagram on the job of 'fixing a hole in a pipe' to estimate the time it would take two plumbers to do the job.

Task	Time	Preceding Activity
A. Find leak	10 min	
B. Switch off water	4 min	A
C. Drain the system	15 min	B
D. Cut out piece of damaged pipe	10 min	C
E. Cut new pipe to required length	5 min	
F. Fit new pipe in place	10 min	D, E
G. Switch on water	4 min	F
H. Check pipe not leaking	10 min	G
I. Clean up	10 min	F

SOLUTIONS TO EXERCISES

S1

a) The class-boundaries are 11.5–15.5, etc. Make sure the *vertical height* of each rectangle in the histogram is adjusted in proportion to the *base* of the rectangle. For example, the heights of the rectangles for the first and last class intervals should be *halved* as the bases of these rectangles are *double* those of the other class intervals.

b)

Weight	0	0.5	1	1.5	2–2.5	3–3.5	4
frequency	6	10	14	20	54	44	12

S2

You need a cumulative frequency and graph, as: in Fig. 11.17.

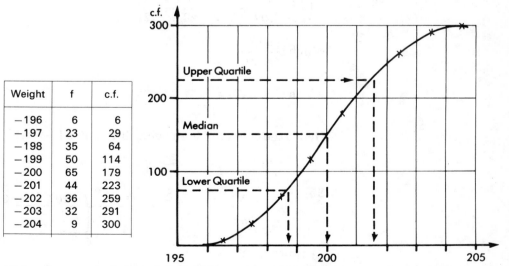

Weight	f	c.f.
−196	6	6
−197	23	29
−198	35	64
−199	50	114
−200	65	179
−201	44	223
−202	36	259
−203	32	291
−204	9	300

Fig. 11.17

Note where we've plotted the points, using 196.5, 197.5 . . . on the horizontal axis as being the most accurate figure for the c.f. due to the giving of information to the nearest gram and rounding off. This is necessary where you can tell this difference easily on the graph.

Look on the $(301) \times \frac{1}{4}$th for the lower quartile, which is $75.25 \rightarrow 198.75$ g

Look on the $(301) \times \frac{3}{4}$th for the upper quartile, which is $225.75 \rightarrow 201.6$ g

Hence the semi-interquartile range is $(201.6 - 198.75) \div 2 = 1.425$ g.

Look on the $(301)/2$th for the median, which is $150.5 \rightarrow 200$ g.

S3

arithmetic mean $= (11 + 14 + 18 + 22 + 27 + 28) \div 6 = 20$.

$$\sum d^2 = (9^2 + 6^2 + 2^2 + 2^2 + 7^2 + 8^2) = 238$$

$$\frac{\sum d^2}{n} = \frac{238}{6} = 39.667$$

standard deviation $= \sqrt{39.667} = 6.3$.

S4

The probability of the first card being an Ace is $\frac{4}{52}$.

The probability of the second being an Ace, given the first is an Ace, is $\frac{3}{51}$.

The probability of the third being an Ace, given the first two are Aces, is $\frac{2}{50}$.

Hence of the fourth being an Ace is ... $\frac{1}{49}$.

Hence the probability that all 4 are Aces is:

$$\frac{4}{52} \times \frac{3}{51} \times \frac{2}{50} \times \frac{1}{49} = 3.7 \times 10^{-6}.$$

S5

The probability is $1 -$ (both being the same)

The probability both being the same is given by:

P(both chocolate) + P(both jellies) + P(both mints),

$$\left(\frac{10}{21} \times \frac{9}{20} \right) + \left(\frac{5}{21} \times \frac{4}{20} \right) + \left(\frac{6}{21} \times \frac{5}{20} \right)$$

which is $\dfrac{90 + 20 + 30}{21 \times 20}$

which is $140/420 = \dfrac{1}{3}$.

Hence the chance of both being different is $1 - \dfrac{1}{3}$ which is $\dfrac{2}{3}$.

S6

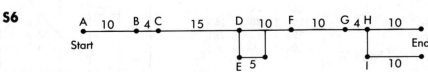

Fig. 11.18

The critical path is ABCDFGH, 63 minutes.

EXAMINATION TYPE QUESTIONS

Q1

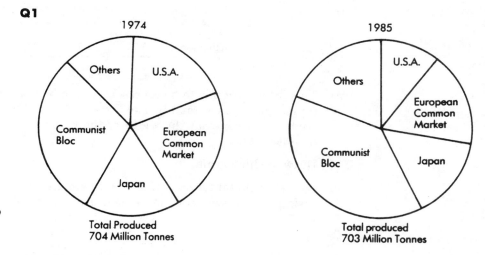

Fig. 11.19

The pie charts in Fig. 11.19 indicate the proportion of steel produced in the world by various economies in 1974 and 1985.
Use these diagrams to answer the following questions.

a) Which economies did not improve their world proportion from 1974 to 1985?
b) i) Measure and state the angle of the sector representing the European Common Market in 1974.
    ii) How many tonnes of steel did the European Common Market produce in 1974?
c) Calculate the percentage increase of the Communist Bloc's proportion of steel production from 1974 to 1985 (NEAB)

Q2

Mrs McAllister, an agent for a firm, kept a record of the time she spent (including travelling) on each customer she saw. During one particular 5 day week, she saw 80 customers and the record of the times spent on them is summarised in Fig. 11.20.

Fig. 11.20

Time (t minutes)	$20 < t \leqslant 25$	$25 < t \leqslant 30$	$30 < t \leqslant 35$	$35 < t \leqslant 40$	$40 < t \leqslant 45$	$45 < t \leqslant 50$
Number of customers	8	10	10	30	18	4

a) Find the mean number of customers Mrs. McAllister saw per day during this week.
b) Mrs McAllister's normal working week is 40 hours. Calculate an estimate of the number of hours overtime she worked during this week.
c) Calculate an estimate of the mean length of time Mrs. McAllister spent per customer.
d) On graph paper, draw a cumulative frequency diagram for this distribution.
e) Use your diagram to estimate
   i) the interquartile range for this distribution
   ii) the number of customers on each of whom Mrs. McAllister spent more than the mean length of time found in part c) (MEG)

Q3

The number of full-time female students in the U.K. in 1991 in various age groups is shown in Fig. 11.21. (Frequencies are given to the nearest thousand.)

Age (years)	16–	20–	25–	35–	45–54	Total
No. (in thousands)	672	139	34	13	4	862

Fig. 11.21

a) This information is to be represented in a histogram using a scale of 2 cm to represent 5 years on the age axis and 4 cm² to represent 100 thousand students. Given that the width of the first rectangle is 1.6 cm, calculate its height.

b) Draw the histogram.

c) By using mid-interval values, estimate the mean age of female students, giving your answer correct to the nearest tenth of a year.   (NEAB)

Q4

A bag contains 5 red discs, 4 white discs and 1 blue disc. Two discs are to be chosen at random, without replacement.

a) Complete the probability tree diagram in Fig. 11.22.

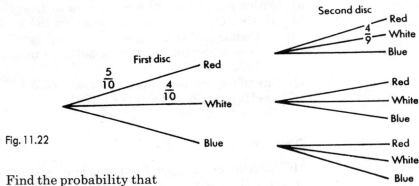

Fig. 11.22

b) Find the probability that
  i) both discs will be red,
  ii) both discs will be blue,
  iii) both discs will be the same colour,
  iv) the two discs will be different colours.   (ULEAC)

Q5

(Give the answers to this question as fractions in their lowest terms.)
In a game, one red dice and one blue dice are used. Both dice are unbiased, but the faces of the red dice are numbered 1, 1, 2, 3, 4, 5 and the faces of the blue dice are numbered 1, 1, 2, 2, 4, 4.

a) The two dice are thrown together, find the probability of each of the following events:
  i) The score on the red dice is an odd number.
  ii) The score on the blue dice is greater than the score on the red dice.
  iii) The scores on the two dice are equal.

b) The two dice are thrown together on two occasions. Find the probability that the score on the blue dice is greater than the score on the red dice on both occasions.   (MEG)

You'll find a diagram . . . not a tree diagram . . . helpful here.

Q6

Part of a children's game involves rolling a normal 6-faced dice, then spinning an arrow as shown in Fig. 11.23.
If on the spinner you get:

a dice—you have another roll of the dice
a spider—you choose a spider part
a foot—you move on one space on a board
a drink—you miss a go.

Fig. 11.23

a)   Find the probability of getting:
   i) a spider
   ii) a foot
   iii) a drink.

b)   To win a game on his next go, John had to
       either roll a 3 on the dice, then spin a spider
           or roll a 5 on the dice, then spin a foot.
     Calculate the probability that John will win on his next go.   (NEAB)

Q7

Mr. Meiring travels to work by car on five days each week. He has to cross three busy junctions. He finds that he is delayed three times a week at the first junction, twice a week at the second junction, and once a week at the third junction. A delay at one junction does not affect a delay at any other junction.

a)   Complete the probability tree diagram in Fig. 11.24, using D for delay, and N for no delay, in the Outcome column.

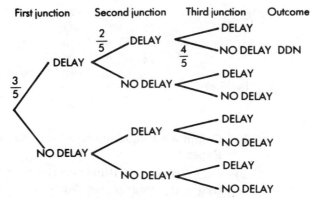

Fig. 11.24

b)   Find the probability that, on any morning he will,
   i) arrive at work without being delayed,
   ii) be delayed at only *one* of the three junctions.   (ULEAC)

Q8

A school entered 50 candidates for GCSE mathematics. There are two papers, each marked out of a maximum of 50. The marks obtained in Paper 1 are shown in Fig. 11.25 and illustrated by the frequency diagram.

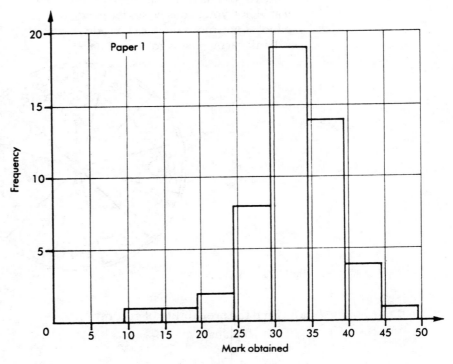

Fig. 11.25

Mark range	0–4	5–9	10–14	15–19	20–24	25–29	30–34	35–39	40–44	45–49
Number of candidates	0	0	1	1	2	8	19	14	4	1

a) Calculate an estimate of the mean mark obtained in Paper 1.
    The marks obtained in Paper 2 are shown in Fig. 11.26.

27	18	31	12	16	37	24	42	15	23
27	27	42	21	3	12	27	24	34	13
9	29	19	32	24	26	33	15	24	25
24	30	23	13	17	6	39	19	18	38
12	18	18	26	31	24	49	12	23	29

Fig. 11.26

b) Compile a frequency table for the marks in Paper 2. Use the same classes as Paper 1.

c) On graph paper, illustrate the data for Paper 2, using the same scales as the frequency diagram for Paper 1.

d) Comment briefly on the differences between the candidate's performances in the two papers. (You may like to use the fact that the mean mark for Paper 2 is 23.6.)   (MEG)

Q9

When a biased 6-sided dice is thrown, a score of 6 is twice as likely as a score of 5; a score of 5 is twice as likely as a score of 4; and scores of 1, 2, 3, 4 are equally likely. Calculate the probability of

    i) a score of 1
    ii) a score of 6
    iii) scoring an even number.

(NEAB)

Q10

In a survey, 100 motorists were asked to record the petrol consumption of their cars in miles per gallon. Each figure was rounded to the nearest mile per gallon and the frequency distribution shown in Fig. 11.27 was obtained.

Fig. 11.27

Miles per gallon	26–30	31–35	36–40	41–45	46–50	51–55	56–60
Frequency	4	6	18	34	20	12	6

a)   i) State the limits of the model class of this distribution.
      ii) Complete the 'less than' cumulative frequency table in Fig. 11.28:

Fig. 11.28

Miles per gallon (less than)	30.5	35.5	40.5	50.5	55.5	65.5
Number of motorists	4	10				

      iii) On graph paper, draw the cumulative frequency curve (ogive) from your completed cumulative frequency table.
b)   Use your cumulative frequency curve to estimate:
      i) the median of the distribution
      ii) the interquartile range.

A 'good' petrol consumption is one which lies between 38 and 52 miles per gallon.

c)   Estimate the number of motorists whose petrol consumption was 'good'.

(NISEAC)

Q11

Five married couples are at a party.

a)   Two people are chosen at random. Find the probability that
      i) they are a married couple,
      ii) one is a man and one is a woman,
      iii) at least one man is chosen.
b)   Four people are chosen at random. Find the probability that
      i) three women and one man are chosen
      ii) no married couple is among the four.

(WJEC)

Q12

Fig. 11.29

Date	Jan. 5	Feb. 16	Mar. 30	May 11	June 22	Aug. 3	Sept. 14	Oct. 26	Dec. 7
Daylight (hours–minutes)	8 h 01 m	10 h 03 m	12 h 48 m	15 h 23 m	16 h 40 m	15 h 19 m	12 h 46 m	10 h 03 m	8 h 02 m

The second line of the table in Fig. 11. 29 gives the length of a 'day' in England (in hours and minutes of daylight) at six-weekly intervals from January 5th, 1995.

a) Complete the table in Fig. 11.30:

Fig. 11.30

Number of weeks after Jan. 5 (x)	0	6						48
Daylight (hours) to one decimal place (y)	8.0	10.1					10.1	8

b) Using scales of 0.2 cm to 1 week and 1 cm to 1 hour along the x and y axes respectively, draw a graph of y against x, joining your points with a smooth curve.

c) i) On the curve, mark the point corresponding to June 1st and label it J.
   ii) Find the hours of daylight on June 1st.

d) i) On your graph, mark the two points at which 'day' is equal to 'night'. Label the left-hand point A and the right-hand point B.
   ii) For how many weeks of the year is 'day' longer than 'night'?
   iii) Estimate the data corresponding to point A. (OCSEB)

Q13

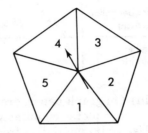

Fig. 11.31

John has a spinner in the shape of a regular pentagon.
Scores of 1, 2, 3, 4, 5 are equally likely when the spinner is spun.
John spins the spinner 200 times and records the scores.

Approximately how many times will he score an even number? (ULEAC)

Q14

On any day during the summer of 1979 the probability that it rained was $\frac{1}{6}$. In 1989, because of climatic changes, the probability that it rained on any day during the summer was only $\frac{1}{10}$.

a) Calculate the probability that any 3 days chosen at random during the summer of 1979 were all wet.

b) Calculate the probability that it rained on a particular date during the summer of 1979 and was dry on the same date in 1989.

Q15

Assume that births are equally likely on each of the seven days of the week. Find the probability that, of two randomly selected people,

a) both were born on a Friday,

b) they were both born on the same day of the week,

c) one will have been born on a Wednesday and the other on a Friday. (NEAB)

Q16

Chess is a game played between two people. Either player can win or the game can end as a draw.
One person has the white pieces and the other person has the black ones.
There is a slight advantage in having white, so a coin is tossed before the game starts. The one who wins the toss plays with the white pieces.

a)   Alwyn and Bernard often play one another at chess. When Alwyn has the white pieces the probability that he will beat Bernard is $\frac{3}{5}$, and the probability that Bernard will win is $\frac{1}{4}$.
    i) Calculate the probability that Alwyn will win the toss and then win the chess match.
    ii) Calculate the probability that Alwyn will win the toss but then lose the chess match.

b)   When Alwyn has the black pieces the probability that he will beat Bernard is $\frac{2}{5}$, and the probability that Bernard will win is $\frac{1}{2}$.
    i) Calculate the probability that Alwyn will lose the toss but then win the chess match.
    ii) Calculate the probability that Alwyn will lose the toss and then lose the chess match.

c)   Use your answers to a) and b) to calculate the percentage of chess matches in which
    i) Alwyn will beat Bernard,
    ii) Bernard beats Alwyn.

d)   What percentage of their chess matches are drawn?   (NEAB)

Q17

An experiment involving a chemical reaction was carried out several times. In each experiment, the temperature of the reaction was taken at the end of one minute.

a)   Complete the table of results shown below.

Temperature (°C)	Frequency	Upper limit for temperature (°C)	Cumulative frequency
41.0–41.1	5	41.15	5
41.2–41.3	2	41.35	7
41.4–41.5	7	41.55	14
41.6–41.7	15	41.75	29
41.8–41.9	7		
42.0–42.1	4		

b)   How many times was the experiment carried out?
c)   On the grid, draw a cumulative frequency polygon to show the reaction temperatures.
d)   Find the interquartile range of the temperatures.
    (Show all construction lines).   (NEAB)

Q18

The lengths, in centimetres, of 10 leaves in a sample were:

5.6,   5.8,   4.9,   6.2,   6.8,   4.8,   5.4,   5.9,   5.3,   5.2

a)   Calculate the standard deviation of these lengths.
b)   The standard deviation of another sample of 10 leaves was 0.432 cm.
    What difference between the two samples is shown by the two standard deviations?   (SEG)

Q19

100 eggs are classified by mass in the following table.

	Mass (g)	Frequency
Extra small	40–42	1
Small	42–46	3
Medium	46–53	25
Standard	53–62	35
Large	62–75	36

a) Draw a histogram to illustrate the data.

b) Calculate estimates of the mean and the standard deviation of this sample.

c) For a normal distribution it would be expected that more than 95% of the distribution would be contained in the interval mean $\pm\,2$ standard deviations. For this sample, using your answers to part b), calculate the numerical limits of this interval and estimate the percentage of this sample which lies within this interval.

Q20

Two plumbers are to replace a radiator. From the given tasks, draw a critical path diagram and find the shortest time the job should be done in.

Replace a radiator

Task	Time	Preceding Activity
A. Buy new radiator	20 min	
B. Switch off water	4 min	
C. Drain the system	15 min	B
D. Take out old radiator	15 min	C
E. Put old radiator in van	3 min	D
F. Put new radiator in place	15 min	A, E
G. Turn on water and fill system	4 min	F
H. Remove air from the system	10 min	G
I. Check for leaks	6 min	G
J. Tidy up	10 min	F

OUTLINE ANSWERS TO EXAM QUESTIONS

A1

a) The ones whose angles have got smaller: Japan, ECM and USA.

b)   i) Any answer between 79° and 83° would be acceptable.

    ii) Your part i) answer $\times\,\dfrac{704}{360}$ = between 154 and 162 million.

c) Again, the angle measurement can be as much as 2° out, but if you were really accurate, the first angle is 107°, the second 138°, hence the proportional increase is $\dfrac{138-107}{107}$. To make this a percentage just multiply this answer by 100 to get 29%.

A2

a) $(8 + 10 + 10 + 30 + 18 + 4) \div 5 = 16$.

b) Figure 11.32 shows how to estimate the total time spent in minutes, which will be 47.7 hours (2860 mins ÷ 60), so she worked approximately 8 hours overtime.

c) $2860 \div 80 = 35.75$ minutes. (36 would do.)

d) See Fig. 11.33.

Time	Halfway (m)	f	m × f
20–25	22.5	8	180
25–30	27.5	10	275
30–35	32.5	10	325
35–40	37.5	30	1125
40–45	42.5	18	765
45–50	47.5	4	190
	Totals	80	2860

Fig. 11.32

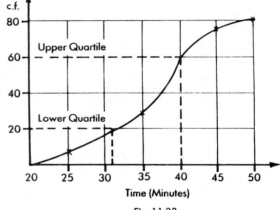

Fig. 11.33

e) i) Upper quartile ($\frac{3}{4}$ × 81)th = 40.5.
    Lower quartile ($\frac{1}{4}$ × 81)th = 31.
    Hence interquartile range = 40.5 − 31 = 9.5 minutes.

    ii) Mean length of 35.75 minutes.
    Read up to the ogive = 33 people below this mark.
    So she would see (80 − 33) = 47 customers for longer than the estimated mean.

A3

a) To represent 672 thousand you need an area of $\dfrac{672}{100} \times 4 = 26.88$ cm², so if width = 1.6 cm, the height $= \dfrac{26.88}{1.6} = 16.8$ cm.

b) The widths and heights of the other rectangles are given in Fig. 11.34.

Age	Width (cm)	f	Height (cm)
16–20	$4 \times \frac{2}{5} = 1.6$	672	$(672 \times 0.04) \div 1.6 = 16.8$
20–25	$5 \times \frac{2}{5} = 2.0$	139	$(139 \times 0.04) \div 2.0 = 2.78$
25–35	$10 \times \frac{2}{5} = 4.0$	34	$(34 \times 0.04) \div 4.0 = 0.34$
35–45	$10 \times \frac{2}{5} = 4.0$	13	$(13 \times 0.04) \div 4.0 = 0.13$
45–54	$9 \times \frac{2}{5} = 3.6$	4	$(4 \times 0.04) \div 3.6 = 0.04$

Fig. 11.34

So your histogram should look like that in Fig. 11.35.

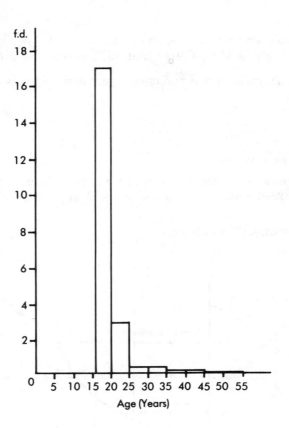

Fig. 11.35

Age	Midway (m)	f (thousand)	m × f
16–20	18	672	12096
20–25	22.5	139	3127.5
25–35	30	34	1020
35–45	40	13	520
45–54	49.5	4	198
	Totals	862	16961.5

Fig. 11.36

c) Your table to estimate this should look like Fig. 11.36.

So your estimated mean will be $16\,961.5 \div 862 = 19.7$ years.

A4

a) See Fig. 11.37.

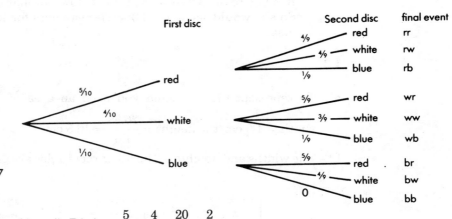

Fig. 11.37

b)   i) $P(rr) = \dfrac{5}{10} \times \dfrac{4}{9} = \dfrac{20}{90} = \dfrac{2}{9}$.

ii) $P(bb) = \dfrac{1}{10} \times 0 = 0$.

iii) $P(\text{same colour}) = P(rr) + P(ww) + P(bb) = \dfrac{2}{9} + \dfrac{4}{10} \times \dfrac{3}{9} + 0 = \dfrac{32}{90}$.

iv) $P(\text{different colours}) = 1 - P(\text{same colour}) = 1 - \dfrac{32}{90} = \dfrac{58}{90}$.

A5

a)   i) $\dfrac{4}{6} = \dfrac{2}{3}$.

The best way to indicate all of the equally likely events to help you find the probability of combined events here is to sketch the following diagrams.

ii)

iii)

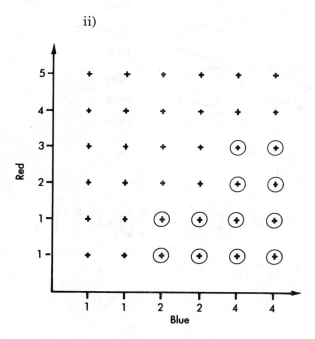

Fig. 11.38

Fig. 11.39

Probability $= \dfrac{12}{36} = \dfrac{1}{3}$

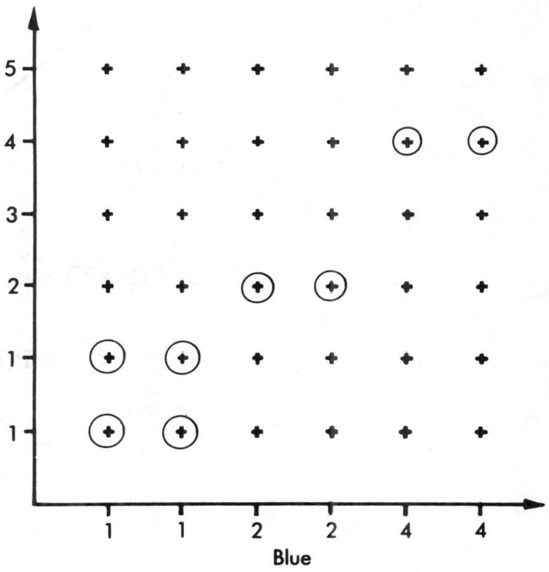

Probability $= \dfrac{8}{36} = \dfrac{2}{9}$

b) $\dfrac{1}{3} \times \dfrac{1}{3} = \dfrac{1}{9}$.

A6

a)   i) $\dfrac{5}{12}$;

ii) $\dfrac{3}{12}$ or $\dfrac{1}{4}$;

iii) $\dfrac{2}{12}$ or $\dfrac{1}{6}$.

b)   A tree diagram may help you to visualise the whole situation, but is not the best method to solve this particular problem.

P(roll 3 then spin a spider) $= \dfrac{1}{6} \times \dfrac{5}{12} = \dfrac{5}{72}$

P(roll 5 then spin a foot) $= \dfrac{1}{6} \times \dfrac{1}{4} = \dfrac{1}{24}$

Add them together to give $\dfrac{5}{72} + \dfrac{1}{24} = \dfrac{8}{72}$

A7

a) See Fig. 11.40.

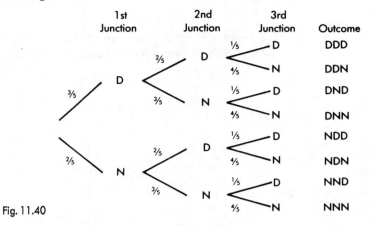

Fig. 11.40

b) i) $P(NNN) = \dfrac{2}{5} \times \dfrac{3}{5} \times \dfrac{4}{5} = \dfrac{24}{125}$

ii) $P(DNN) + P(NDN) + P(NND) = \left(\dfrac{3}{5} \cdot \dfrac{3}{5} \cdot \dfrac{4}{5}\right) + \left(\dfrac{2}{5} \cdot \dfrac{2}{5} \cdot \dfrac{4}{5}\right) + \left(\dfrac{2}{5} \cdot \dfrac{3}{5} \cdot \dfrac{1}{5}\right)$

$= \dfrac{36}{125} + \dfrac{16}{125} + \dfrac{6}{125} = \dfrac{58}{125}$

A8

a) Use the table of values as in Fig. 11.41:

Mark range	Midway (m)	f	m × f
0–4	2	0	0
5–9	7	0	0
10–14	12	1	12
15–19	17	1	17
20–24	22	2	44
25–29	27	8	216
30–34	32	19	608
35–39	37	14	518
40–44	42	4	168
45–49	47	1	47
	Totals	50	1630

Fig. 11.41

Hence the estimated mean = $1630 \div 50 = 32.6$.

b) You should have a table of values as in Fig. 11.42.

Mark range	0–4	5–9	10–14	15–19	20–24	25–29	30–34	35–39	40–44	45–49
Number of candidates	1	2	6	10	10	9	6	3	2	1

Fig. 11.42

c) You should have a diagram as in Fig. 11.43:

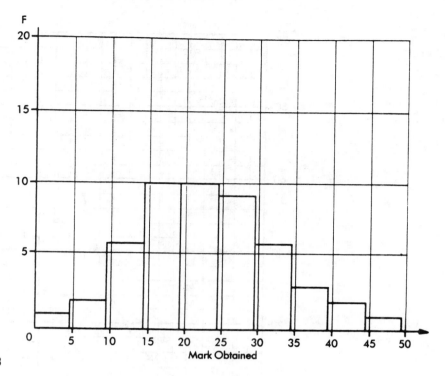

Fig. 11.43

d) They performed better on paper 1 than on paper 2 as the mean marks of 32.6 on paper1 and 23.6 on paper 2 suggest. However, paper 2 has a better range and spread of marks than does paper 1. You could say that paper 1 was a good GCSE paper as most of the students gained over half marks, where paper 2 was not, as most of the students scored less than half marks.

A9

Let the probability of scoring a 4 be x, then the table in Fig. 11.44 illustrates each probability.

Score	1	2	3	4	5	6
Probability	x	x	x	x	$2x$	$4x$

Fig. 11.44

Hence where the total of the probabilities is 1, then $10x = 1$ and so $x = 0.1$,
hence   i) $P(1) = 0.1$
ii) $P(6) = 0.4$
iii) $P(2 \text{ or } 4 \text{ or } 6) = 0.1 + 0.1 + 0.4 = 0.6$.

A10

a)   i) Modal class is 41–50.
ii) See Fig. 11.45.

(Less than) Miles per gallon	30.5	35.5	40.5	45.5	50.5	55.5	60.5
No. of motorists	4	10	28	62	82	94	100

Fig. 11.45

iii) You should have an ogive as in Fig. 11.46.

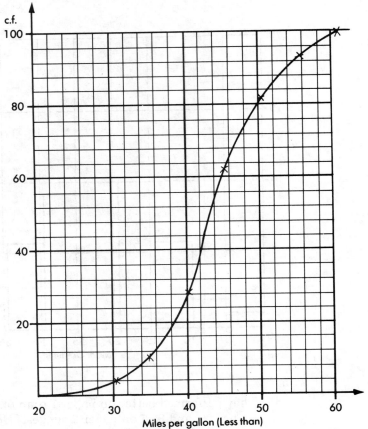

Fig. 11.46

b) i) Median—read off the (101)/2 = $50\frac{1}{2}$th on the c.f. to give 43.8 mpg.
    ii) Upper quartile read off the (101) × $\frac{3}{4}$ = 75.75th on the c.f. to give 48.5 mpg.
    Lower quartile read off the (101)/4 = 25.25th on the c.f. to give 40 mpg.
    Hence the interquartile range is 48.5 − 40 = 8.5 mpg.

c) Reading up to the ogive and hence the c.f. from 38 and 52 miles you get 17 and
    86 respectively. Hence the number of motorists in between this that have
    'good' petrol consumption is 86 − 17 = 69.

A11

a) i) The first person can be anybody, then the probability that the next person
    is married to the first person will be $\frac{1}{9}$.

    ii) Can choose either 'man then woman' *or* 'woman then man', so the
    probability is P(MW) + P(WM) = $\left(\frac{5}{10} \times \frac{5}{9}\right) + \left(\frac{5}{10} \times \frac{5}{9}\right) = \frac{50}{90} = \frac{5}{9}$.

    iii) The quickest way is to find 1 − P(no men).

    P(no men) = P(women then women) = $\frac{5}{10} \times \frac{4}{9} = \frac{20}{90} = \frac{2}{9}$,

    hence answer = $1 - \frac{20}{90} = \frac{70}{90} = \frac{7}{9}$.

    The alternative is to choose either 'man then woman' *or* 'woman then
    man' *or* 'man then man', so the probability is $\frac{50}{90} + \left(\frac{5}{10} \times \frac{4}{9}\right) = \frac{70}{90} = \frac{7}{9}$.

b) Choose either (WWWM) or (WWMW) or (WMWW) or (MWWW)
    i) which in effect is 4 × $\left(\frac{5}{10} \times \frac{4}{9} \times \frac{3}{8} \times \frac{5}{7}\right) = 0.238$

ii) P(first person) = 1 it can be anybody

P(next person *not* married to first) = $\dfrac{8}{9}$

P(next person *not* married to either of first two) = $\dfrac{6}{8}$

P(next person *not* married to either of first three) = $\dfrac{4}{7}$ hence the

probability is $1 \times \dfrac{8}{9} \times \dfrac{6}{8} \times \dfrac{4}{7} = 0.381$.

A12

a) See Fig. 11.47.

Numbers of weeks after Jan. 5th (x)	0	6	12	18	24	30	36	42	48
Daylight (hours) to one decimal place	8.0	10.1	12.8	15.4	16.7	15.3	12.8	10.1	8.0

Fig. 11.47

b) See Fig. 11.48.

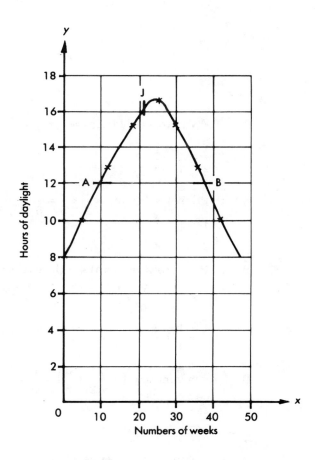

Fig. 11.48

c) i) June 1st is 21 weeks after January 5th.
   ii) Hours of daylight on June 1st = 16.3 = 16 hours 18 min.

d) i) See Fig. 11.48, points A and B.
   ii) This is the number of weeks between A and B, which is 28 weeks.
   iii) Point A is 10 weeks after January 5th, which is 70 days after January 5th, which corresponds to March 16th.

A13

$$P(\text{even number}) = \frac{2}{5}$$

$$\text{estimated number of even numbers} = \frac{2}{5} \times 200 = 80.$$

A14

a) $\dfrac{1}{6} \times \dfrac{1}{6} \times \dfrac{1}{6} = \dfrac{1}{216}$

b) $\dfrac{1}{6} \times \dfrac{9}{10} = \dfrac{3}{20}$

A15

a) $\dfrac{1}{7} \times \dfrac{1}{7} = \dfrac{1}{49}$

b) They could both be born on Sunday *or* Monday *or* etc.

$$= \left(\frac{1}{7} \times \frac{1}{7}\right) + \left(\frac{1}{7} \times \frac{1}{7}\right) + \cdots \text{etc} = \frac{1}{49} \times 7 = \frac{1}{7}$$

c) $\dfrac{1}{7} \times \dfrac{1}{7} = \dfrac{1}{49}$

A16

a)   i) $P(\text{win toss}) \times P(\text{win}) = \dfrac{1}{2} \times \dfrac{3}{5} = \dfrac{3}{10}$

    ii) $\dfrac{1}{2} \times \dfrac{1}{4} = \dfrac{1}{8}$

b)   i) $P(\text{lose}) \times P(\text{win}) = \dfrac{1}{2} \times \dfrac{2}{5} = \dfrac{1}{5}$

    ii) $\dfrac{1}{2} \times \dfrac{1}{2} = \dfrac{1}{4}$

c)   i) $P(\text{win toss and win}) + P(\text{lose toss and win})$

$$\frac{3}{10} + \frac{1}{5} = \frac{5}{10} = \frac{1}{2}$$

    ii) $\dfrac{1}{8} + \dfrac{1}{4} = \dfrac{3}{8}$

d)   Drawn games $= 1 - \left(\dfrac{1}{2} + \dfrac{3}{8}\right) = \dfrac{1}{8} = \dfrac{1}{8} \times 100\% = 12.5\%$

A17

a)   41.8–41.9   7   41.95   36
      42.0–42.1   4   42.15   40

b)   40

d)   upper quartile   41.78
      lower quartile   41.44
      interquartile range = 41.78–41.44 = 0.34.

A18

a)   the arithmetic mean $= 55.9 \div 10 = 5.59$

$$\Sigma d^2 = (-0.01)^2 + (-0.21)^2 + (0.69)^2 + (-0.61)^2 + (-1.21)^2 + (0.79)^2$$
$$+ (0.19)^2 + (-0.31)^2 + (0.29)^2 + (0.39)^2$$
$$= 3.349$$

$$\frac{\Sigma d^2}{n} = \frac{3.349}{10} = 0.3349$$

$$\text{s.d.} = \sqrt{0.3349} = 0.58$$

b)   this sample has a greater variety of leaf sizes.

A19

b)

Mass	m	f	fm	d	d^2	fd^2
40–42	41	1	41	17.89	320.0	320
42–46	44	3	132	14.89	221.7	665
46–53	49.5	25	1237.5	9.39	88.2	2205
53–62	57.5	35	2012.5	1.39	1.9	66.5
62–75	68.5	36	2466	−9.61	92.4	3326
		100	5889			6582

estimated mean $= 5889 \div 100 = 58.89$

$$\frac{\Sigma fd^2}{n} = \frac{6582}{100} = 65.82$$

$$\text{s.d.} = \sqrt{(65.82)} = 8.1$$

c) ± 2 s.d. $= \pm 16.2 \Rightarrow$ norm dist is 42.69–75.09
all except the 'extra small' lie in the sample $\Rightarrow 99\%$.

A20

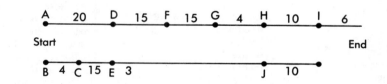

Fig. 11.49

The 'Critical Path is: A, D, F, G, H, I. which is 70 mins.

GRADE CHECKLIST

For a Grade B you should:

Be able to: ■ Construct and interpret cumulative frequency diagrams.
             ■ Calculate probabilities of combined events.

For a Grade A you should also:

Be able to: ■ Construct and interpret histograms. Use 'sampling' to investigate a 'population'
             ■ Use tree diagrams.

For a Grade A* you should also:

Be able to: ■ Calculate standard deviation.
             ■ Interpret and construct critical path analysis diagrams.

INDEX